METHUEN LIBRARY REPRINTS

WALTER SAVAGE LANDOR.
Ætat 74.

THE
COMPLETE WORKS
OF
WALTER SAVAGE LANDOR

EDITED BY

T. EARLE WELBY

VOLUME I

BARNES & NOBLE, Inc.
New York
METHUEN & CO. Ltd
London

PREFACE

FIVE of the minor publications of Walter Savage Landor are lost, but, as regards most of them, to the bibliographer rather than the reader.[1] Much of his extant work, however, has been allowed to remain unreprinted, much has been reprinted in an indolent dependence on the arbitrary and careless Forster, and therefore inaccurately. The present edition, whatever its defects, will be found to be much fuller and, I venture to hope, more faithful in text than its predecessors.

Since it issues from the publishing house which gave its imprint to John Forster's *The Works and Life of Walter Savage Landor*, 8 vols., 1876, it is desirable to say at once that it is not a mere revised edition of Forster, but has been prepared in the main independently, and is based on material made available by the generosity of Mr. Thomas J. Wise and Mr. Stephen Wheeler.

To catalogue the omissions and errors of Forster, many of them till now unremedied, might be ungracious in me, and would certainly

---

[1] The lost publications are :—

(1) *Sponsalia Polyxenæ*. Pistoja, 1819. The only recorded copy was that in the possession of the late Willard Fiske in 1899. Wise and Wheeler safely assume that this piece was identical with the poem bearing the same title in *Idyllia Heroica Decem*, 1820.

(2) *To the Burgesses of Warwick*. A pamphlet of eight 8vo pages.

(3) *Palinodia*. A short companion piece to "Gaffer Lockhart," which latter was reprinted in *Dry Sticks Fagoted*, 1858. The *Two Poems* were printed originally on a half-sheet of which no example is extant.

(4) *Two Poems*. 1852. The text of one is preserved in Forster's *Landor*, 1869, vol. ii. p. 534; the text of the other in *Last Fruit*, 1853, p. 429.

(5) *Letters of a Canadian*, 1862. A pamphlet printed in London, now completely lost.

PREFACE

be tiresome to the reader : reference to a few of the more serious will suffice to show that this edition is not superfluous. To the capital work of Landor as a writer of prose, Forster in 1876 added several Conversations for which he deserves our gratitude, but totally ignored no less than ten others, produced between 1852 and 1860, all of them characteristic and several of them equal to all but the very greatest of Landor's work in this kind. Of the miscellaneous prose, he neglected the *Commentary on Trotter's Memoir of Mr. Fox*, the claims of which had been justly pressed on him by Lord Houghton; neglected *High and Low Life in Italy*, originally printed serially in Leigh Hunt's *Monthly Repository* in successive numbers from that of August 1837 to April 1838; neglected the *Letter to R. W. Emerson*; neglected the great mass of Landor's letters to the Press. As regards Landor's verse, Forster omitted 195 of the miscellaneous pieces printed in *Dry Sticks*, 131 of the pieces in *Heroic Idylls*, and, to mention a particular poem, gave the incomparable " I strove with none " only in his biography. That his arrangement of the material he did use was sometimes unhappy, that he perpetuated the textual errors of earlier issues, are counts in the indictment that need not be pressed. Enough has been said to show that Forster's edition was grievously incomplete.

Some of his omissions were made good, and certain of his errors corrected, in 1891 by Mr. Crump. This scholarly editor, however, failed to fill all the gaps left by Forster. Thus, adding three items to the *Imaginary Conversations*, he passed over seven Conversations, which are here first included in a collected edition of Landor, passed over various other prose compositions, and even excluded some of the verse given by Forster. Unlike Forster, he took the trouble to notice variants, but was not consistent in this policy, and in certain instances fell victim to transcribers, printers, or the fatigue of so arduous a task as the editing of Landor. His notes, to which, however, I frankly record my obligations, were not wholly free from error.

Of sectional reprints and of selections it can hardly be required of me to say much. The most generally used of the selections,

PREFACE

Sir Sidney Colvin's, must be commended for drawing on some of the then and still neglected writings; and despite his acquiescence in at least one gross misreading, and his omission of " Dirce," one of the poet's three highest achievements in lyrical epigram, his little volume long ago placed him high among the few who have loyally served Landor. But no assembly of reprints and anthologies round the eight volumes of Forster and the ten of Crump can yield the reader patient enough to turn from book to book, backwards and forwards, the full and accurate text needed for the apprehension of Landor in all the moods of his experience and all the science with which he used the instruments of verse and prose. Chill as may be some pages of Landor, vexatious as may be some, here is a master who must be read as a whole if he is to be rightly appreciated.

In editing work so frequently rewrought, I had open to me several courses. I might have acted in accordance with the wish once expressed by Swinburne for an edition that should give the text of the first editions, later versions being noted marginally. Or I might have adopted the latest text sanctioned or perforce acquiesced in by a writer in exile who delegated to friends the duty of seeing his work through the press, and have ignored earlier versions as condemned by Landor. Or I might, in a hedonistic spirit, have chosen now an earlier, now a later version.

The last of these courses is that which I should recommend to an anthologist. At least, I venture to suggest it reverently to Swinburne as an admirable occupation for eternity, illimitable time and Swinburne's instinct for Landor being the conditions requisite for the task. That any lesser judge should presume, and summarily, to choose between version and version throughout the writings of Landor would be an intolerable exhibition of arrogance.

This method ruled out, it seemed to me there was little reason to hesitate. The adoption of the text of first editions would have had consequences very detrimental to the reading of Landor for pleasure. At certain points it would have necessitated footnotes running to a page or more ; at certain others it would have thrust on the reader a version so unfamiliar as to be disconcerting. With

PREFACE

what feelings would readers have viewed a page on which a line of text was weighed down by a massive footnote ? With what feelings would they have perused in the main text the "Rose Aylmer" of 1806 when they were counting on the consummated perfection of 1831 ?

Influenced by such considerations, I decided to adopt everywhere the latest text for which, with whatever reservations, the authority of Landor can be invoked, but to record everywhere variants provided by earlier editions. Verbal changes are thus noticed throughout, but I have felt it permissible to notice changes in spelling only to the extent necessary for illustration of Landor's habits at various stages of his career, and changes in punctuation have been treated on a similar principle, except where they affect the meaning.

From explanatory and appreciative annotation I have for the most part abstained. Landor is not the reading of ignorant, indolent, unsensitive persons. This abstinence commended itself to me the more because I would discourage that view of Landor according to which he was engaged, in the *Imaginary Conversations* and certain other of his works, in reproducing as precisely as he could the lineaments and situations of the characters of antiquity. Moving in the ancient world with the freedom of a scholar who relies on his memory rather than on repeated and narrowly purposed consultation of authorities, and shaping and expanding his material with the liberty of a creative artist, Landor was concerned, as a rule, for nothing more than plausibility in his representation of historical personages and events. To draw attention to every stroke of characterization for which there is no justification in history, to every conscious or unconscious defiance of chronology, is to suggest that Landor is failing in an enterprise which he, in fact, rarely entered upon. With some exceptions, he made the people of his Conversations and dramatic poems in his own likeness, caring only to secure the minimum of historical colour necessary for illusion. Remembering this, I have noted departures from historical truth or probability only when there was some special reason for doing so. As to sources, I have in general avoided speculation, and I will add that it is apt to result in absurdity ; for Landor's sources were often

viii

PREFACE

less recondite than those which an ingenious scholarship discovers for him, and when his richly stored memory did not suffice him, he readily condescended to an ordinary work of general reference or to a specialized modern treatise.

A profusion of notes is not proof of industry, and I must ask the reader to believe that my usual asceticism in regard to all but bibliographical and textual notes does not mean that I have grudged pains over my edition of this noble master. But I must make it clear that thrice my labour would have availed me little if I had not enjoyed the advantage of using the material collected by Mr. Wise and Mr. Wheeler. I am indebted to them jointly for their great Bibliography : there I am but one of their many debtors. Where I am under peculiar obligations to Mr. Wise is for the hospitality of the Ashley Library, with its matchless collection of first and early editions of Landor ; and my special obligation to Mr. Stephen Wheeler arises out of the fact that I have almost everywhere had the benefit of his minute textual criticism. I have further to acknowledge with gratitude the sympathetic interest taken in this edition, from the time when it was a project without a publisher, by Sir Edmund Gosse. Finally, I have to record my appreciation of assistance given me by my cousin, Mrs. Thomas, in checking the textual variations of Landor.

Since I have reserved for a biographical and critical monograph, to be issued by the same publishers, what I have to say of the character and achievements of Walter Savage Landor, I will not stand longer between readers and the graciously austere entertainment offered them in these volumes. But it is impossible to conclude this Preface without one word of homage to the noble and aloof master whom I have been privileged to edit, one word of thanksgiving for the good fortune enjoyed by the least of his students.

T. EARLE WELBY.

CONTENTS

IMAGINARY CONVERSATIONS OF GREEKS AND ROMANS

GREEK

THE AUTHOR TO THE READER OF THE IMAGINARY CONVERSATIONS[1]

Avoid a mistake in attributing to the writer any opinions in this book but what are spoken under his own name. The introduction of characters now or recently existing has been censured; but among the relics of antiquity the censurer probably has been gratified at finding an allusion to the contemporaries of the authors: let him be consistent and acquiescent, and believe that the dialogues now before him may be also among the relics of antiquity. A few public men of small ability are introduced, to show better the proportions of the great; as a painter would situate a beggar under a triumphal arch, or a camel against a pyramid.

[1] From " Avoid " to " name " reproduces the substance of a sentence in the Preface to the ed. of 1824, p. xi. From " A few public men " to " pyramid " is taken, with slight alteration, from the Dedication of that volume, the words originally following on " introduced " (" such as emperors and ministers of modern art ") having been deleted.

ORIGINAL DEDICATION TO THE FIRST COLLECTED EDITION OF LANDOR'S WRITINGS

JULIUS HARE,

WITHOUT WHOSE PATIENCE AND ASSIDUITY IN SUPERINTENDING THE PRESS, WHILE I WAS RESIDENT IN ITALY, THE " IMAGINARY CONVERSATIONS " NEVER WOULD HAVE BEEN PUBLISHED IN MY LIFE-TIME;

AND

JOHN FORSTER,

BY WHOSE EXERTION AND SOLICITUDE A COMPLETE EDITION OF MY WRITINGS IS NOW LAID BEFORE THE READER;

ACCEPT MY THANKS.

RETAIN, CONTINUE, AND, IF POSSIBLE, INCREASE YOUR FRIENDSHIP FOR ME, AND RECEIVE FOR YOUR OWN WORKS ALL THE FAVOUR YOU WOULD ATTRACT TO MINE.

WALTER SAVAGE LANDOR.

IMAGINARY CONVERSATIONS OF GREEKS AND ROMANS

GREEK

I. ACHILLES AND HELENA

(Imag. Convers. Gk. and Rom., 1853 ; *Wks.*, ii., 1876 ; in verse, *Hellenics*, 2nd ed., 1859 ; *Wks.*, vii., 1876.)

HELENA. Where am I ? Desert me not, O ye blessed from above ! ye twain who brought me hither !

Was it a dream ?

Stranger ! thou seemest thoughtful ; couldst thou [1] answer me ? Why so silent ? I beseech and implore thee, speak.

ACHILLES. Neither thy feet nor the feet of mules have borne thee where thou standest. Whether in the hour of departing sleep, or at what hour of the morning, I know not, O Helena, but Aphroditè and Thetis, inclining to my prayer, have, as thou art conscious, led thee into these solitudes. To me also have they shown the way ; that I might behold the pride of Sparta, the marvel of the earth, and— how my heart swells and agonises at the thought !—the cause of innumerable woes to Hellas.

HELENA. Stranger ! thou art indeed one whom the Goddesses or Gods might lead, and glory in ; such is thy stature, thy voice, and thy demeanour ; but who, if earthly, art thou ?

ACHILLES. Before thee, O Helena, stands Achilles, son of Peleus. Tremble not, turn not pale, bend not thy knees, O Helena !

HELENA. Spare me, thou Goddess-born ! thou cherished and only son of silver-footed Thetis ! Chryseïs and Briseïs ought to soften and content thy heart. Lead not me also into captivity. Woes too surely have I brought down on Hellas : but woes have been mine alike, and will for ever be.

---

[1] Between "thou" and "answer" we should doubtless insert "not."

ACHILLES. Daughter of Zeus! what word hast thou spoken! Chryseïs, child of the aged priest who performs in this land due sacrifices to Apollo, fell to the lot of another; an insolent and unworthy man, who hath already brought more sorrows upon our people than thou hast, so that dogs and vultures prey on the brave who sank without a wound. Briseïs is indeed mine; the lovely and dutiful Briseïs. He, unjust and contumelious, proud at once and base, would tear her from me. But, Gods above! in what region has the wolf with impunity dared to seize upon the kid which the lion hath taken?

Talk not of being led into servitude. Could mortal be guilty of such impiety? Hath it never thundered on these mountain-heads? Doth Zeus, the wide-seeing, see all the earth but Ida? doth he watch over all but his own? Capaneus and Typhöeus less offended him, than would the wretch whose grasp should violate the golden hair of Helena. And dost thou still tremble? irresolute and distrustful!

HELENA. I must tremble; and more and more.

ACHILLES. Take my hand: be confident: be comforted.

HELENA. May I take it? may I hold it? I am comforted.

ACHILLES. The scene around us, calm and silent as the sky itself, tranquillises thee; and so it ought. Turnest thou to survey it? perhaps it is unknown to thee.

HELENA. Truly; for since my arrival I have never gone beyond the walls of the city.

ACHILLES. Look then around thee freely, perplexed no longer. Pleasant is this level eminence, surrounded by broom and myrtle, and crisp-leaved beech and broad dark pine above. Pleasant the short slender grass, bent by insects as they alight on it or climb along it, and shining up into our eyes, interrupted by tall sisterhoods of grey lavender, and by dark-eyed cistus, and by lightsome citisus, and by little troops of serpolet running in disorder here and there.

HELENA. Wonderful! how didst thou ever learn to name so many plants?

ACHILLES. Chiron taught me them, when I walked at his side while he was culling herbs for the benefit of his brethren. All these he taught me, and at least twenty more; for wonderous was his wisdom, boundless his knowledge, and I was proud to learn.

Ah look again! look at those little yellow poppies; they appear to be just come out to catch all that the sun will throw into their

2

cups : they appear in their joyance and incipient dance to call upon the lyre to sing among them.

HELENA. Childish ! for one with such a spear against his shoulder ; terrific even its shadow ; it seems to make a chasm across the plain.

ACHILLES. To talk or to think like a child is not always a proof of folly : it may sometimes push aside heavy griefs where the strength of wisdom fails. What art thou pondering, Helena ?

HELENA. Recollecting the names of the plants. Several of them I do believe I had heard before, but had quite forgotten ; my memory will be better now.

ACHILLES. Better now ? in the midst of war and tumult ?

HELENA. I am sure it will be, for didst thou not say that Chiron taught them ?

ACHILLES. He sang to me over the lyre the lives of Narcissus and Hyacynthus, brought back by the beautiful Hours, of silent unwearied feet, regular as the stars in their courses. Many of the trees and bright-eyed flowers once lived and moved, and spoke as we are speaking. They may yet have memories, although they have cares no longer.

HELENA. Ah ! then they have no memories ; and they see their own beauty only.

ACHILLES. Helena ! thou turnest pale, and droopest.

HELENA. The odour of the blossoms, or of the gums, or the highth of the place, or something else, makes me dizzy. Can it be the wind in my ears ?

ACHILLES. There is none.

HELENA. I could wish there were a little.

ACHILLES. Be seated, O Helena !

HELENA. The feeble are obedient : the weary may rest even in the presence of the powerful.

ACHILLES. On this very ground where we are now reposing, they who conducted us hither told me, the fatal prize of beauty was awarded. One of them smiled ; the other, whom in duty I love the most, looked anxious, and let fall some tears.

HELENA. Yet she was not one of the vanquished.

ACHILLES. Goddesses contended for it ; Helena was afar.

HELENA. Fatal was the decision of the arbiter ! But could not the venerable Peleus, nor Pyrrhus the infant so

3

beautiful and so helpless, detain thee, O Achilles, from this sad sad war ?

ACHILLES. No reverence or kindness for the race of Atreus brought me against Troy ; I detest and abhor both brothers : but another man is more hateful to me still. Forbear we to name him. The valiant, holding the hearth as sacred as the temple, is never a violator of hospitality. He carries not away the gold he finds in the house ; he folds not up the purple linen worked for solemnities, about to convey it from the cedar chest to the dark ship, together with the wife confided to his protection in her husband's absenec, and sitting close and expectant by the altar of the gods.

It was no merit in Menelaüs to love thee ; it was a crime in another—I will not say to love, for even Priam or Nestor might love thee—but to avow it, and act on the avowal.

HELENA. Menelaüs, it is true, was fond of me, when Paris was sent by Aphroditè to our house. It would have been very wrong to break my vow to Menelaüs, but Aphroditè urged me by day and by night, telling me that to make her break hers to Paris would be quite inexpiable. She told Paris the same thing at the same hour ; and as often. He repeated it to me every morning : his dreams tallied with mine exactly. At last——

ACHILLES. The last is not yet come. Helena! by the Immortals! if ever I meet him in battle I transfix him with this spear.

HELENA. Pray do not. Aphroditè would be angry and never forgive thee.

ACHILLES. I am not sure of that ; she soon pardons. Variable as Iris, one day she favours and the next day she forsakes.

HELENA. She may then forsake *me*.

ACHILLES. Other deities, O Helena, watch over and protect thee. Thy two brave brothers are with those deities now, and never are absent from their higher festivals.

HELENA. They could protect me were they living, and they would. O that thou couldst but have seen them !

ACHILLES. Companions of my father on the borders of the Phasis, they became his guests before they went all three to hunt the boar in the brakes of Kalydon. Thence too the beauty of a woman brought many sorrows into brave men's breasts, and caused many tears to hang long and heavily on the eyelashes of matrons.

HELENA. Horrible creatures !—boars I mean.

4

ACHILLES AND HELENA

Didst thou indeed see my brothers at that season? Yes, certainly.

ACHILLES. I saw them not, desirous though I always was of seeing them, that I might have learnt from them, and might have practised with them, whatever is laudable and manly. But my father, fearing my impetuosity, as he said, and my inexperience, sent me away. Soothsayers had foretold some mischief to me from an arrow : and among the brakes many arrows might fly wide, glancing from trees.

HELENA. I wish thou hadst seen them, were it only once. Three such youths together the blessed sun will never shine upon again.

O my sweet brothers ! how they tended me ! how they loved me ! how often they wished me to mount their horses and to hurl their javelins. They could only teach me to swim with them ; and when I had well learnt it I was more afraid than at first. It gratified me to be praised for anything but swimming.

Happy, happy hours ! soon over ! Does happiness always go away before beauty ? It must go then : surely it might stay that little while. Alas ! dear Kastor ! and dearer Polydeukès ! often shall I think of you as ye were (and oh ! as I was) on the banks of the Eurotas.

Brave noble creatures ! they were as tall, as terrible, and almost as beautiful, as thou art. Be not wroth ! Blush no more for me.

ACHILLES. Helena ! Helena ! wife of Menelaüs ! my mother is reported to have left about me only one place vulnerable : I have at last found where it is. Farewell !

HELENA. O leave me not ! Earnestly I entreat and implore thee, leave me not alone. These solitudes are terrible : there must be wild beasts among them ; there certainly are Fauns and Satyrs. And there is Cybèlè, who carries towers and temples on her head ; who hates and abhors Aphroditè, who persecutes those *she* favours, and whose priests are so cruel as to be cruel even to themselves.

ACHILLES. According to their promise, the Goddesses who brought thee hither in a cloud will in a cloud reconduct thee, safely and unseen, into the city.

Again, O daughter of Leda and of Zeus, farewell !

5

II. ÆSOP AND RHODOPÈ

EGYPT, BETWEEN 620 AND 560 B.C.

(*Bk. of Beauty*, 1844 ; *Wks.*, ii., 1846 ; *Imag. Convers. Gk. and Rom.*, 1853 ; *Wks.*, ii., 1876.)

ÆSOP. Albeit thou approachest me without any sign of derision, let me tell thee before thou advancest a step nearer, that I deem thee more hard-hearted than the most petulant of those other young persons, who are pointing and sneering from the door-way.

RHODOPÈ. Let them continue to point and sneer at me : they are happy ; so am I ; but are you ? Think me hard-hearted, O good Phrygian ! but graciously give me the reason for thinking it ; other wise I may be unable to correct a fault too long overlooked by me, or to deprecate a grave infliction of the Gods.

ÆSOP. I thought thee so, my little maiden, because thou camest toward me without the least manifestation of curiosity.

RHODOPÈ. Is the absence of curiosity a defect ?

ÆSOP. None whatever.

RHODOPÈ. Are we blamable in concealing it if we have it ?

ÆSOP. Surely not. But it is feminine ; and where none of it comes forward, we may suspect that other feminine appurtenances, such as sympathy for example, are deficient. Curiosity slips in among you before the passions are awake : curiosity comforts your earliest cries ; curiosity intercepts your latest. For which reason Dædalus, who not only sculptured but painted admirably, represents her in the vestibule of the Cretan labyrinth as a Goddess.

RHODOPÈ. What was she like ?

ÆSOP. There now ! Like ? Why, like Rhodopè.

RHODOPÈ. You said I have nothing of the kind.

ÆSOP. I soon discovered my mistake in this, and more than this, and not altogether to thy disadvantage.

RHODOPÈ. I am glad to hear it.

ÆSOP. Art thou ? I will tell thee then how she was depicted :

6

for I remember no author who has related it. Her lips were half-open ; her hair flew loosely behind her, designating that she was in haste ; it was more disordered, and it was darker, than the hair of Hope is represented, and somewhat less glossy. Her cheeks had a very fresh colour, and her eyes looked into every eye that fell upon them ; by her motion she seemed to be on her way into the labyrinth.

RHODOPÈ. O how I wish I could see such a picture !

ÆSOP. I do now.

RHODOPÈ. Where ? where ? Troublesome man ! Are you always so mischievous ? but your smile is not ill-natured. I can not help thinking that the smiles of men are pleasanter and sweeter than of women ; unless of the women who are rather old and decrepit, who seem to want help, and who perhaps are thinking that we girls are now the very images of what *they* were formerly. But girls never look at me so charmingly as you do, nor smile with such benignity ; and yet, O Phrygian, there are several of them who really are much handsomer.

ÆSOP. Indeed ? Is that so clear ?

RHODOPÈ. Perhaps in the sight of the Gods they may not be, who see all things as they are. But some of them appear to me to be very beautiful.

ÆSOP. Which are those ?

RHODOPÈ. The very girls who think me the ugliest of them all. How strange !

ÆSOP. That they should think thee so ?

RHODOPÈ. No, no : but that nearly all the most beautiful should be of this opinion ; and the others should often come to look at me, apparently with delight, over each other's shoulder or under each other's arm, clinging to their girdle or holding by their sleeve and hanging a little back, as if there were something about me unsafe. They seem fearful regarding me; for there are many venomous things in this country, of which we have none at home.

ÆSOP. And some which we find all over the world. But thou art too talkative.

RHODOPÈ. Now indeed you correct me with great justice, and with great gentleness. I know not why I am so pleased to talk with you. But what you say to me is different from what others say : the thoughts, the words, the voice, the look, all different. And yet reproof is but little pleasant, especially to those who are unused to it.

Æsop. Why didst thou not spring forward and stare at me, having heard as the rest had done, that I am unwillingly a slave, and indeed not over-willingly a deformed one ?

Rhodopè. I would rather that neither of these misfortunes had befallen you.

Æsop. And yet within the year thou wilt rejoice that they have.

Rhodopè. If you truly thought so, you would not continue to look at me with such serenity. Tell me why you say it.

Æsop. Because by that time thou wilt prefer me to the handsomest slave about the house.

Rhodopè. For shame ! vain creature !

Æsop. By the provision of the Gods, the under-sized and distorted are usually so. The cork of vanity buoys up their chins above all swimmers on the tide of life. But, Rhodopè, my vanity has not yet begun.

Rhodopè. How do you know that my name is Rhodopè ?

Æsop. Were I malicious I would inform thee, and turn against thee the tables on the score of vanity.

Rhodopè. What can you mean ?

Æsop. I mean to render thee happy in life, and glorious long after. Thou shalt be sought by the powerful, thou shalt be celebrated by the witty, and thou shalt be beloved by the generous and the wise. Xanthus may adorn the sacrifice, but the Immortal shall receive it from the altar.

Rhodopè. I am but fourteen years old, and Xanthus is married. Surely he would not rather love me than one to whose habits and endearments he has been accustomed for twenty years.

Æsop. It seems wonderful : but such things do happen.

Rhodopè. Not among us Thracians. I have seen in my childhood men older than Xanthus, who, against all remonstrances and many struggles, have fondled and kissed, before near relatives, wives of the same age, proud of exhibiting the honorable love they bore toward them : yet in the very next room, the very same day, scarcely would they press to their bosoms while you could (rather slowly) count twenty, nor kiss for half the time, beautiful young maidens, who, casting down their eyes, never stirred, and only said " Don't ! Don't ! "

Æsop. What a rigid morality is the Thracian ! How courageous the elderly ! and how enduring the youthful !

ÆSOP AND RHODOPÈ

RHODOPÈ. Here in Egypt we are nearer to strange creatures; to men without heads, to others who ride on dragons.

ÆSOP. Stop there, little Rhodopè! In all countries we live among strange creatures. However, there are none such in the world as thou hast been told of since thou camest hither.

RHODOPÈ. Oh yes there are. You must not begin by shaking my belief, and by making me know less than others of my age. They all talk of them : nay, some creatures not by any means prettier, are worshipped here as deities : I have seen them with my own eyes. I wonder that you above all others should deny the existence of prodigies.

ÆSOP. Why dost thou wonder at it particularly in me ?

RHODOPÈ. Because when you were brought hither yesterday, and when several of my fellow-maidens came around you, questioning you about the manners and customs of your country, you began to tell them stories of beasts who spoke, and spoke reasonably.

ÆSOP. They are almost the only people of my acquaintance who do.

RHODOPÈ. And you call them by the name of *people ?*

ÆSOP. For want of a nobler and a better. Didst thou hear related what I had been saying ?

RHODOPÈ. Yes, every word, and perhaps more.

ÆSOP. Certainly more ; for my audience was of females. But canst thou repeat any portion of the narrative ?

RHODOPÈ. They began by asking you whether all the men in Phrygia were like yourself.

ÆSOP. Art thou quite certain that this was the real expression they used ? Come : no blushes. Do not turn round.

RHODOPÈ. It had entirely that meaning.

ÆSOP. Did they not inquire if all Phrygians were such horrible monsters as the one before them ?

RHODOPÈ. O heaven and earth ! this man is surely omniscient. Kind guest ! do not hurt them for it. Deign to repeat to me, if it is not too troublesome, what you said about the talking beasts.

ÆSOP. The innocent girls asked me many questions, or rather half-questions ; for never was one finished before another from the same or from a different quarter was begun.

RHODOPÈ. This is uncivil : I would never have interrupted you.

ÆSOP. Pray tell me why all that courtesy.

9

RHODOPÈ. For fear of losing a little of what you were about to say, or of receiving it somewhat changed. We never say the same thing in the same manner when we have been interrupted. Beside, there are many who are displeased at it ; and if you had been, it would have shamed and vexed me.

ÆSOP. Art thou vexed so easily ?

RHODOPÈ. When I am ashamed I am. I shall be jealous if you are kinder to the others than to me, and if you refuse to tell me the story you told them yesterday.

ÆSOP. I have never yet made anyone jealous ; and I will not begin to try my talent on little Rhodopè.

They asked me who governs Phrygia at present. I replied that the Phrygians had just placed themselves under the dominion of a sleek and quiet animal, half-fox, half-ass, named Alopiconos.[1] At one time he seems fox almost entirely; at another, almost entirely ass.

RHODOPÈ. And can he speak ?

ÆSOP. Few better.

RHODOPÈ. Are the Phrygians contented with him ?

ÆSOP. They who raised him to power and authority rub their hands rapturously : nevertheless, I have heard several of the principal ones, in the very act of doing it, breathe out from closed teeth, " *The cursed fox !* " and others, " *The cursed ass !* "

RHODOPÈ. What has he done ?

ÆSOP. He has made the nation the happiest in the world, they tell us.

RHODOPÈ. How ?

ÆSOP. By imposing a heavy tax on the necessaries of life, and thus making it quite independent.

RHODOPÈ. O Æsop ! I am ignorant of politics, as of everything else. We Thracians are near Phrygia : our kings, I believe, have not conquered it : what others have ?

ÆSOP. None : but the independence which Alopiconos has conferred upon it, is conferred by hindering the corn of other lands, more fertile and less populous, from entering it, until so many of the inhabitants have died of famine and disease, that there will be imported just enough for the remainder.

---

[1] " Alopiconos " : probably a reference to Lord Liverpool ; Premier in 1815, when the duty to be levied on all corn imported into the country at less than 84s. the quarter was made prohibitive.

ÆSOP AND RHODOPE

RHODOPĖ. Holy Jupiter! protect my country! and keep for ever its asses and its foxes wider apart!

Tell me more. You know many things that have happened in the world. Beside the strange choice you just related, what is the most memorable thing that has occurred in Phrygia since the Trojan war?

ÆSOP. An event more memorable preceded it; but nothing since will appear to thee so extraordinary.

RHODOPĖ. Then tell me only that.

ÆSOP. It will interest thee less, but the effect is more durable than of the other. Soon after the dethronement of Saturn, with certain preliminary ceremonies, by his eldest son Jupiter, who thus became the legitimate king of Gods and men, the lower parts of nature on our earth were likewise much affected. At this season the water in all the rivers of Phrygia was running low, but quietly, so that the bottom was visible in many places, and grew tepid and warm and even hot in some. At last it became agitated and excited: and loud bubbles rose up from it, audible to the ears of Jupiter, declaring that it had an indefeasible right to exercise its voice on all occasions, and of rising to the surface at all seasons. Jupiter, who was ever much given to hilarity, laughed at this; but the louder he laughed, the louder bubbled the mud, beseeching him to thunder and lighten and rain in torrents, and to sweep away dams and dykes and mills and bridges and roads, and moreover all houses in all parts of the country that were not built of mud. Thunder rolled in every quarter of the heavens: the lions and panthers were frightened and growled horribly: the foxes, who are seldom at fault, began to fear for the farm-yards; and were seen with vertical tails, three of which, if put together, would be little stouter than a child's whip for whipping-tops, so thoroughly soaked were they and draggled in the mire: not an animal in the forest could lick itself dry: their tongues ached with attempting it. But the mud gained its cause, and rose above the river-sides. At first it was elated by success; but it had floated in its extravagance no long time before a panic seized it, at hearing out of the clouds the fatal word *teleutaion*, which signifies *final*. It panted and breathed hard; and, at the moment of exhausting the last remnant of its strength, again it prayed to Jupiter, in a formulary of words which certain borderers of the principal stream suggested, imploring him that it might stop and subside. It did so. The borderers enriched their fields with it, carting it off, tossing it about, and breaking it into powder. But the streams were too dirty for decent men to bathe in them ; and scarcely a fountain in all Phrygia had as much pure water, at its very source, as thou couldst carry on thy head in an earthen jar. For several years afterward there were pestilential exhalations, and drought and scarcity, throughout the country.

RHODOPÈ. This is indeed a memorable event ; and yet I never heard of it before.

ÆSOP. Dost thou like my histories ?

RHODOPÈ. Very much indeed.

ÆSOP. Both of them ?

RHODOPÈ. Equally.

ÆSOP. Then, Rhodopè, thou art worthier of instruction than anyone I know. I never found an auditor, until the present, who approved of each ; one or other of the two was sure to be defective in style or ingenuity : it showed an ignorance of the times or of mankind : it proved only that the narrator was a person of contracted views, and that nothing pleased him.

RHODOPÈ. How could you have hindered, with as many hands as Gyas, and twenty thongs in each, the fox and ass from uniting ? or how could you prevail on Jupiter to keep the mud from bubbling ? I have prayed to him for many things more reasonable, and he has never done a single one of them ; except the last, perhaps.

ÆSOP. What was it ?

RHODOPÈ. That he would bestow on me power and understanding to comfort the poor slave from Phrygia.

ÆSOP. On what art thou reflecting ?

RHODOPÈ. I do not know. Is reflection that which will not lie quiet on the mind, and which makes us ask ourselves questions we can not answer ?

ÆSOP. Wisdom is but that shadow which we call reflection ; dark always, more or less, but usually the most so where there is the most light around it.

RHODOPÈ. I think I begin to comprehend you ; but beware lest anyone else should. Men will hate you for it, and may hurt you ; for they will never bear the wax to be melted in the ear, as your words possess the faculty of doing.

ÆSOP. They may hurt me, but I shall have rendered them a service first.

12

ÆSOP AND RHODOPÈ

RHODOPÈ. O Æsop! if you think so, you must soon begin to instruct me how I may assist you, first in performing the service, and then in averting the danger : for I think you will be less liable to harm if I am with you.

ÆSOP. Proud child !

RHODOPÈ. Not yet ; I may be then.

ÆSOP. We must converse about other subjects.

RHODOPÈ. On what rather ?

ÆSOP. I was accused by thee of attempting to unsettle thy belief in prodigies and portents.

RHODOPÈ. Teach me what is right and proper in regard to them, and in regard to the gods of this country who send them.

ÆSOP. We will either let them alone, or worship them as our masters do. But thou mayst be quite sure, O Rhodopè, that if there were any men without heads, or any who ride upon dragons, they would have been worshipped as deities long ago.

RHODOPÈ. Ay ; now you talk reasonably : so they would : at least I think so : I mean only in this country. In Thrace we do not think so unworthily of the gods : we are too afraid of Cerberus for that.

ÆSOP. Speak lower ; or thou wilt raise ill blood between him and Anubis. His three heads could hardly lap milk when Anubis with only one could crack the thickest bone.

RHODOPÈ. Indeed ! how proud you must be to have acquired such knowledge.

ÆSOP. It is the knowledge which men most value, as being the most profitable to them ; but I possess little of it.

RHODOPÈ. What then will you teach me ?

ÆSOP. I will teach thee, O Rhodopè, how to hold Love by both wings, and how to make a constant companion of an ungrateful guest.

RHODOPÈ. I think I am already able to manage so little a creature.

ÆSOP. He hath managed greater creatures than Rhodopè.

RHODOPÈ. They had no scissors to clip his pinions, and they did not slap him soon enough on the back of the hand. I have often wished to see him ; but I never have seen him yet.

ÆSOP. Nor anything like ?

RHODOPÈ. I have touched his statue ; and once I stroked it down, all over ; very nearly. He seemed to smile at me the more for it, until I was ashamed. I was then a little girl : it was long ago : a year at least.

ÆSOP. Art thou sure it was such a long while since ?

RHODOPÈ. How troublesome ! Yes ! I never told anybody but you : and I never would have told you, unless I had been certain that you would find it out by yourself, as you did what those false foolish girls said concerning you. I am sorry to call them by such names, for I am confident that on other things and persons they never speak maliciously or untruly.

ÆSOP. Not about thee ?

RHODOPÈ. They think me ugly and conceited, because they do not look at me long enough to find out their mistake. I know I am not ugly, and I believe I am not conceited : so I should be silly if I were offended, or thought ill of them in return. But do you yourself always speak the truth, even when you know it ? The story of the mud, I plainly see, is a mythos. Yet, after all, it is difficult to believe ; and you have scarcely been able to persuade me, that the beasts in any country talk and reason, or ever did.

ÆSOP. Wherever they do, they do one thing more than men do.

RHODOPÈ. You perplex me exceedingly : but I would not disquiet you at present with more questions. Let me pause and consider a little, if you please. I begin to suspect that, as gods formerly did, you have been turning men into beasts, and beasts into men. But, Æsop, you should never say the thing that is untrue.

ÆSOP. We say and do and look no other all our lives.

RHODOPÈ. Do we never know better ?

ÆSOP. Yes ; when we cease to please, and to wish it ; when death is settling the features, and the cerements are ready to render them unchangeable.

RHODOPÈ. Alas ! alas !

ÆSOP. Breathe, Rhodopè, breathe again those painless sighs : they belong to thy vernal season. May thy summer of life be calm, thy autumn calmer, and thy winter never come.

RHODOPÈ. I must die then earlier.

ÆSOP. Laodameia died ; Helen died ; Leda, the beloved of Jupiter, went before. It is better to repose in the earth betimes than to sit up late ; better, than to cling pertinaciously to what we feel crumbling under us, and to protract an inevitable fall. We may

14

enjoy the present while we are insensible of infirmity and decay: but the present, like a note in music, is nothing but as it appertains to what is past and what is to come. There are no fields of amaranth on this side of the grave : there are no voices, O Rhodopè, that are not soon mute, however tuneful : there is no name, with whatever emphasis of passionate love repeated, of which the echo is not faint at last.

RHODOPÈ. O Æsop! let me rest my head on yours : it throbs and pains me.

ÆSOP. What are these ideas to thee ?

RHODOPÈ. Sad, sorrowful.

ÆSOP. Harrows that break the soil, preparing it for wisdom. Many flowers must perish ere a grain of corn be ripened. And now remove thy head : the cheek is cool enough after its little shower of tears.

RHODOPÈ. How impatient you are of the least pressure ?

ÆSOP. There is nothing so difficult to support imperturbably as the head of a lovely girl, except her grief. Again upon mine ! forgetful one ! Raise it, remove it, I say. Why wert thou reluctant ? why wert thou disobedient ? Nay, look not so. It is I (and thou shalt know it) who should look reproachfully.

RHODOPÈ. Reproachfully ? did I ? I was only wishing you would love me better, that I might come and see you often.

ÆSOP. Come often and see me, if thou wilt ; but expect no love from me.

RHODOPÈ. Yet how gently and gracefully you have spoken and acted, all the time we have been together. You have rendered the most abstruse things intelligible, without once grasping my hand, or putting your fingers among my curls.

ÆSOP. I should have feared to encounter the displeasure of two persons if I had.

RHODOPÈ. And well you might. They would scourge you, and scold me.

ÆSOP. That is not the worst.

RHODOPÈ. The stocks too, perhaps.

ÆSOP. All these are small matters to the slave.

RHODOPÈ. If they befell you, I would tear my hair and my cheeks, and put my knees under your ancles. Of whom should you have been afraid ?

Æsop. Of Rhodopè and of Æsop. Modesty in man, O Rhodopè, is perhaps the rarest and most difficult of virtues : but intolerable pain is the pursuer of its infringement. Then follow days without content, nights without sleep, throughout a stormy season, a season of impetuous deluge which no fertility succeeds.

Rhodopè. My mother often told me to learn modesty, when I was at play among the boys.

Æsop. Modesty in girls is not an acquirement, but a gift of nature : and it costs as much trouble and pain in the possessor to eradicate, as the fullest and firmest lock of hair would do.

Rhodopè. Never shall I be induced to believe that men at all value it in themselves, or much in us, although from idleness or from rancour they would take it away from us whenever they can.

Æsop. And very few of you are pertinacious : if you run after them, as you often do, it is not to get it back.

Rhodopè. I would never run after anyone, not even you : I would only ask you, again and again, to love me.

Æsop. Expect no love from me. I will impart to thee all my wisdom, such as it is ; but girls like our folly best. Thou shalt never get a particle of mine from me.

Rhodopè. Is love foolish ?

Æsop. At thy age and at mine. I do not love thee : if I did, I would the more forbid thee ever to love *me*.

Rhodopè. Strange man !

Æsop. Strange indeed. When a traveller is about to wander on a desert, it is strange to lead him away from it ; strange to point out to him the verdant path he should pursue, where the tamarisk and lentisk and acacia wave overhead, where the reseda is cool and tender to the foot that presses it, and where a thousand colours sparkle in the sunshine, on fountains incessantly gushing forth.

Rhodopè. Xanthus has all these ; and I could be amid them in a moment.

Æsop. Why art not thou ?

Rhodopè. I know not exactly. Another day perhaps. I am afraid of snakes this morning. Beside, I think it may be sultry out of doors. Does not the wind blow from Libya ?

Æsop. It blows as it did yesterday when I came over, fresh across the Ægean, and from Thrace. Thou mayst venture into the morning air.

ÆSOP AND RHODOPÈ

RHODOPÈ. No hours are so adapted to study as those of the morning. But will you teach me ? I shall so love you if you will.

ÆSOP. If thou wilt *not* love me, I will teach thee.

RHODOPÈ. Unreasonable man !

ÆSOP. Art thou aware what those mischievous little hands are doing ?

RHODOPÈ. They are tearing off the golden hem from the bottom of my robe ; but it is stiff and difficult to detach.

ÆSOP. Why tear it off ?

RHODOPÈ. To buy your freedom. Do you spring up, and turn away, and cover your face from me ?

ÆSOP. My freedom ! Go, Rhodopè ! Rhodopè ! This, of all things, I shall never owe to thee.

RHODOPÈ. Proud man ! and you tell me to go ! do you ? do you ? Answer me at least. Must I ? and so soon ?

ÆSOP. Child ! begone !

RHODOPÈ. O Æsop, you are already more my master than Xanthus is. I will run and tell him so ; and I will implore of him, upon my knees, never to impose on *you* a command so hard to obey.

SECOND CONVERSATION

(*Bk. of Beauty*, 1845 ; *Imag. Convers. Gk. and Rom.*, 1853 ; *Wks.*, ii., 1876.)

ÆSOP. And so, our fellow-slaves are given to contention on the score of dignity ?

RHODOPÈ. I do not believe they are much addicted to contention : for, whenever the good Xanthus hears a signal of such misbehaviour, he either brings a scourge into the midst of them, or sends our lady to scold them smartly for it.

ÆSOP. Admirable evidence against their propensity !

RHODOPÈ. I will not have you find them out so, nor laugh at them.

ÆSOP. Seeing that the good Xanthus and our lady are equally fond of thee, and always visit thee both together, the girls, however envious, can not well or safely be arrogant, but must of necessity yield the first place to thee.

RHODOPÈ. They indeed are observant of the kindness thus bestowed upon me : yet they afflict me by taunting me continually with what I am unable to deny.

Æsop. If it is true, it ought little to trouble thee ; if untrue, less. I know, for I have looked into nothing else of late, no evil can thy heart have admitted : a sigh of thine before the gods would remove the heaviest that could fall on it. Pray tell me what it may be. Come, be courageous ; be cheerful. I can easily pardon a smile if thou empleadest me of curiosity.

Rhodopè. They remark to me that enemies or robbers took them forcibly from their parents—and that—and that——

Æsop. Likely enough : what then ? Why desist from speaking ? why cover thy face with thy hair and hands ? Rhodopè ! Rhodopè ! dost thou weep moreover ?

Rhodopè. It is so sure !

Æsop. Was the fault thine ?

Rhodopè. O that it were !—if there was any.

Æsop. While it pains thee to tell it, keep thy silence ; but when utterance is a solace, then impart it.

Rhodopè. They remind me (oh ! who could have had the cruelty to relate it ?) that my father, my own dear father——

Æsop. Say not the rest : I know it : his day was come.

Rhodopè. —sold me, sold me. You start : you did not at the lightning last night, nor at the rolling sounds above. And do you, generous Æsop ! do you also call a misfortune a disgrace ?

Æsop. If it is, I am among the most disgraceful of men. Didst thou dearly love thy father ?

Rhodopè. All loved him. He was very fond of me.

Æsop. And yet sold thee ! sold thee to a stranger !

Rhodopè. He was the kindest of all kind fathers, nevertheless. Nine summers ago, you may have heard perhaps, there was a grievous famine in our land of Thrace

Æsop. I remember it perfectly.

Rhodopè. O poor Æsop ! and were you too famishing in your native Phrygia ?

Æsop. The calamity extended beyond the narrow sea that separates our countries. My appetite was sharpened ; but the appetite and the wits are equally set on the same grindstone.

Rhodopè. I was then scarcely five years old : my mother died the year before : my father sighed at every funereal, but he sighed more deeply at every bridal, song. He loved me because he loved her who bore me : and yet I made him sorrowful whether I cried or

18

smiled. If ever I vexed him, it was because I would not play when he told me, but made him, by my weeping, weep again.

ÆSOP. And yet he could endure to lose thee ! he, thy father ! Could any other ? could any who lives on the fruits of the earth, endure it ? O age, that art incumbent over me ! blessed be thou ; thrice blessed ! Not that thou stillest the tumults of the heart, and promisest eternal calm, but that, prevented by thy beneficence, I never shall experience this only intolerable wretchedness.

RHODOPÈ. Alas ! alas !

ÆSOP. Thou art now happy, and shouldst not utter that useless exclamation.

RHODOPÈ. You said something angrily and vehemently when you stepped aside. Is it not enough that the handmaidens doubt the kindness of my father ? Must so virtuous and so wise a man as Æsop blame him also ?

ÆSOP. Perhaps he is little to be blamed ; certainly he is much to be pitied.

RHODOPÈ. Kind heart ! on which mine must never rest !

ÆSOP. Rest on it for comfort and for counsel when they fail thee : rest on it, as the deities on the breast of mortals, to console and purify it.

RHODOPÈ. Could I remove any sorrow from it, I should be contented.

ÆSOP. Then be so ; and proceed in thy narrative.

RHODOPÈ. Bear with me a little yet. My thoughts have over-powered my words, and now themselves are overpowered and scattered.

Forty-seven days ago (this is only the forty-eighth since I beheld you first) I was a child ; I was ignorant, I was careless.

ÆSOP. If these qualities are signs of childhood, the universe is a nursery.

RHODOPÈ. Affliction, which makes many wiser, had no such effect on me. But reverence and love (why should I hesitate at the one avowal more than at the other ?) came over me, to ripen my understanding.

ÆSOP. O Rhodopè ! we must loiter no longer upon this discourse.

RHODOPÈ. Why not ?

ÆSOP. Pleasant is yonder beanfield, seen over the high papyrus when it waves and bends : deep laden with the sweet heaviness of its odour is the listless air that palpitates dizzily above it : but Death is lurking for the slumberer beneath its blossoms.

RHODOPÈ. You must not love then !—but may not I ?

ÆSOP. We will—but——

RHODOPÈ. *We !* O sound that is to vibrate on my breast for ever ! O hour ! happier than all other hours since time began ! O gracious Gods ! who brought me into bondage !

ÆSOP. Be calm, be composed, be circumspect. We must hide our treasure that we may not lose it.

RHODOPÈ. I do not think that you can love me ; and I fear and tremble to hope so. Ah, yes ; you have said you did. But again you only look at me, and sigh as if you repented.

ÆSOP. Unworthy as I may be of thy fond regard, I am not unworthy of thy fullest confidence : why distrust me ?

RHODOPÈ. Never will I—never, never. To know that I possess your love, surpasses all other knowledge, dear as is all that I receive from you. I should be tired of my own voice if I heard it on aught beside : and, even yours is less melodious in any other sound than *Rhodopè*.

ÆSOP. Do such little girls learn to flatter ?

RHODOPÈ. Teach me how to speak, since you could not teach me how to be silent.

ÆSOP. Speak no longer of me, but of thyself ; and only of things that never pain thee.

RHODOPÈ. Nothing can pain me now.

ÆSOP. Relate thy story then, from infancy.

RHODOPÈ. I must hold your hand : I am afraid of losing you again.

ÆSOP. Now begin. Why silent so long ?

RHODOPÈ. I have dropped all memory of what is told by me and what is untold.

ÆSOP. Recollect a little. I can be patient with this hand in mine.

RHODOPÈ. I am not certain that yours is any help to recollection.

ÆSOP. Shall I remove it ?

RHODOPÈ. O ! now I think I can recall the whole story. What did you say ? did you ask any question ?

ÆSOP. None, excepting what thou hast answered.

RHODOPÈ. Never shall I forget the morning when my father, sitting in the coolest part of the house, exchanged his last measure of grain for a chlamys of scarlet cloth fringed with silver. He watched

20

the merchant out of the door, and then looked wistfully into the corn-chest. I, who thought there was something worth seeing, looked in also, and, finding it empty, expressed my disappointment, not thinking however about the corn. A faint and transient smile came over his countenance at the sight of mine. He unfolded the chlamys, stretched it out with both hands before me, and then cast it over my shoulders. I looked down on the glittering fringe and screamed with joy. He then went out; and I know not what flowers he gathered, but he gathered many; and some he placed in my bosom, and some in my hair. But I told him with captious pride, first that I could arrange them better, and again that I would have only the white. However, when he had selected all the white, and I had placed a few of them according to my fancy, I told him (rising in my slipper) he might crown me with the remainder. The splendour of my apparel gave me a sensation of authority. Soon as the flowers had taken their station on my head, I expressed a dignified satisfaction at the taste displayed by my father, just as if I could have seen how they appeared! But he knew that there was at least as much pleasure as pride in it, and perhaps we divided the latter (alas! not both) pretty equally. He now took me into the marketplace, where a concourse of people was waiting for the purchase of slaves. Merchants came and looked at me; some commending, others disparaging; but all agreeing that I was slender and delicate. that I could not live long, and that I should give much trouble. Many would have bought the chlamys, but there was something less saleable in the child and flowers.

ÆSOP. Had thy features been coarse and thy voice rustic, they would all have patted thy cheeks and found no fault in thee.

RHODOPÈ. As it was, every one had bought exactly such another in time past, and been a loser by it. At these speeches I perceived the flowers tremble slightly on my bosom, from my father's agitation. Although he scoffed at them, knowing my healthiness, he was troubled internally, and said many short prayers, not very unlike imprecations, turning his head aside. Proud was I, prouder than ever, when at last several talents were offered for me, and by the very man who in the beginning had undervalued me the most, and prophesied the worst of me. My father scowled at him, and refused the money. I thought he was playing a game, and began to wonder what it could be, since I never had seen it played before. Then I fancied it might be some celebration because plenty had returned to the city, insomuch that my father had bartered the last of the corn he hoarded. I grew more and more delighted at the sport. But soon there advanced an elderly man, who said gravely, " Thou hast stolen this child : her vesture alone is worth above a hundred drachmas. Carry her home again to her parents, and do it directly, or Nemesis and the Eumenides will overtake thee." Knowing the estimation in which my father had always been holden by his fellow-citizens, I laughed again, and pinched his ear. He, although naturally choleric, burst forth into no resentment at these reproaches, but said calmly, " I think I know thee by name, O guest ! Surely thou art Xanthus the Samian. Deliver this child from famine."

Again I laughed aloud and heartily ; and, thinking it was now my part of the game, I held out both my arms and protruded my whole body towards the stranger. He would not receive me from my father's neck, but he asked me with benignity and solicitude if I was hungry : at which I laughed again, and more than ever : for it was early in the morning, soon after the first meal, and my father had nourished me most carefully and plentifully in all the days of the famine. But Xanthus, waiting for no answer, took out of a sack, which one of his slaves carried at his side, a cake of wheaten bread and a piece of honey-comb, and gave them to me. I held the honey-comb to my father's mouth, thinking it the most of a dainty. He dashed it to the ground ; but, seizing the bread, he began to devour it ferociously. This also I thought was in play ; and I clapped my hands at his distortions. But Xanthus looked on him like one afraid, and smote the cake from him, crying aloud, " Name the price." My father now placed me in his arms, naming a price much below what the other had offered, saying, " The gods are ever with thee, O Xanthus ; therefore to thee do I consign my child." But while Xanthus was counting out the silver, my father seized the cake again, which the slave had taken up and was about to replace in the wallet. His hunger was exasperated by the taste and the delay. Suddenly there arose much tumult. Turning round in the old woman's bosom who had received me from Xanthus, I saw my beloved father struggling on the ground, livid and speechless. The more violent my cries, the more rapidly they hurried me away ; and many were soon between us. Little was I suspicious that he had suffered the pangs of famine long before : alas ! and he had suffered them for me. Do I weep while I am telling you they ended ? I could not have closed his eyes ; I was too young : but I might have received his last breath ; the only comfort of an orphan's bosom. Do you now think him blamable, O Æsop ?

ÆSOP. It was sublime humanity : it was forbearance and self-denial which even the immortal Gods have never shown us. He could endure to perish by those torments which alone are both acute and slow ; he could number the steps of death and miss not one : but he could never see thy tears, nor let thee see his. O weakness above all fortitude ! Glory to the man who rather bears a grief corroding his breast, than permits it to prowl beyond, and to prey on the tender and compassionate ! Women commiserate the brave, and men the beautiful. The dominion of Pity has usually this extent, no wider. Thy father was exposed to the obloquy not only of the malicious, but also of the ignorant and thoughtless, who condemn in the unfortunate what they applaud in the prosperous. There is no shame in poverty or in slavery, if we neither make ourselves poor by our improvidence nor slaves by our venality. The lowest and highest of the human race are sold : most of the intermediate are also slaves, but slaves who bring no money in the market.

RHODOPÈ. Surely the great and powerful are never to be purchased : are they ?

ÆSOP. It may be a defect in my vision, but I can not see greatness on the earth. What they tell me is great and aspiring, to me seems little and crawling. Let me meet thy question with another. What monarch gives his daughter for nothing ? Either he receives stone walls and unwilling cities in return, or he barters her for a parcel of spears and horses and horsemen, waving away from his declining and helpless age young joyous life, and trampling down the freshest and the sweetest memories. Midas in the highth of prosperity would have given his daughter to Lycaon,[1] rather than to the gentlest, the most virtuous, the most intelligent of his subjects. Thy father threw wealth aside, and, placing thee under the protection of Virtue, rose up from the house of Famine to partake in the festivals of the Gods.

Release my neck, O Rhodopè ! for I have other questions to ask of thee about him.

[1] Lycaon, son of Pelasgus, slayer of his guests.

RHODOPÈ. To hear thee converse on him in such a manner, I can do even that.

ÆSOP. Before the day of separation was he never sorrowful? Did he never by tears or silence reveal the secret of his soul?

RHODOPÈ. I was too infantine to perceive or imagine his intention. The night before I became the slave of Xanthus, he sat on the edge of my bed. I pretended to be asleep: he moved away silently and softly. I saw him collect in the hollow of his hand the crumbs I had wasted on the floor, and then eat them, and then look if any were remaining. I thought he did so out of fondness for me, remembering that, even before the famine, he had often swept up off the table the bread I had broken, and had made me put it between his lips. I would not dissemble very long, but said,

" Come, now you have wakened me, you must sing me asleep again, as you did when I was little."

He smiled faintly at this, and, after some delay, when he had walked up and down the chamber, thus began:

" I will sing to thee one song more, my wakeful Rhodopè! my chirping bird! over whom is no mother's wing! That it may lull thee asleep, I will celebrate no longer, as in the days of wine and plenteousness, the glory of Mars, guiding in their invisibly rapid onset the dappled steeds of Rhæsus. What hast thou to do, my little one, with arrows tired of clustering in the quiver? How much quieter is thy pallet than the tents which whitened the plain of Simöis! What knowest thou about the river Eurotas? What knowest thou about its ancient palace, once trodden by assembled Gods, and then polluted by the Phrygian? What knowest thou of perfidious men or of sanguinary deeds?

" Pardon me, O goddess who presidest in Cythera! I am not irreverent to thee, but ever grateful. May she upon whose brow I lay my hand, praise and bless thee for evermore!

" Ah yes! continue to hold up above the coverlet those fresh and rosy palms clasped together: her benefits have descended on thy beauteous head, my child! The Fates also have sung, beyond thy hearing, of pleasanter scenes than snow-fed Hebrus; of more than dim grottoes and sky-bright waters. Even now a low murmur swells upward to my ear: and not from the spindle comes the sound, but from those who sing slowly over it, bending all three their tremulous heads together. I wish thou couldst hear it; for

24

seldom are their voices so sweet. Thy pillow intercepts the song perhaps : lie down again, lie down, my Rhodopè ! I will repeat what they are saying :

" ' Happier shalt thou be, nor less glorious, than even she, the truly beloved, for whose return to the distaff and the lyre the portals of Tænarus flew open. In the woody dells of Ismarus, and when she bathed among the swans of Strymon, the nymphs called her Eurydicè. Thou shalt behold that fairest and that fondest one hereafter. But first thou must go unto the land of the lotos, where famine never cometh, and where alone the works of man are immortal.'

" O my child ! the undeceiving Fates have uttered this. Other powers have visited me, and have strengthened my heart with dreams and visions. We shall meet again, my Rhodopè ! in shady groves and verdant meadows, and we shall sit by the side of those who loved us."

He was rising : I threw my arms about his neck, and, before I would let him go, I made him promise to place me, not by the side, but between them : for I thought of her who had left us. At that time there were but two, O Æsop !

You ponder : you are about to reprove my assurance in having thus repeated my own praises. I would have omitted some of the words, only that it might have disturbed the measure and cadences, and have put me out. They are the very words my dearest father sang ; and they are the last : yet, shame upon me ! the nurse (the same who stood listening near, who attended me into this country) could remember them more perfectly : it is from her I have learnt them since ; she often sings them, even by herself.

ÆSOP. So shall others. There is much both in them and in thee to render them memorable.

RHODOPÈ. Who flatters now ?

ÆSOP. Flattery often runs beyond Truth, in a hurry to embrace her ; but not here. The dullest of mortals, seeing and hearing thee, would never misinterpret the prophecy of the Fates.

If, turning back, I could overpass the vale of years, and could stand on the mountain-top, and could look again far before me at the bright ascending morn, we would enjoy the prospect together ; we would walk along the summit hand in hand, O Rhodopè, and we would only sigh at last when we found ourselves below with others.

III. SOLON AND PISISTRATUS

ATHENS, ABOUT 560 B.C.

(Philosophical Museum, i., 1832 ; *Ablett's Lit. Hours,* 1837 ; *Wks.,* ii., 1846 ; *Imag. Convers. Gk. and Rom.,* 1853 ; *Wks.,* ii., 1876.)

PISISTRATUS. Here is a proof, Solon, if any were wanting, that either my power is small or my inclination to abuse it : you speak just as freely to me as formerly, and add unreservedly, which you never did before, the keenest sarcasms and the bitterest reproaches. Even such a smile as that, so expressive of incredulity and contempt, would arouse a desire of vengeance, difficult to control, in any whom you could justly call impostor and usurper.

SOLON. I do you no injustice, Pisistratus, which I should do if I feared you. Neither your policy nor your temper, neither your early education nor the society you have since frequented, and whose power over the mind and affections you can not at once throw off, would permit you to kill or imprison, or even to insult or hurt me. Such an action, you well know, would excite in the people of Athens as vehement a sensation as your imposture of the wounds, and you would lose your authority as rapidly as you acquired it. This however, you also know, is not the consideration which hath induced me to approach you, and to entreat your return, while the path is yet open, to reason and humanity.

PISISTRATUS. What inhumanity, my friend, have I committed ?

SOLON. No deaths, no tortures, no imprisonments, no stripes : but worse than these ; the conversion of our species into a lower ; a crime which the poets never feigned, in the wild attempts of the Titans or others who rebelled against the Gods, and against the order they established here below.

PISISTRATUS. Why then should you feign it of me ?

SOLON. I do not feign it : and you yourself shall bear me witness that no citizen is further removed from falsehood, from the perversion of truth by the heat of passion, than Solon. Choose between the

26

friendship of the wise and the adulation of the vulgar.   Choose, do I
say, Pisistratus ?   No, you can not : your choice is already made.
Choose then between a city in the dust and a city flourishing.

PISISTRATUS. How so ? who could hesitate ?

SOLON. If the souls of the citizens are debased, who cares whether
its walls and houses be still upright or thrown down ?   When free
men become the property of one, when they are brought to believe
that their interests repose on him alone, and must arise from him,
their best energies are broken irreparably.   They consider his will
as the rule of their conduct, leading to emolument and dignity,
securing from spoliation, from scorn, from contumely, from chains,
and seize this compendious blessing (such they think it) without
exertion and without reflection.   From which cause alone there are
several ancient nations so abject, that they have not produced in
many thousand years as many rational creatures as we have seen
together round one table in the narrowest lane of Athens.

PISISTRATUS. But, Solon, you yourself are an example, ill treated
as you have been, that the levity of the Athenian people requires
a guide and leader.

SOLON. There are those who, by their discourses and conduct,
inflate and push forward this levity, that the guide and leader may
be called for ; and who then offer their kind services, modestly, and
by means of friends, in pity to the weakness of their fellow-citizens,
taking care not only of their follies, but also their little store of
wisdom, putting it out to interest where they see fit, and directing
how and where it shall be expended. Generous hearts ! the
Lacedemonians themselves, in the excess of their democracy, never
were more zealous that corn and oil should be thrown into the
common stock, than these are that minds should, and that no one
swell a single line above another.   Their own meanwhile are fully
adequate to all necessary and useful purposes, and constitute them
a superintending Providence over the rest.

PISISTRATUS. Solon, I did not think you so addicted to derision :
you make me join you.   This in the latter part is a description of
despotism ; a monster of Asia, and not yet known even in the most
uncivilised region of Europe.   For the Thracians and others, who
have chieftains, have no kings, much less despots.   In speaking of
them we use the word carelessly, not thinking it worth our while to
form names for such creatures, any more than to form collars and

bracelets for them, or rings (if they use them) for their ears and noses.

SOLON. Preposterous as this is, there are things more so, under our eyes : for instance, that the sound should become lame, the wise foolish, and this by no affliction of disease or age. You go further ; and appear to wish that a man should become a child again : for what is it else, when he has governed himself, that he should go back to be governed by another ? and for no better reason than because, as he is told, that other has been knocked down and stabbed. Incontrovertible proofs of his strength, his prudence, and the love he has been capable of conciliating in those about him !

PISISTRATUS. Solon ! it would better become the gravity of your age, the dignity of your character, and the office you assume of adviser, to address me with decorous and liberal moderation, and to treat me as you find me.

SOLON. So small a choice of words is left us, when we pass out of Atticism into barbarism, that I know not whether you, distinguished as you are both for the abundance and the selection of them, would call yourself in preference *king* [1] or *tyrant*. The latter is usually the most violent, at least in the beginning ; the former the most pernicious. Tyrants, like ravens and vultures, are solitary : they either are swept off, or languish and pine away, and leave no brood in their places. Kings,[1] as the origin of them is amid the swamps and wildernesses, take deeper root, and germinate more broadly in the loose and putrescent soil, and propagate their likenesses for several generations ; a brood which (such is the power of habitude) does not seem monstrous, even to those whose corn, wine, and oil, it swallows up every day, and whose children it consumes in its freaks and festivals. I am ignorant under what number of them, at the present day, mankind in various countries lies prostrate ; just as ignorant as I am how many are the desarts and caverns of the earth, or the eddies and whirlpools of the sea ; but I should not be surprised to find it stated that, in Asia and Africa, there may be a dozen, greater or less. Europe has never been amazed at such a portent, either in the most corrupted or the most uncivilised of her nations, as a hereditary chief in possession of absolute power.

PISISTRATUS. The first despots were tyrannical and cruel.

SOLON. And so the last will be. This is wanting, on some

[1] 1st ed. reads : " *despot* or *tyrant*," and " *Despots*."

28

occasions, to arouse a people from the lethargy of servitude ; and therefore I would rather see the cruelest usurper than the mildest king. Under him men lose the dignity of their nature : under the other they recover it.

PISISTRATUS. Hereditary kings [1] too have been dethroned.

SOLON. Certainly : for, besotted as those must be who have endured them, some subject at last hath had the hardihood and spirit to kick that fellow in the face and trample on him, who insists that the shoe must fit him because it fitted his father and grandfather, and that, if his foot will not enter, he will pare and rasp it.

PISISTRATUS. The worst of wickedness is that of bearing hard on the unfortunate, and near it is that of running down the fortunate : yet these are the two commonest occupations of mankind. We are despised if we are helpless ; we are teased by petulance and tormented by reprehension if we are strong. One tribe of barbarians would drag us into their own dry desarts, and strip us to the skin : another would pierce us with arrows for being naked. What is to be done ?

SOLON. Simpler men run into no such perplexities. Your great wisdom, O Pisistratus, will enable you in some measure to defend your conduct ; but your heart is the more vulnerable from its very greatness.

PISISTRATUS. I intend to exert the authority that is conferred on me by the people, in the maintenance of your laws, knowing no better.

SOLON. Better there may be, but you will render worse necessary ; and would you have it said hereafter by those who read them, " Pisistratus was less wise than Solon " ?

PISISTRATUS. It must be said ; for none among men hath enjoyed so high a character as you, in wisdom and integrity.

SOLON. Either you lie now, Pisistratus, or you lied when you abolished my institutions.

PISISTRATUS. They exist, and shall exist, I swear to you.

SOLON. Yes, they exist like the letters in a burnt paper, which are looked down on from curiosity, and just legible, while the last of the consuming fire is remaining, but they crumble at a touch, and indeed fly before it, weightless and incoherent.

Do you desire, Pisistratus, that your family shall inherit your

[1] 1st ed. reads : " *despots.*"

anxieties ? If you really feel none yourself, which you never will persuade me, nor (I think) attempt it, still you may be much happier, much more secure and tranquil, by ceasing to possess what you have acquired of late, provided you cease early ; for long possession of any property makes us anxious to retain it, and insensible, if not to the cares it brings with it, at least to the real cause of them. Tyrants will never be persuaded that their alarms and sorrows, their perplexity and melancholy, are the product of tyranny : they will not attribute a tittle of them to their own obstinacy and perverseness, but look for it all in another's. They would move everything and be moved by nothing ; and yet lighter things move them than any other particle of mankind.

PISISTRATUS. You are talking, Solon, of mere fools.

SOLON. The worst of fools, Pisistratus, are those who once had wisdom. Not to possess what is good is a misfortune ; to throw it away is a folly : but to change what we know hath served us, and would serve us still, for what never has and never can, for what on the contrary hath always been pernicious to the holder, is the action of an incorrigible idiot. Observations on arbitrary power can never be made usefully to its possessors. There is not a foot-page about them at the bath whose converse on this subject is not more reasonable than mine would be. I could adduce no argument which he would not controvert, by the magical words " practical things " and " present times " : a shrug of the shoulder would overset all that my meditations have taught me in half a century of laborious inquiry and intense thought. " These are theories," he would tell his master, " fit for Attica before the olive was sown among us. Old men must always have their way. Will their own grey beards never teach them that time changes things ? "

One fortune, hath ever befallen those whom the indignant Gods have cursed with despotical power ; to feed upon falsehood, to loath and sicken at truth, to avoid the friendly, to discard the wise, to suspect the honest, and to abominate the brave. Like grubs in rotten kernels, they coil up for safety in dark hollowness, and see nothing but death in bursting from it. Although they place violence in the highest rank of dignities and virtues, and draw closely round their bodies those whose valour, from the centre to the extremities, should animate the state, yet they associate the most intimately with singers, with buffoons, with tellers of tales, with prodigies of

30

eating and drinking, with mountebanks, with diviners. These captivate and enthrall their enfeebled and abject spirits ; and the first cry that rouses them from their torpor is the cry that demands their blood. Then would it appear by their countenances, that all they had scattered among thousands, had come secretly back again to its vast repository, and was issuing forth from every limb and feature, from every pore, from every hair upon their heads.

What is man at last, O Pisistratus, when he is all he hath ever wished to be ! the fortunate, the powerful, the supreme ! Life in its fairest form (such he considers it) comes only to flatter and deceive him. Disappointments take their turn, and harass him : weakness and maladies cast him down : pleasures catch him again when he rises from them, to misguide and blind and carry him away : ambition struggles with those pleasures, and only in struggling with them seems to be his friend ; they mar one another, and distract him : enemies encompass him ; associates desert him ; rivalries thwart, persecutions haunt him ; another's thoughts molest and injure him ; his own do worse than join with them : and yet he shudders and shrinks back at nothing so much as the creaking of that door by which alone there is any escape.

Pisistratus ! O Pisistratus ! do we tire out the patience of mankind, do we prey upon our hearts, for this ? Does Nature crave it ? Does Wisdom dictate it ? Can Power avert it ? Descend then from a precipice, it is difficult to stand, it is impossible to repose on. Take the arm that would lead you and support you back, and restore you to your friends and country. He who places himself far above them, is (any child might tell you) far from them. What on earth can be imagined so horrible and disheartening, as to live without ever seeing one creature of the same species ! Being a tyrant or despot, you are in this calamity. Imprisonment in a dungeon could not reduce you to it : false friends have done that for you which enemies could but attempt. If such is the harvest of their zeal, when they are unsated and alert, what is that which remains to be gathered in by you, when they are full and weary ? Bitterness ; the bitterness of infamy ! And how will you quench it ? By swallowing the gall of self-reproach !

Let me put to you a few questions, near to the point : you will answer them, I am confident, easily and affably.

Pisistratus, have you not felt yourself the happier, when in the fulness of your heart, you have made a large offering to the Gods ?

PISISTRATUS. Solon, I am not impious : I have made many such offerings to them, and have always been the happier.

SOLON. Did they need your sacrifice ?

PISISTRATUS. They need nothing from us mortals ; but I was happy in the performance of what I have been taught is my duty.

SOLON. Piously, virtuously, and reasonably said, my friend. The Gods did not indeed want your sacrifice : they, who give everything, can want nothing. The Athenians do want a sacrifice from you : *they* have an urgent necessity of something ; the necessity of that very thing which you have taken from them, and which it can cost you nothing to replace. You have always been happier, you confess, in giving to the Gods what you could have yourself used in your own house : believe me, you will not be less so in giving back to your fellow-citizens what you have taken out of theirs and what you very well know they will seize when they can, together with your property and life. You have been taught, you tell me, that sacrifice to the Gods is a duty : be it so : but who taught you it? Was it a wiser man than you or I ? Or was it at a time of life when your reason was more mature than at present, or your interests better understood ? No good man ever gave anything without being the more happy for it, unless to the undeserving, nor ever took anything away without being the less so. But here is anxiety and suspicion, a fear of the strong, a subjection to the weak ; here is fawning, in order to be fawned on again, as among suckling whelps half awake. He alone is the master of his fellow-men, who can instruct and improve them ; while he who makes the people another thing from what it was, is master of that other thing, but not of the people. And supposing we could direct the city exactly as we would, is our greatness to be founded on this ? A ditcher may do greater things : he may turn a torrent (a thing even more turbid and more precipitate) by his ditch. A sudden increase of power, like a sudden increase of blood, gives pleasure ; but the new exitement being once gratified, the pleasure ceases.

I do not imagine the children of the powerful to be at any time more contented than the children of others, although I concede that the powerful themselves may be so for some moments, paying however very dearly for those moments, by more in quantity and in

32

value. Give a stranger, who has rendered you no service, four talents : the suddenness of the gift surprises and delights him : take them away again, saying, " Excuse me ; I intended them for your brother ; yet, not wholly to disappoint you, I give you two." What think you ; do you augment or diminish that man's store of happiness ?

PISISTRATUS. It must depend on his temper and character : but I think in nearly all instances you would diminish it.

SOLON. Certainly. When we can not have what we expect, we are dissatisfied ; and what we have ceases to afford us pleasure. We are like infants ; deprive them of one toy, and they push the rest away, or break them, and turn their faces from you, crying inconsolably.

If you desire an increase of happiness, do not look for it, O Pisistratus, in an increase of power. Follow the laws of nature on the earth. Spread the seeds of it far and wide : your crop shall be in proportion to your industry and liberality. What you concentrate in yourself, you stifle : you propagate what you communicate.

Still silent ? Who is at the door ?

PISISTRATUS. The boys.

SOLON. Come, my little fugitives ! turn back again hither ! come to me, Hippias and Hipparchus ! I wish you had entered earlier ; that you might have witnessed my expostulation with your father, and that your tender age might have produced upon him the effect my declining one has failed in. Children, you have lost your patrimony. Start not, Pisistratus ! I do not tell them that you have squandered it away : no, I will never teach them irreverence to their parent : aid me, I entreat you, to teach them reverence. Do not, while the thing is recoverable, deprive them of filial love, of a free city, of popular esteem, of congenial sports, of kind confidence, of that which all ages run in pursuit of, equals. Children seek those of the same age, men those of the same condition. Misfortunes come upon all : who can best ward them off ? not those above us nor those below, but those on a level with ourselves. Tell me, Pisistratus, what arm hath ever raised up the pillow of a dying despot ? He hath loosened the bonds of nature : in no hour, and least of all in the last, can they be strengthened and drawn together. It is a custom, as you know, for you have not yet forgotten all our

customs, to conduct youths with us when we mark the boundaries
of our lands, that they may give their testimony on any suit about
them in time to come.. Unfortunate boys ! their testimony cannot
be received ; the landmarks are removed from their own inheritance
by their own father.   Armed men are placed in front of them for
ever, and their pleasantest walks throughout life must be guarded
by armed men.   Who would endure it ? one of the hardest things
to which the captive, or even the criminal, is condemned.   The
restraints which everyone would wish away, are eternally about
them ; those which the best of us require through life, are removed
from them on entering it.   Their passions not only are uncontrolled,
but excited, fed, and flattered, by all around, and mostly by their
teachers.   Do not expose them to worse monsters than the young
Athenians were exposed to in the time of Theseus.   Never hath our
city, before or since, endured such calamity, such ignominy.   A
king, a conqueror, an injured and exasperated enemy, imposed
them : shall a citizen, shall a beneficent man, shall a father, devise
more cruel and more shameful terms, and admit none but his own
offspring to fulfill them ?   That monster perhaps was fabulous.   O
that these were so ! and that pride, injustice, lust, were tractable
to any clue or conquerable by any courage of despotism !

Weak man ! will sighing suffocate them ? will holding down
the head confound them ?

Hippias and Hipparchus ! you are now the children of Solon, the
orphans of Pisistratus.   If I have any wisdom, it is the wisdom of
experience : it shall cost you nothing from me, from others much.   I
present to you a fruit which the Gods themselves have fenced round,
not only from the animals, but from most men ; one which I have
nurtured and watched day and night for seventy years, reckoning
from the time when my letters and duties were first taught me ; a
lovely, sweet, and wholesome fruit, my children, one which, like the
ambrosia of the blessed in Olympus, grows by participation and
enjoyment.

You receive it attentively and gratefully : your father, who ought
to know its value, listens and rejects it.   I am not angry with him
for this ; and, if I censure him before you, I blame myself also in his
presence.   Too frequently have I repeated my admonition : I am
throwing my time away, I who have so little left me : I am consuming my heart with sorrow, when sorrow and solicitudes should have

34

ceased; and for whom? for him principally who will derive no good from it, and will suffer none to flow on others, not even on those the dearest to him. Think, my children, how unwise a man is Solon, how hard a man Pisistratus, how mistaken in both are the Athenians. Study to avoid our errors, to correct our faults, and by simplicity of life, by moderation in your hopes and wishes, to set a purer and (grant it, Heaven!) a more stabile example than we have done.

IV. ANACREON AND POLYCRATES

Circa 535-515 B.C.

(*Imag. Convers.*, iii., 1828 ; with alterations, *Wks.*, i., 1846 ;
Imag. Convers. Gk. and Rom., 1853.)

POLYCRATES. Embrace me, my brother poet.

ANACREON. What have you written, Polycrates ?

POLYCRATES. Nothing.   But invention is the primary part of us ;
and the mere finding of a brass ring in the belly of a dogfish, has
afforded me a fine episode in royalty.   You could not have made so
much out of it.

ANACREON. I have heard various stories this morning about the
matter : and, to say the truth, my curiosity led me hither.

POLYCRATES. It was thus.   I ordered my cook to open, in the
presence of ten or twelve witnesses, a fat mullet, and to take out of
it an emerald ring, which I had laid aside from the time when, as you
may remember, I felt some twitches of the gout in my knuckle.

ANACREON.[1] The brass ring was really found in a fish some time
ago : might not a second seem suspicious ?   And with what object
is this emerald one extracted from such another mine ?

POLYCRATES. To prove the constancy and immutability of my
fortune.   It is better for a prince to be fortunate than wise : people
know that his fortune may be communicated, his wisdom not ; and,
if it could, nobody would take it who could as readily carry off a
drachma.   In fact, to be fortunate is to be powerful, and not only
without the danger of it, but without the displeasure.

ANACREON. Ministers are envied, princes never ; because envy
can exist there only where something (as people think) may be raised
or destroyed.   You were proceeding very smoothly with your
reflections, Polycrates, but, with all their profundity, are you unaware that mullets do not eat such things ?

POLYCRATES. True ; the people however swallow anything ; and,

---

[1] 1st ed. reads : " ANACREON. With what object ? "

36

the further out of the course of nature the action is, the greater name for good fortune, or rather for the favour of divine providence, shall I acquire.

ANACREON. Is that the cook yonder?

POLYCRATES. Yes; and he also has had some share of the same gifts. I have rewarded him with an Attic talent : he seems to be laying the gold pieces side by side, or in lines and quincunxes, just as if they were so many dishes.

ANACREON. I go to him and see—— By Jupiter ! my friend, you have made no bad kettle of fish of it to-day—— The fellow does not hear me. Let us hope, Polycrates, that it may not break in turning out. If your cook was remunerated so magnificently, what must you have done for the fisherman !

POLYCRATES. He was paid the price of his fish.

ANACREON. Royally said and done ! Your former plan was more extensive. To feign that a brazen ring was the ring of Gyges is indeed in itself no great absurdity [1] ; but to lay claim to the kingdom of Lydia by the possession of it, was extravagant.[2] Crœsus is unwarlike and weak, confident and supercilious, and you had prepared the minds of his officers by your liberality, not to mention the pity and sorrow we put together over our wine, ready to pour it forth on the bleeding hearts of his subjects, treated so ungenerously for their fidelity. Yet your own people might require, at least once a-year, the proof of your invisibility in public by putting on the brazen ring.

POLYCRATES. I had devised as much : nothing is easier than an optical deception, at the distance that kings on solemn occasions keep from the people. A cloud of incense rising from under the floor through several small apertures, and other contrivances were in readiness.[3] But I abandoned my first design, and thought of

[1] 1st ed. adds : " for as much may be done by brass as by gold, in the proper place."

[2] Crœsus had ceased to be King of Lydia before Polycrates became Tyrant of Samos.

[3] 1st ed. inserts here : " The orientals, founders of this fable, teach us by it that we princes should see everything and be unseen. Those who relate it are ignorant of its meaning. Gyges, it is said, was a shepherd. Until I recollected his condition I had sealed my orders with the seal of the fisherman, and submitting all things to the will of Fortune, or of Providence, I was inclined to owe my elevation to this their instrument, to follow the conduct of the shepherd, and to be merely the vice-regent of one or other, according to time and circumstances. On recalling to mind my own ring I abandoned my first design, discarded my shepherd and fisherman, and thought of conquering," etc.

37

conquering Lydia, instead of claiming it from inheritance. For, the ring of a fisherman would be too impudent a fabrication, in the claim of a kingdom or even of a village, and my word upon other occasions might be doubted. Crœsus is superstitious : there are those about him who will persuade him not to contend with a man so signally under the protection of the Gods.[1]

ANACREON. Can not you lay aside all ideas of invasion, and rest quiet and contented here ?

POLYCRATES. No man, O Anacreon, can rest anywhere quiet in his native country who has deprived his fellow-citizens of their liberties ; contented are they only who have taken nothing from another ; and few even of those. As, by eating much habitually, we render our bodies by degrees capacious of more, and uncomfortable without it, so, after many acquisitions, we think new ones necessary. Hereditary kings invade each other's dominions from the feelings of children, the love of having and of destroying ; their education being always bad, and their intellects for the most part low and narrow. But we who have great advantages over them in our mental faculties, these having been constantly exercised and exerted, and in our knowledge of men, wherein the least foolish of them are quite deficient, find wars and civil tumults absolutely needful to our stability and repose.

ANACREON. By Hercules ! you people in purple are very like certain sea-fowls I saw in my voyage from Teios hither. In fine weather they darted upward and downward, sidelong and circuitously, and fished and screamed as if all they seized and swallowed was a torment to them : again, when it blew a violent gale, they appeared to sit perfectly at their ease, buoyant upon the summit of the waves.

POLYCRATES.[2] After all, I cannot be thought to have done any great injury to my friends the citizens of Samos. It is true I have taken away what you ingenious men call their liberties : but have you never, my friend Anacreon, snatched from a pretty girl a bracelet or locket, or other such trifle ?

ANACREON. Not without her permission, and some equivalent.

---

[1] 1st ed. inserts here : " but rather to implore my alliance against the Persian. Now, as I have subverted the laws of Samos, my authority can only be insured by the King of Kings. In Samos I shall always be safe from him, in Lydia from the Samians, if ever they rebell."

[2] From here to " counsel " added in 2nd ed.

ANACREON AND POLYCRATES

POLYCRATES. I likewise have obtained the consent of the people, and have rendered them a great deal more than an equivalent. Formerly they called one another the most opprobrious names in their assemblies, and sometimes even fought there ; now they never do. I entertained from the very beginning so great a regard for them, that I punished one of my brothers with death, and the other with banishment, for attempting to make divisions among them, and for impeding the measures I undertook to establish unanimity and order. My father had consented to bear alone all the toils of government ; and filial piety induced me to imitate his devotion to the commonwealth. The people had assembled to celebrate the festival of Juno, and had crowded the avenues of her temple so unceremoniously and indecorously, that I found it requisite to slay a few hundreds to her glory. King Lygdamus of Naxos lent me his assistance in this salutary operation, well knowing that the cause of royalty in all countries, being equally sacred, should be equally secure.

ANACREON. My sweet Polycrates ! do not imagine that I, or any wise man upon earth, can be interested in the fate of a nation that yields to the discretion of one person. But pray avoid those excesses which may subject the Graces to the Tempests. Let people live in peace and plenty, for your own sake ; and go to war then only when beauteous slaves are wanting. Even then it is cheaper to buy them of the merchant, taking care that at every importation you hire a philosopher or poet to instruct them in morality and religion. The one will demonstrate that obedience is a virtue ; the other, that it is a pleasure. If age stimulates the senses, or if youth is likely to return (as the ring did), not a syllable can I add against the reasonableness of conquests to assuage the wants of either.

POLYCRATES. The people in all countries must be kept in a state of activity : for men in cities, and horses in stables, grow restive by standing still. It is the destination of both to be patted, ridden, and whipped. The riding is the essential thing; the patting and whipping are accessories ; and few are very careful or expert in timing them.

ANACREON. In courts, where silliness alone escapes suspicion, we must shake false lights over the shallows, or we shall catch nothing. But, O Polycrates ! I am not in the court of a prince : I am in the house of a friend. I might flatter you, if flattery could make you happier : but, as you have neglected nothing which could render my

39

abode with you delightful, I would omit no precaution, no suggestion, which may secure and prolong my blessings. Do not believe that every poet is dishonest, because most are. Homer was not ; Solon is not ; I doubt at times whether I myself am ; in despite of your inquisitive eye. My opinion of your wisdom is only shaken by your assumption of royalty, since I can not think it an act of discretion to change tranquillity for alarm, or friends for soldiers, or a couch for a throne, or a sound sleep for a broken one. If you doubt whether I love you (and every prince may reasonably entertain that doubt of every man around him), yet you can not doubt that I am attached to your good fortune, in which I have partaken to my heart's content, and in which I hope to continue a partaker.

POLYCRATES. May the Gods grant it !

ANACREON. Grant it yourself, Polycrates, by following my counsel.[1] Everything is every man's over which his senses extend. What you can enjoy is yours ; what you can not, is not. Of all the islands in the world the most delightful and the most fertile is Samos. Crete and Cyprus are larger ; what then ? The little Teios, my own native country, affords more pleasure than any one heart can receive : not a hill in it but contains more beauty and more wine than the most restless and active could enjoy. Teach the Samiots, O Polycrates, to refuse you and each other no delight that is reciprocal and that lasts. Royalty is the farthest of all things from reciprocity, and what delight it gives must be renewed daily, and with difficulty. In the order of nature, flowers grow on every side of us : why take a ploughshare to uproot them ? We may show our strength and dexterity in guiding it for such a purpose, but not our wisdom. Love, in its various forms, according to our age, station, and capacity, is the only object of reasonable and just desire. I prefer that which is the easiest to give and to return : you, since you have chosen royalty, have taken the most difficult in both : yet by kindness and courtesy you may conciliate those minds, which, once abased by royalty, never can recover their elasticity and strength, unless in the fires of vengeance. The Gods avert it from you, my friend ! Do not inure your people to war : but instead of arming and equipping them, soften them more and more by peace and luxury. Let your deceit in the ring be your last : for men will rather be subjugated than deceived, not knowing, or not reflecting, that they must have

[1] End of passage added in 2nd ed.

been deceived before they could be subjugated. Let you and me keep this secret : that of the cook is hardly so safe.

POLYCRATES. Perfectly, or death would have sealed it ; although my cook is, you know, an excellent one, and would be a greater loss to me than any native of the island. A tolerably good minister of state may be found in any cargo of slaves that lands upon the coast. Interest ensures fidelity. As for difficulty, I see none : to handle great bodies requires little delicacy. He would make in a moment a hole through a mud-wall who could never make the eye of a needle : and it is easier to pick up a pompion than a single grain of dust. With you however who have lived among such people, and know them thoroughly, I need not discourse long about them, nor take the trouble to argue how impossible it is to blunder on so wide and smooth a road, where every man is ready with a lamp if it is dark or with a cart if it is miry. You know that a good cook is the peculiar gift of the gods. He must be a perfect creature from the brain to the palate, from the palate to the finger's end. Pleasure and displeasure, sickness and health, life and death, are consigned to his arbitration. It would be little to add that he alone shares with royalty the privilege of exemption from every punishment but capital : for it would be madness to flog either, and turn it loose.

The story of the ring will be credited as long as I want it ; probably all my life, perhaps after. For men are swift to take up a miracle, and slow to drop it ; and woe to the impious wretch who would undeceive them ! They never will believe that I can be unprosperous, until they see me put to death : some, even then, would doubt whether it were I, and others whether I were really dead, the day following. As we are in no danger of any such event, let us go and be crowned for the feast, and prove whether the mullet has any other merits than we have yet discovered.

Come, Anacreon, you must write an ode to Fortune, not forgetting her favorite.

ANACREON. I dare not, before I have written one to Juno, the patroness of Samos : but, as surely as you are uncrucified, I will do it then. Pardon me however if I should happen to praise the beauty of her eyes, for I am used to think more about the Goddess who has the loveliest ; and, even if I began with the Furies, I should end in all likelihood with *her*.

POLYCRATES. Follow [1] your own ideas. You can not fail, however, to descant on the facility with which I acquired my power, and the unanimity by which I retain it, under the guidance and protection of our patroness. I had less trouble in becoming the master of Samos than you will have in singing it. Indeed, when I consider how little I experienced, I wonder that liberty can exist in any country where there is one wise and resolute man.

ANACREON. And I that tyranny can, where there are two.

POLYCRATES. What! Anacreon, are even you at last so undisguisedly my adversary?

ANACREON. Silly creature! behold the fruit of royalty! Rottenness in the pulp, and bitterness in the kernel.

Polycrates, if I had uttered those words before the people, they would have stoned me for being your enemy . . . for being a traitor! This is the expression of late, not applied to those who betray, but to those who resist or traverse the betrayer. To such a situation are men reduced when they abandon self-rule! I love you from similarity of studies and inclinations, from habit, from gaiety of heart, and because I live with you more conveniently than in a meaner house and among coarser slaves. As for the Samiots, you can not suppose me much interested about them. Beauty itself is the less fierce from servitude ; and there is no person, young or old, who does not respect more highly the guest of Polycrates than the poet of Teios. You, my dear friend, who are a usurper, for which courage, prudence, affability, liberality, are necessary, would surely blush to act no better or more humanely than a hereditary and established king, the disadvantages of whose condition you yourself have stated admirably. Society is not yet trodden down and forked together by you into one and the same rotten mass, with rank weeds covering the top and sucking out its juices.[2] Circe, when she transformed the companions of Ulysses into swine, took no delight in drawing their tusks and ringing their snouts, but left them, by special grace, in quiet and full possession of their new privileges and dignities. The rod of enchantment was the only rod she used among them, finding a pleasanter music in the choruses of her nymphs than in the grunts and squeals of her subjects.

---

[1] From here to " patroness " added in 2nd ed.
[2] 1st ed. inserts : " though somewhat soiled the straws are yet distinct, and may be assorted out for different uses as you want them."

ANACREON AND POLYCRATES

POLYCRATES. Now, tell me truly, Anacreon, if you knew of a conspiracy against me, would you reveal it ?

ANACREON. I would ; both for your sake and for the conspirators. Even were I not your guest and friend, I would dissuade from every similar design.

POLYCRATES. In some points, however, you [1] appear to have a fellow feeling with the seditious. You differ from them in this : you would not take the trouble to kill me, and could not find a convenient hour to run away.

ANACREON. I am too young for death, too old for flight, and too comfortable for either. As for killing you, I find it business enough to kill a kid as a sacrifice to Bacchus. Answer me as frankly as I answered you. If by accident you met a girl carried off by force would you stop the ravisher ?

POLYCRATES. Certainly, if she were pretty : if not, I would leave the offence to its own punishment.

ANACREON. If the offence had been perpetrated to its uttermost extent, if the girl were silent, and if the brother unarmed should rush upon the perpetrator armed——

POLYCRATES. I would catch him by the sleeve and stop him.

ANACREON. I would act so in this business of yours. You have deflowered the virgin. Whether the action will bring after it the full chastisement, I know not : nor whether the laws will ever wake upon it, or, waking upon it, whether they will not hold their breath and lie quiet. Weazels, and other animals that consume our corn, are strangled or poisoned, as may happen : usurpers and conquerors must be taken off quietly in one way only, lest many perish in the attempt, and lest it fail. No conspiracy of more than two persons ought ever to be entered into on such a business. Hence the danger is diminished to those concerned, and the satisfaction and glory are increased. Statues can be erected to two, not to many ; gibbets can be erected as readily to many as to few ; and would be ; for most conspiracies have been discovered and punished, while hundreds of usurpers have been removed by their cooks, their cup-bearers, and their mistresses, as easily, and with as little noise or notice, as a dish from the table, or a slipper from the bed-side.

Banish the bloated and cloudy ideas of war and conquest. Continue to eat while you have anything in your mouth, particularly if

[1] 1st ed. reads : " POLYCRATES. You ... feeling. ANACREON. Answer me," etc.

43

sweet or savoury, and only think of filling it again when it is empty.

Crœsus hath no naval force, nor have the Persians : they desire the fish but fear the water, and will mew and purr over you until they fall asleep and forget you, unless you plunge too loud and glitter too near. They would have attacked you in the beginning, if they had ever wished to do it, or been ignorant that kings have an enemy the less on the ruin of every free nation. I do not tell you to sit quiet, any more than I would a man who has a fever or an ague, but to sit as quiet as your condition will permit. If you leave to others their enjoyments, they will leave yours to you. Tyrants never perish from tyranny, but always from folly ; when their fantasies build up a palace for which the earth has no foundation. It then becomes necessary, they think, to talk about their similitude to the Gods, and to tell the people, " We have a right to rule you, just as they have a right to rule us : the duties they exact from us, we exact from you : we are responsible to none but to them."

POLYCRATES. Anacreon ! Anacreon ! who, in the name of Hermes, ever talked thus since the reign of Salmoneus ? People who would listen to such inflated and idle arrogance, must be deprived, not of their liberties only, but their senses. Lydians or Carians, Cappadocians or Carmanians, would revolt at it : I myself would tear the diadem from my brow, before I would commit such an outrage on the dignity of our common nature. A little fallacy, a little fraud and imposture, may be requisite to our office, and principally on entering it ; there is however no need to tell the people that we, on our consciences, lay the public accounts before Jupiter for his signature ; that, if there is any surplus, we will return it hereafter ; but that, as honest and pious men, their business is with him, not with us.

My dear Anacreon, you reason speciously, which is better in most cases than reasoning soundly ; for many are led by it and none offended. But as there are pleasures in poetry which I can not know, in like manner there are pleasures in royalty which you can not. Say what you will, we have this advantage over you. Sovrans and poets alike court us ; they alike treat you with malignity and contumely. Do you imagine that Hylactor, supposing him to feign a little in regard to me, really would on any occasion be so enthusiastic in your favour as he was in mine ?

44

ANACREON AND POLYCRATES

ANACREON. You allude to the village-feast, in which he requested from your hand the cup you had poured a libation from, and tasted ?

POLYCRATES. The very instance I was thinking on.

ANACREON. Hylactor [1] tells a story delightfully, and his poetry is better than most poets will allow.

POLYCRATES. I do not think it—I speak of the poetry.

ANACREON. Now, my dear Polycrates, without a word of flattery to you, on these occasions you are as ignorant as a goat-herd.

POLYCRATES. I do not think *that* either.

ANACREON. Who does, of himself ? Yet poetry and the degrees of it are just as difficult to mark and circumscribe, as love and beauty. [2]

POLYCRATES. Madman !

ANACREON. All are madmen who first draw out hidden truths.

POLYCRATES. You are envious of Hylactor, because on that day I had given him a magnificent dress, resembling those of the Agathyrsi.

ANACREON. I can go naked at my own expense. I would envy him (if it gave me no trouble) his lively fancy, his convivial fun, and his power to live in a crowd, which I can do no longer than a trout can in the grass. What I envied on that day, I had. When with eyes turned upward to you, modestly and reverentially, he entreated the possession of the beechen bowl out of which you had taken *one* draught, I, with like humility of gesture and similar tone of voice, requested I might be possessor of the barrel out of which you had taken *but* one. The people were silent at his request ; they were rapturous at mine : one excepted.

POLYCRATES. And what said he ?

ANACREON. " By Bacchus ! " he exclaimed, " I thought syco-phants were the most impudent people in the world : but, Anacreon, verily thou surpassest them : thou puttest them out of countenance, out of breath, man ! "

Your liberality was, as usual, enough for us ; and, if Envy must come in, she must sit between us. Really the dress, coarse as it was, that you gave Placoeis, the associate of Hylactor, would have covered Tityus : nay, would have made winding-sheets, and ample ones, for

[1] 1st ed. reads : " Hylactor, if he were not a sycophant, would be admirable : he tells," etc.

[2] 1st ed. inserts : " All men are affected by them more or less : no man could ever say exactly what proportions they bore in any one object to another. We shall see ten Iliads before we see one right criticism on good poetry."

45

all the giants, if indeed their mother Earth enwrapt their bones in any. Meditating the present of such another investiture, you must surprise or scale Miletus ; for if, in addition to the sheep of Samos, the cows and oxen, the horses and swine, the goats and dogs, were woolly, the fleeces of ten years would be insufficient. As Placoeis moved on, there were exclamations of wonder on all sides, at all distances. " Another Epeüs * must have made that pageant ! " was the cry : and many were trodden under foot from wishing to obtain a sight of the rollers. His heat, like the sun's, increased as he proceeded ; and those who kept egg-stalls and fish-stalls cursed him and removed them.

POLYCRATES. We [1] will feast again no less magnificently when I return from my victory on the continent. There are delicate perfumes and generous wines and beautiful robes at Sardis.

* Framer of the *Trojan Horse.*—W. S. L.
[1] " We . . . Sardis " added in 2nd ed.

V. XERXES AND ARTABANUS

Circa 480 B.C.

(*Imag. Convers. Gk. and Rom.*, 1853 ; *Wks.*, ii., 1876.)

ARTABANUS. Many nations, O Xerxes, have risen higher in power, but no nation rose ever to the same elevation in glory as the Greek.

XERXES. For which reason, were there no other, I would destroy it ; then all the glory this troublesome people have acquired will fall unto me in addition to my own.

ARTABANUS. The territory, yes ; the glory, no. The solid earth may yield to the mighty : one particle of glory is never to be detached from the acquirer and possessor.

XERXES. Artabanus ! Artabanus ! thou speakest more like an Athenian than a Persian. If thou forgettest thy country, remember at least thy race.

ARTABANUS. I owe duty and obedience to my King ; I owe truth both to King and country. Years have brought me experience.

XERXES. And timidity.

ARTABANUS. Yes, before God.

XERXES. And not before the monarch ?

ARTABANUS. My last word said it.

XERXES. I too am pious ; yea, even more devout than thou. Was there ever such a sacrifice as that of the thousand beeves, which on the Mount of Ilion I offered up in supplication to Athenè ? I think it impossible the gods of Hellas should refuse me victory over such outcasts and barbarians in return for a thousand head of cattle. Never was above a tenth of the number offered up to them before. Indeed, I doubt whether a tenth of that tenth come not nearer to the amount : for the Greeks are great boasters, and, in their exceeding cleverness and roguery, would chuckle at cheating the eagerly expectant and closely observant Gods. What sayest thou ?

ARTABANUS. About the Greeks I can say nothing to the contrary : but about the Gods a question is open. Are they more vigorous, active, and vigilant, for the thousand beeves ? Certain it is that every Mede and Persian in the army would have improved in condition after feasting on them : as they might all have done for many days.

XERXES. But their feasting or fasting could have no influence on the Gods, who, according to their humour at the hour, might either laugh or scowl at them.

ARTABANUS. I know not the will of Him above ; for there is only one ; as our fathers and those before them have taught us. Ignorant Greeks, when they see the chariot of His representative drawn before thee by white horses, call Him Zeus.

XERXES. Mithra, the sun, we venerate.

ARTABANUS. Mithra we call the object of our worship. One sits above the sun, observes it, watches it, and replenishes it perpetually with His own light to guide the walk of the seasons. He gives the sun its beauty, its strength, its animation.

XERXES. I worship Him devoutly. But if one God can do us good, fifty can do us more, aided by demigods and heroes.

ARTABANUS. Could fifty lamps in a royal chamber add light to it when open to the meridian ?

XERXES. No doubt they could.

ARTABANUS. Are they wanted ?

XERXES. Perhaps not. They must be, even there, if the sun should go behind a cloud.

ARTABANUS. God avert the omen !

XERXES. I have better omens in abundance. I am confident, I am certain of success. The more powerful and the more noble of the Greeks, the Athenians, Spartans, Thessalians, are with me, or ready to join me.

ARTABANUS. How many of them, fugitives from their country, or traitors to it, can be trusted ?

XERXES. The Aleuadai from Larissa, country of Achilles, whose sepulchral mound we visited, offer me their submission and the strongholds on the borders of their territory. The descendants of Pisistratus, with the King of Sparta, are under my protection, and obedient to my will. They who have been stripped of power, lawful or unlawful, are always the most implacable enemies of their country. Whether they return to it by force or by treachery, or by persuasion and the fickleness of the people, they rule with rigour.

48

XERXES AND ARTABANUS

Ashamed of complicity and cowardice, the rabble, the soldiery, the priests, the nobles, hail them with acclamations, and wait only to raise louder, until his death, natural or violent (but violent and natural are here the same), shall deliver them again from their bondage. Then cometh my hand afresh over the people and draweth it gently back unto me. Resistance is vain. Have I not commanded the refractory and insolent sea to be scourged? and not for disobeying my orders, which it never dared, but in my absence for destroying my bridge. The sentence hath already been carried into execution. Never more in my proximity and to my detriment will it presume to be tumultuous and insurgent.

ARTABANUS. O King! thy power is awful, is irresistible; but can the waves feel? *

XERXES. Mutineers can; and these waves were mutineers. They hiss and roar and foam, and swell and sink down again; and never are quiet. This, O Artabanus, is so like undisciplined men, that it appears to me they also may feel. Whether they do or not, terror is stricken into the hearts of the beholders. No exertion of superior power but works upon the senses of mankind. Men are always the most obedient to, and follow the most vociferously, those who can and who do chastise, whether them or others. A trifle of benefit, bestowed on them afterward, drops like balm into the wound: but balm the most precious and the most sanitary drops insensibly on an unwounded part. Behold! here come into my presence, to be reviewed at my leisure, the silver shields. To what perfect discipline have I brought my army! Its armature is either the admiration or the terror of the universe. What sayest thou?

ARTABANUS. Certainly our Median and Persian cavalry is excellent. In regard to the armature, which former kings and generals devised, I entreat the liberty to remark, that its brightness and gorgeousness are better adapted to attract the fancies of women and boys, than to strike terror into martial men.

XERXES. Look thou again, if thine eyes can endure the splendour, look thou again at my body-guard, and at their silver shields, and at their spears with golden pomegranates at the nearer end.

ARTABANUS. Permit me to inquire, of what utility are these

---

* Dead men, it is said, have been whipped under the Czar Nicholas; but they were alive and hale when the whipping began.—W. S. L.

golden pomegranates ? They stick not into the ground, which sometimes is needful ; they are injurious to the arm in grasping, more injurious in evolution, and may sometimes be handles for the enemy. Metal breast-plates, metal corselets, metal shields, silver or brass, are unwieldy and wearisome, not only by the weight but by the heat, especially at that season of the year when armies are most in activity.

XERXES. What wouldst thou have ? What wouldst thou suggest ?

ARTABANUS: I would have neither horse-hair nor plumage, nor other ornament, on the helmet, which are inconvenient to the soldier, but are convenient to the enemy. Helmets, alike for cavalry and infantry, should in form be conical, or shaped as the keel of a ship. In either case, a stroke of the sword, descending on it, would more probably glance off, without inflicting a wound. But I would render them less heavy, and less subject to the influence of heat and cold.

XERXES. Impossible ! How ?

ARTABANUS. There are materials. Cork, two fingers breadth in thickness, covered with well-seasoned, strained, and levigated leather, would serve the purpose both for helmet and corselet, and often turn aside, often resist, both sword and spear.

XERXES. My younger soldiers, especially the officers, would take little pride in such equipment.

ARTABANUS. The pride of the officer ought to be in the efficiency and comfort of the soldier. Latterly I have been grieved to see vain and idle young persons introduce alterations, which wiser men laugh at, and by which the enemy only, and their tailor, can profit. We should be more efficient if we were less decorative.

XERXES. Efficient ! what can excell us ?

ARTABANUS. Ah my King ! Our ancestors have excelled *their* ancestors in various improvements and inventions : our children may excell *us*. Where is that beyond which there is nothing ? Great would be our calamity, for great our disgrace and shame, if barbarians, in any action, however slight and partial, should discomfit the smallest part of our armies. And there are barbarians whose bodies are more active, whose vigilance more incessant, whose abstinence more enduring, and whose armour is less impedimental, than ours. I blush at some of our bravest and best generals giving way so easily to fantastical and inexperienced idlers, who never saw a battle even from a balcony or a tower. Who is he that would not respect and venerate grey hairs? but, seeing such dereliction of dignity, such relaxation of duty, such unworthy subserviency, who can? Every soldier should be able to swim, and should have every facility for doing it. Corselets of the form I described, would enable whole bodies of troops to cross broad and deep rivers, and would save a great number of pontoons, and their carriages, and their bullocks. No shield would be necessary; so that every soldier, Mede and Persian, would have one hand the more out of two. Let the barbarous nations in our service use only their own weapons; it is inexpedient and dangerous to instruct them in better.

XERXES. There is somewhat of wisdom, but not much, O Artabanus, in thy suggestions; had there been more, the notions would first have occurred to me. But with the arms which our men already bear we are perfectly a match for the Greeks, who, seeing our numbers, will fly.

ARTABANUS. Whither? From one enemy to another? Believe me, sir, neither Athenian nor Spartan will ever fly. If he loses this one battle, he loses life or freedom; and he knows it.

XERXES. I would slay only the armed. The women and children I would in part divide among the bravest of my army, and in part I would settle on the barren localities of my dominions, whereof there are many.

ARTABANUS. Humanely and royally spoken; but did it never once occur to an observer so sagacious, that thousands and tens of thousands, in your innumerable host, would gladly occupy and cultivate those desert places, in which an Athenian would pine away? Immense tracts of your dominions are scantily inhabited. Two million men are taken from agriculture and other works of industry, of whom probably a third would have married, another third would have had children born unto them from the wives they left behind: of these thousands and tens of thousands God only knows how many may return. Not only losses are certain; but wide fields must lie uncultivated, much cattle be the prey of wild beasts throughout the empire, and more of worse depredators, who never fear the law, but always the battle, and who skulk behind and hide themselves, to fall upon what unprotected property has been left by braver men. Unless our victory and our return be speedy, your providence in collecting stores, during three entire years, will have been vain. Already the greater part (four-fifths at the lowest computation) hath been consumed. Attica and Sparta could not supply a sufficiency for two millions of men additional, and three hundred thousand horses, two months. Provender will soon be wanting for the sustenance of their own few cattle : summer heats have commenced ; autumn is distant, and unpromising.

XERXES. Disaffection ! disaffection ! Artabanus, beware ! I love my father's brother ; but not even my father's brother shall breathe despondency or disquietude into my breast. Well do I remember thy counsel against this expedition.

ARTABANUS. Thou thyself for awhile, O king, and before I gave my counsel, didst doubt and hesitate.

XERXES. The holy Dream enlightened me : and thou also wert forced to acknowledge the visitation of the same. Awful and superhuman was the Apparition. Never had I believed that even a deity would threaten Xerxes. A second time, when I had begun again to doubt and hesitate, it appeared before me ; the same stately figure, the same menacing attitude, nearer and nearer. Thou wilt acknowledge, O Artabanus, that in this guise, or one more terrible, he came likewise unto thee.

ARTABANUS. Commanded by my king to enter his chamber and to sleep in his bed, I did so. Discourse on the invasion of Greece had animated some at supper, and depressed others. Wine was poured freely into the cups equally of these and of those. Mardonius, educated by the wisest of the Mages, and beloved by all of them, was long in conference with his old preceptor. Toward the close they were there alone. Wearied, and fearful of offending, I retired, and left them together. The royal bedchamber had many tapers in various parts of it : by degrees they grew more and more dim, breathing forth such odours as royalty alone is privileged to inhale. Slumber came over me ; heavy sleep succeeded.

XERXES. It was thus with me, the first night and the second. Mardonius would never have persuaded me, had dreams and visions been less constant and less urgent. What pious man ought to resist them ? Nevertheless, I am still surrounded and trammelled by perplexities.

52

XERXES AND ARTABANUS

ARTABANUS. The powerful, the generous, the confiding, always are ; kings especially.

XERXES. Mardonius, I begin to suspect, is desirous of conquering Greece principally in order to become satrap of that country.

ARTABANUS. He is young ; he may be and ought to be ambitious, but I believe him to be loyal.

XERXES. Artabanus ! thou art the only one about me who never spoke ill, or hinted it, of another.

ARTABANUS. I have never walked in the path of evil-doers, and know them not.

XERXES. Fortunate am I that a man so wise and virtuous hath come over to my opinion. The Vision was irresistible.

ARTABANUS. It confirmed, not indeed my opinion, but the words formerly told me by a Mage now departed.

XERXES. What words ? Did he likewise foresee and foretell my conquest of Hellas ?

ARTABANUS. I know not whether he foresaw it : certainly he never foretold it unto me. But wishing to impress on my tender mind (for I was then about the age of puberty) the power appertaining to the Mages, he declared to me, among other wonders, that the higher of them could induce sleep, of long continuance and profound, by a movement of the hand ; could make the sleeper utter his inmost thoughts ; could inspire joy or terror, love or hatred ; could bring remote things and remote persons near, even the future, even the dead. Is it impossible that the Dream was one of them ?

XERXES. I am quite lost in the darkness of wonder ; for never hast thou been known to utter an untruth, or a truth disparaging to the Mages. Their wisdom is unfathomable ; their knowledge is unbounded by the visible world in which we live : their empire is vast even as mine. But take heed : who knows but the Gods themselves are creatures of their hands ! My hair raises up my diadem at the awful thought.

ARTABANUS. The just man, O Xerxes, walks humbly in the presence of his God, but walks fearlessly. Deities of many nations are within thy tents ; and each of them is thought the most powerful, the only true one, by his worshiper. Some, it is reported, are jealous ; if so, the worshiper is, or may be, better than they are. The courts and pavilions of others are represented by their hymners as filled with coals and smoke, and with chariots and instruments of slaughter. These are the deities of secluded regions and gloomy imaginations. We are now amid a people of more lively and more genial faith.

XERXES. I think their Gods are easy to propitiate, and worth propitiating. The same singer who celebrated the valour of Achilles, hath described in another poem the residence of these Gods [1]; where they lead quiet lives above the winds and tempests; where frost never binds the pure illimitable expanse; where snow never whirls around; where lightning never quivers; but temperate warmth and clearest light are evermore about them.

Such is the description which the sons of Hipparchus have translated for my amusement from the singer.

ARTABANUS. Whatever be the quarrels in the various tents, extending many and many parasangs in every direction, there is no quarrel or disturbance about the objects of veneration. Barbarous are many of the nations under thee, but none so barbarous. There may be such across the Danube and across the Adriatic; old regions of fable; countries where there are Læstrigons and Cyclopses, and men turned into swine; there may be amid the wastes of Scythia, where Gryphons are reported to guard day and night treasures of gold buried deep under the rocks, and to feed insatiably on human blood and marrow; but none, O happy king, within the regions, interminable as they are, under the beneficent sway of thy sceptre.

XERXES. The huntsman knows how to treat dogs that quarrel in the kennel; moreover he perceives the first symptoms of the rabid, and his arrow is upon the string.

Ancient times and modern have seen annihilated two great armies; the greatest of each; that of Xerxes and that of Napoleon. Xerxes was neither the more ambitious of these invaders nor the more powerful, but greatly the more provident. Three years together he had been storing magazines in readiness for his expedition, and had collected fresh provisions in abundance on his march. Napoleon marched where none had been or could be collected, instead of taking the road by Danzic, in which fortress were ample stores for his whole army until it should reach Petersburg by the coast. No hostile fleet could intercept such vessels as would convey both grain and munition. The nobility of Moscow would have rejoiced at the destruction of a superseding city, become the seat of empire. Whether winter came on ten days earlier or later, snow

---

[1] Homer, *Od.*, vi. 42 ; Landor, *Wks.*, iv. 273.

XERXES AND ARTABANUS

was sure to blockade and famish the army in Moscow; the importation of provisions (had sufficiency existed within reach) and the march northward, were equally impracticable. Napoleon left behind him a signal example that strategy is only a constituent part of a commander. In his Russian campaign even this was wanting. Xerxes lost his army not so totally as Napoleon lost his: Xerxes in great measure by the valour and skill of his enemy; Napoleon by his own imprudence. The faith of Xerxes was in his Dream, Napoleon's in his Star: the Dream was illusory, the Star a falling one.—W. S. L.

VI. PERICLES AND SOPHOCLES

Circa 460 B.C.

(Imag. Convers., ii., 1824, and 1826 ; *Wks.*, i., 1846 ; *Imag. Convers.*
Gk. and Rom., 1853 ; *Wks.*, ii., 1876.)

PERICLES. O Sophocles ! is there in the world a city so beautiful
as Athens ?   Congratulate me, embrace me ; the Piræus and the
Pœcilè are completed this day * ; my glory is accomplished ; behold
it founded on the supremacy of our fellow-citizens.

SOPHOCLES. And it arises, O Pericles, the more majestically from
the rich and delightful plain of equal laws.   The Gods have bestowed
on our statuaries and painters a mighty power, enabling them
to restore our ancestors unto us, some in the calm of thought,
others in the tumult of battle, and to present them before our
children when we are gone.

PERICLES. Shall it be so ?   Alas, how worthless an incumbrance,
how wearisome an impediment is life, if it separate us from the better
of our ancestors, not in our existence only, but in our merit [1] !   We
are little by being seen among men ; because that phasis of us
only is visible which is exposed toward them and which most resembles them : we become greater by leaving the world, as the sun
appears to be on descending below the horizon.   Strange reflection !
humiliating truth ! that nothing on earth, no exertion, no endow-
ment, can do so much for us as a distant day.   And deep indeed,
O Sophocles, must be the impression made upon thy mind by these
masterly works of art, if they annihilate in a manner the living ;

* Their decorations only ; for the structures were finished before.   The
propylæa of Pericles were entrances to the citadel : other works of consummate
beauty were erected as ornaments to the city, but chiefly in the Pœcilè, where
also was seen the Temple of Cybèlè, with her statue by Phidias.—W. S. L.

[In the 1826 ed. this note is much longer.   Most of it was added to " Pallavicini
and Landor " in 1846.]

[1] In 1824 ed. : " merits."

if they lower in thee that spirit which hath often aroused by one touch, or rather flash, the whole Athenian people at thy tragedies, and force upon thee the cold and ungenial belief, the last which it appears to be their nature to inculcate, that while our children are in existence it can cease to be among them.

SOPHOCLES. I am only the interpreter of the heroes and divinities who are looking down on me. When I survey them I remember their actions, and when I depart from them I visit the regions they illustrated.

Neither the Goddesses on Ida nor the Gods before Troy were such rivals as our artists. Æschylus hath surpassed me * : I must excell Æschylus. O Pericles, thou conjurest up Discontent from the bosom of Delight, and givest her an elevation of mien and character she never knew before : thou makest every man greater than his competitor, and not in his own eyes but in another's. We want historians : thy eloquence will form the style, thy administration will supply the materials. Beware, O my friend, lest the people hereafter be too proud of their city, and imagine that to have been born in Athens is enough.

PERICLES. And this indeed were hardly more irrational, than the pride which cities take sometimes in the accident of a man's birth within their walls, of a citizen's whose experience was acquired, whose virtues were fostered, and perhaps whose services were performed, elsewhere.

SOPHOCLES. They are proud of having been the cradles of great men, then only when great men can be no longer an incumbrance or a reproach to them. Let them rather boast of those who spend the last day in them than the first ; [1] this is always accidental, that is generally by choice ; for, from something like instinct, we wish to close our eyes upon the world in the places we love best, the child in its mother's bosom, the patriot in his country. When we are born we are the same as others : at our decease we may induce our friends, and oblige our enemies, to acknowledge that others are not the same as we. It is folly to say, Death levels the whole

---

* Sophocles gained the first prize for which he contended with Æschylus, and was conscious that he had not yet deserved the superiority, which enthusiasm on the one side and jealousy on the other are always ready to grant a vigorous young competitor. The character of Sophocles was frank and liberal, as was remarkably proved on the death of his last rival, Euripides.—W. S. L.

[1] Colon in ed. of 1824.

human race : for it is only when he hath stripped men of everything external, that their deformities can be clearly discovered, or their worth correctly ascertained. Gratitude is soon silent ; a little while longer and Ingratitude is tired, is satisfied, is exhausted, or sleeps. Lastly fly off the fumes of party-spirit [1] ; the hottest and most putrid ebullition of self-love. We then see before us and contemplate calmly [2] the creator of our customs, the ruler of our passions, the arbiter of our pleasures, and, under the Gods, the disposer of our destiny. What then, I pray thee, is there dead ? Nothing more than that which we can handle, cast down, bury ; and surely not he who is yet to progenerate a more numerous and far better race, than during the few years it was permitted us to converse with him.

PERICLES. When I reflect on Themistocles, on Aristides, and on the greatest of mortal men, Miltiades, I wonder how their country-men can repeat their names, unless in performing the office of expiation.*

SOPHOCLES. Cities are ignorant that nothing is more disgraceful to them than to be the birth-places of the illustriously good, and not afterward the places of their residence ; that their dignity consists in adorning them with distinctions, in entrusting to them the regulation of the commonwealth, and not in having sold a crust or cordial to the nurse or midwife.

PERICLES. O Zeus and Pallas [3] ! grant a right mind to the Athenians ! If, throughout so many and such eventful ages, they have been found by you deserving of their freedom, render them more and more worthy of the great blessing you bestowed on them !

---

[1] " Partyspirit " in ed. of 1824.

[2] Commas in ed. of 1826 after " us " and " calmly."

* There are some who may deem this reflection unsuitable to Pericles. He saw injustice in others, and hated it : yet he caused the banishment of Cimon, as great a man as any of the three. It is true he had afterward the glory of proposing and of carrying to Sparta the decree of his recall. Let us contemplate the brighter side of his character, his eloquence, his wit, his clemency, his judg-ment, his firmness, his regularity, his decorousness, his domesticity ; let us then unite him with his predecessor, and acknowledge that such illustrious rivals never met before or since, in enmity or in friendship. Could the piety attributed to Pericles have belonged to a scholar of Anaxagoras ? Eloquent men often talk like religious men : and where should the eloquence of Pericles be more inflamed by enthusiasm than in the midst of his propylæa, at the side of Sophocles, and before the Gods of Phidias ?—W. S. L.

[3] In 1st ed. : " Jove and Minerva."

58

PERICLES AND SOPHOCLES

May the valour of our children defend this mole for ever; and constantly may their patriotism increase and strengthen among these glorious reminiscences !   Shield them from the jealousy of surrounding states, from the ferocity of barbarian kings, and from the perfidy of those who profess the same religion !   Teach them that between the despot and the free all compact is a cable of sand, and every alliance unholy [1] !   And, O givers of power and wisdom ! remove from them the worst and wildest of illusions, that happiness, liberty, virtue, genius, will be fostered or long respected, much less attain their just ascendency, under any other form of government !

Sophocles. May the Gods hear thee, Pericles, as they have always done ! or may I, reposing in my tomb, never know that they have not heard thee !

I smile on imagining how trivial would thy patriotism and ideas of government appear to Chloros.[2]   And indeed much wiser men, from the prejudices of habit and education, have undervalued them, preferring the dead quiet of their wintry hives to our breezy spring of life and busy summer.   The countries of the vine and olive are more subject to hailstorms than the regions of the north : yet is it not better that some of the fruit should fall than that none should ripen ?

Pericles. Quit these creatures ; let them lie warm and slumber ; they are all they ought to be, all they can be.   But prythee who is Chloros, that he should deserve to be named by Sophocles ?

Sophocles. He was born somewhere on the opposite coast of Euboea, and sold as a slave in Persia to a man who dealt largely in that traffic, and who also had made a fortune by displaying to the public four remarkable proofs of ability : [2] first, by swallowing at a draught an amphora of the strongest wine ; secondly, by standing up erect and modulating his voice like a sober man when he was drunk ; thirdly, by acting to perfection like a drunken man when he was sober ; and fourthly, by a most surprising trick indeed, which it is reported he learnt in Babylonia : one would have sworn he had a blazing fire in his mouth ; take it out, and it is nothing but a lump of ice.   The king, before whom he was

---

[1] In 2nd ed. : " and alliance most unholy."

[2] " Chloros " : apparently Viscount Castlereagh.   Pitt is intended by the Persian conjuror.   The former conjuror is Fox.

admitted to play his tricks, hated him at first, and told him that the last conjuror had made him cautious of such people, he having been detected in filching from the royal tiara one of the weightiest jewels : but talents forced their way. As for Chloros, I mention him by the name under which I knew him ; he has changed it since ; for although the dirt wherewith it was encrusted kept him comfortable at first, when it cracked and began to crumble it was incommodious.

The barbarians have commenced, I understand, to furbish their professions and vocations with rather whimsical skirts and linings : thus for instance a chessplayer is *lion-hearted* and *worshipful ;* a drunkard is *serenity* and *highness ;* a hunter of fox, badger, polecat, fitchew, and weazel, is *excellency* and *right honourable ;* while, such is the delicacy of distinction, a rat-catcher is considerably less : he however is *illustrious*, and appears, as a tail to a comet, in the train of a legation, holding a pen between his teeth to denote his capacity for secretary, and leading a terrier in the right hand, and carrying a trap baited with cheese and anise-seed in the left.

It is as creditable among them to lie with dexterity as it is common among the Spartans to steal. Chloros, who performed it with singular frankness and composure, had recently a cock's feather mounted on his turban, in place of a hen's, and the people was commanded to address him by the title of *most noble.* His brother Alexaretes [1] was employed at a stipend of four talents to detect an adultress in one among the royal wives : he gave no intelligence in the course of several months : the king on his return cried angrily, " What hast thou been doing ? hast thou never found her out ? " He answered, " Thy servant, O king, hath been doing more than finding out an adultress : he hath, O king, been making one."

PERICLES. I have heard the story with this difference, that the bed-ambassador being as scantily gifted with facetiousness as with perspicacity, the reply was framed satirically by some other courtier, who, imitating his impudence, had forgotten his dulness. But about the reward of falsehood, that is wonderful, when we read that formerly the Persians were occupied many years in the sole study of truth.

[1] Lord Charles Stewart, afterwards 3rd Marquis of Londonderry.

PERICLES AND SOPHOCLES

SOPHOCLES. How difficult then must they have found it! No [1] wonder they left it off the first moment they could conveniently. The grandfather of Chloros [2] was honest : he carried a pack upon his shoulders, in which pack were contained the coarser linens of Caria : these he retailed among the villages of Asia and Greece, but principally in the islands. He died : on the rumour of war the son and grandson, then an infant, fled : the rest is told. In Persia no man inquires how another comes to wealth or power, the suddenness of which appears to be effected by some of the demons or genii of their songs and stories. Chloros grew rich, was emancipated from slavery, and bought several slaves himself. One of these was excessively rude and insolent to me : I had none near enough to chastise him, so that I requested of his master, by a friend, to admonish and correct him at his leisure. My friend informs me that Chloros, crossing his legs, and drawing his cock's feather through the thumb and finger, asked languidly who I was, and receiving the answer, said, " I am surprised at his impudence : Pericles himself could have demanded nothing more." My friend remarked that Sophocles was no less sensible of an affront than Pericles. " True," replied he, " but he has not the power of expressing his sense of it quite so strongly. For an affront to Pericles, who could dreadfully hurt me, I would have imprisoned my whole gang, whipped them with wires, mutilated them, turned their bodies into safes for bread and water, or cooled their prurient tongues with hemlock : but no slave shall ever shrug a shoulder the sorer or eat a leek the less for Sophocles."

PERICLES. The ideas of such a man on government must be curious : I am persuaded he would prefer the Persian to any. I forgot to mention that, according to what I hear this morning, the great king has forbidden strange ships to sail within thirty parasangs of his coasts, and has claimed the dominion of half ours.

SOPHOCLES. Where is the scourge with which Xerxes lashed the ocean ? Were it not better laid on the back of a madman than placed within his hand ?

PERICLES. It hath been observed by those who look deeply into the history of physics, that all royal families become at last insane.

---

[1] In this, and several similarly framed sentences, or pieces of sentences, there was originally no break, the 1826 ed. reading " found it ! no wonder," etc.

[2] Viscount Castlereagh's great-grandfather was an alderman of Belfast.

61

Immoderate power, like other intemperance, leaves the progeny weaker and weaker, until Nature, as in compassion, covers it with her mantle and it is seen no more, or until the arm of indignant man sweeps it from before him.

We must ere long excite the other barbarians to invade the territories of this, and before the cement of his new acquisitions shall have hardened. Large conquests break readily off from an empire by their weight, while smaller stick fast. A wide and rather waste kingdom should be interposed between the policied states and Persia, by the leave of Chloros. Perhaps he would rather, in his benevolence, unite us with the great and happy family of his master. Despots are wholesale dealers in equality; and, father Zeus! was ever equality like this?

SOPHOCLES. My dear Pericles!—do excuse a smile—is not that the best government which, whatever be the form of it, we ourselves are called upon to administer?

PERICLES. The Piræus and the Pœcilè have a voice of their own wherewith to answer thee, O Sophocles! and the Athenians, exempt from war, famine, tax, debt, exile, fine, imprisonment, delivered from monarchy, from oligarchy, and from anarchy, walking along their porticoes, inhaling their sea-breezes, crowning their Gods daily for fresh blessings, and their children for deserving them, reply to this voice by the symphony of their applause. Hark! my words are not idle. Hither come the youths and virgins, the sires and matrons; hither come citizen and soldier——

SOPHOCLES. A solecism from Pericles! Has the most eloquent of men forgotten the Attic language? has he forgotten the language of all Greece? Can the father of his country be ignorant that he should have said hither *comes?* for citizen and soldier is one.

PERICLES. The fault is graver than the reproof, or indeed than simple incorrectness of language: my eyes misled my tongue: a large portion of the citizens is armed.

O what an odour of thyme and bay and myrtle, and from what a distance, bruised by the procession!

SOPHOCLES. What regular and full harmony! What a splendour and effulgence of white dresses! painful to aged eyes and dangerous to young.

PERICLES. I can distinguish many voices from among others. Some of them have blessed me for defending their innocence before the judges ; some for exhorting Greece to unanimity ; some for my choice of friends. Ah surely those sing sweetest ! those are the voices, O Sophocles ! that shake my heart with tenderness, a tenderness passing love, and excite it above the trumpet and the cymbal. Return we to the Gods ∶ the crowd is waving the branches of olive, calling us by name, and closing to salute us.

SOPHOCLES. O citadel of Pallas, more than all other citadels may the goddess of wisdom and of war protect thee ! and never may strange tongue be heard within thy walls, unless from captive king !

Live, Pericles ! and inspire into thy people the soul that once animated these heroes round us.

Hail, men of Athens ! Pass onward ; leave me ; I follow. Go ; behold the Gods, the demigods, and Pericles !

Artemidoros ! come to my right. No : better walk between us ; else they who run past may knock the flute out of your hand, or push it every now and then from the lip ! Have you received the verses I sent you in the morning ? soon enough to learn the accents and cadences ?

ARTEMIDOROS. Actaios brought them to me about sunrise ; and I raised myself up in bed to practise them, while he sat on the edge of it, shaking the dust off his sandals all over the chamber, by beating time.

SOPHOCLES. Begin we.

> The colours of thy waves are not the same
> Day after day, Poseidon [1] ? nor the same
> The fortunes of the land wherefrom arose
> Under thy trident the brave friend of man.
> Wails have been heard from women, sterner breasts
> Have sounded with the desperate pang of grief,
> Grey hairs have strown these rocks : here Ægeus cried,
> "O Sun ! careering over Sipylos,
> If desolation (worse than ever there
> Befell the mother, and those heads her own
> Would shelter when the deadly darts flew round)

---

[1] The 1st ed., 1824, reads " Neptune " for " Poseidon." The utterance of Ægeus, there spelled " Egeus," is separated from the preceding lines. Instead of " careering over Sipylos " the reading of 1824 is " careering o'er the downs of Sipylus." The punctuation also differs slightly. Crump merely reproduces Forster, with Forster's misprint.

IMAGINARY CONVERSATIONS : GREEK

Impend not o'er my house in gloom so long,
Let one swift cloud illumined by thy chariot
Sweep off the darkness from that doubtful sail."

Deeper and deeper came the darkness down ;
The sail itself was heard ; his eyes grew dim ;
His knees tottered beneath him, but availed
To bear him till he plunged into the deep.

Sound, fifes ! there is a youthfulness of sound
In your shrill voices : sound again, ye lips
That Mars delights in.   I will look no more
Into the time behind for idle goads
To stimulate faint fancies : hope itself
Is bounded by the starry zone of glory.
On one bright point we gaze, one wish we breathe,

Athens ! be ever as thou art this hour,
Happy and strong, a Pericles thy guide.[1]

---

[1] At the end of this Conversation there is in the ed. of 1824 a lengthy note.   See appendix to the final volume of *Imag. Con.* in the present edition.

VII. DIOGENES AND PLATO

Circa 370 B.C.

(*Imag. Convers.*, iv., 1829 ; *Wks.*, i., 1846 ; *Imag. Convers. Gk. and Rom.*, 1853 ; *Wks.*, ii., 1876.)

DIOGENES. Stop ! stop ! come hither ! Why lookest thou so scornfully and askance upon me ?

PLATO. Let me go ; loose me ; I am resolved to pass.

DIOGENES. Nay then, by Jupiter and this tub ! thou leavest three good ells of Milesian cloth behind thee. Whither wouldst thou amble ?

PLATO. I am not obliged in courtesy to tell you.

DIOGENES. Upon whose errand ? Answer me directly.

PLATO. Upon my own.

DIOGENES. O ! then I will hold thee yet awhile. If it were upon another's, it might be a hardship to a good citizen, though not to a good philosopher.

PLATO. That can be no impediment to my release : you do not think me one.

DIOGENES. No, by my father Jove !

PLATO. Your father !

DIOGENES. Why not ? Thou shouldst be the last man to doubt it. Hast not thou declared it irrational to refuse our belief to those who assert that they are begotten by the Gods, though the assertion (these are thy words) be unfounded on reason or probability ? In me there is a chance of it : whereas in the generation of such people as thou art fondest of frequenting, who claim it loudly, there are always too many competitors to leave it probable.

PLATO. Those who speak against the great, do not usually speak from morality, but from envy.

DIOGENES. Thou hast a glimpse of the truth in this place ; but as thou hast already shown thy ignorance in attempting to prove to me what a *man* is, ill can I expect to learn from thee what is a *great man*.

PLATO. No doubt your experience and intercourse will afford me the information.

DIOGENES. Attend, and take it. The great man is he who hath nothing to fear and nothing to hope from another. It is he who, while he demonstrates the iniquity of the laws, and is able to correct them, obeys them peaceably. It is he who looks on the ambitious both as weak and fraudulent. It is he who hath no disposition or occasion for any kind of deceit, no reason for being or for appearing different from what he is. It is he who can call together the most select company when it pleases him.

PLATO. Excuse my interruption. In the beginning of your definition I fancied that you were designating your own person, as most people do in describing what is admirable ; now I find that you have some other in contemplation.

DIOGENES. I thank thee for allowing me what perhaps I *do* possess, but what I was not then thinking of ; as is often the case with rich possessors : in fact, the latter part of the description suits me as well as any portion of the former.

PLATO. You may call together the best company, by using your hands in the call, as you did with me ; otherwise I am not sure that you would succeed in it.

DIOGENES. My thoughts are my company : I can bring them together, select them, detain them, dismiss them. Imbecile and vicious men can not do any of these things. Their thoughts are scattered, vague, uncertain, cumbersome : and the worst stick to them the longest ; many indeed by choice, the greater part by necessity, and accompanied, some by weak wishes, others by vain remorse.

PLATO. Is there nothing of greatness, O Diogenes ! in exhibiting how cities and communities may be governed best, how morals may be kept the purest, and power become the most stabile ?

DIOGENES. *Something* of greatness does not constitute the great man. Let me however see him who hath done what thou sayest : he must be the most universal and the most indefatigable traveller, he must also be the oldest creature upon earth.

PLATO. How so ?

DIOGENES. Because he must know perfectly the climate, the soil,

66

the situation, the peculiarities, of the races, of their allies, of their enemies : he must have sounded their harbours, he must have measured the quantity of their arable land and pasture, of their woods and mountains : he must have ascertained whether there are fisheries on their coasts, and even what winds are prevalent.* On these causes, with some others, depend the bodily strength, the numbers, the wealth, the wants, the capacities, of the people.

PLATO. Such are low thoughts.

DIOGENES. The bird of wisdom flies low, and seeks her food under hedges : the eagle himself would be starved if he always soared aloft and against the sun. The sweetest fruit grows near the ground, and the plants that bear it require ventilation and lopping. Were this not to be done in thy garden, every walk and alley, every plot and border, would be covered with runners and roots, with boughs and suckers. We want no poets or logicians or metaphysicians to govern us : we want practical men, honest men, continent men, unambitious men, fearful to solicit a trust, slow to accept, and resolute never to betray one. Experimentalists may be the best philosophers : they are always the worst politicians. Teach people their duties, and they will know their interests. Change as little as possible, and correct as much.

Philosophers are absurd from many causes, but principally from laying out unthriftily their distinctions. They set up four virtues : fortitude, prudence, temperance, and justice. Now a man may be a very bad one, and yet possess three out of the four. Every cut-throat must, if he has been a cut-throat on many occasions, have more fortitude and more prudence than the greater part of those whom we consider as the best men. And what cruel wretches, both executioners and judges, have been strictly just ! how little have they cared what gentleness, what generosity, what genius, their sentence hath removed from the earth ! Temperance and beneficence contain all other virtues. Take them home, Plato, split them, expound them ; do what thou wilt with them, if thou but use them.

Before I gave thee this lesson, which is a better than thou ever gavest anyone, and easier to remember, thou wert accusing me of invidiousness and malice against those whom thou callest the

* Parts of knowledge which are now general, but were then very rare, and united in none.—W. S. L.

great, meaning to say the powerful. Thy imagination, I am well aware, had taken its flight toward Sicily, where thou seekest thy great man, as earnestly and undoubtingly as Ceres sought her Persephonè. Faith! honest Plato, I have no reason to envy thy worthy friend Dionysius. Look at my nose! A lad seven or eight years old threw an apple at me yesterday, while I was gazing at the clouds, and gave me nose enough for two moderate men. Instead of such a godsend, what should I have thought of my fortune if, after living all my life-time among golden vases, rougher than my hand with their emeralds and rubies, their engravings and embossments, among Parian caryatides and porphyry sphinxes, among philosophers with rings upon their fingers and linen next their skin, and among singing-boys and dancing-girls, to whom alone thou speakest intelligibly—I ask thee again, what should I in reason have thought of my fortune, if, after these facilities and superfluities, I had at last been pelted out of my house, not by one young rogue, but by thousands of all ages, and not with an apple (I wish I could say a rotten one), but with pebbles and broken pots ; and, to crown my deserts, had been compelled to become the teacher of so promising a generation ? Great men, forsooth ! thou knowest at last who they are.

PLATO. There are great men of various kinds.

DIOGENES. No, by my beard, are there not.

PLATO. What ! are there not great captains, great geometricians, great dialecticians ?

DIOGENES. Who denied it ? A great man was the postulate. Try thy hand now at the powerful one.

PLATO. On seeing the exercise of power, a child can not doubt who is powerful, more or less ; for power is relative. All men are weak, not only if compared to the Demiurgos, but if compared to the sea or the earth, or certain things upon each of them, such as elephants and whales. So placid and tranquil is the scene around us, we can hardly bring to mind the images of strength and force, the precipices, the abysses——

DIOGENES. Prythee hold thy loose tongue, twinkling and glittering like a serpent's in the midst of luxuriance and rankness. Did never this reflection of thine warn thee that, in human life, the precipices and abysses would be much further from our admiration, if we were less inconsiderate, selfish, and vile ? I will not however

68

stop thee long, for thou wert going on quite consistently. As thy great men are fighters and wranglers, so thy mighty things upon the earth and sea are troublesome and intractable incum brances. Thou perceivedst not what was greater in the former case, neither art thou aware what is greater in this. Didst thou feel the gentle air that passed us ?

PLATO. I did not, just then.

DIOGENES. That air, so gentle, so imperceptible to thee, is more powerful not only than all the creatures that breathe and live by it ; not only than all the oaks of the forest, which it rears in an age and shatters in a moment ; not only than all the monsters of the sea, but than the sea itself, which it tosses up into foam, and breaks against every rock in its vast circumference ; for it carries in its bosom, with perfect calm and composure, the incontrollable ocean and the peopled earth, like an atom of a feather.

To the world's turmoils and pageantries is attracted, not only the admiration of the populace, but the zeal of the orator, the enthusiasm of the poet, the investigation of the historian, and the contemplation of the philosopher : yet how silent and invisible are they in the depths of air ! Do I say in those depths and deserts ? No ; I say at the distance of a swallow's flight ; at the distance she rises above us, ere a sentence brief as this could be uttered.

What are its mines and mountains ? Fragments welded up and dislocated by the expansion of water from below ; the mostpart reduced to mud, the rest to splinters. Afterward sprang up fire in many places, and again tore and mangled the mutilated carcase, and still growls over it.

What are its cities and ramparts, and moles and monuments ? segments of a fragment, which one man puts together and another throws down. Here we stumble upon thy great ones at their work. Show me now, if thou canst, in history, three great warriors, or three great statesmen, who have acted otherwise than spiteful children.

PLATO. I will begin to look for them in history when I have discovered the same number in the philosophers or the poets. A prudent man searches in his own garden after the plant he wants, before he casts his eyes over the stalls in Kenkrea or Keramicos.

Returning to your observation on the potency of the air, I am not ignorant or unmindful of it. May I venture to express my opinion to you, Diogenes, that the earlier discoverers and distributers of wisdom (which wisdom lies among us in ruins and remnants, partly distorted and partly concealed by theological allegory), meant by Jupiter the air in its agitated state, by Juno the air in its quiescent. These are the great agents, and therefore called the king and queen of the gods. Jupiter is denominated by Homer the *compeller of clouds :* Juno receives them, and remits them in showers to plants and animals.

I may trust you, I hope, O Diogenes !

DIOGENES. Thou mayst lower the Gods in my presence, as safely as men in the presence of Timon.

PLATO. I would not lower them : I would exalt them.

DIOGENES. More foolish and presumptuous still !

PLATO. Fair words, O Sinopean ! I protest to you my aim is truth.

DIOGENES. I can not lead thee where of a certainty thou mayst always find it ; but I will tell thee what it is. Truth is a point ; the subtlest and finest ; harder than adamant ; never to be broken, worn away, or blunted. Its only bad quality is, that it is sure to hurt those who touch it ; and likely to draw blood, perhaps the life-blood, of those who press earnestly upon it. Let us away from this narrow lane skirted with hemlock, and pursue our road again through the wind and dust, toward the *great* man and the *powerful.* Him I would call the powerful one, who controls the storms of his mind, and turns to good account the worst accidents of his fortune. The great man, I was going on to demonstrate, is somewhat more. He must be able to do this, and he must have an intellect which puts into motion the intellect of others.

PLATO. Socrates then was your great man.

DIOGENES. He was indeed ; nor can all thou hast attributed to him ever make me think the contrary. I wish he could have kept a little more at home, and have thought it as well worth his while to converse with his own children as with others.

PLATO. He knew himself born for the benefit of the human race.

DIOGENES. Those who are born for the benefit of the human race, go but little into it : those who are born for its curse, are crowded.

PLATO. It was requisite to dispell the mists of ignorance and error.

DIOGENES. Has he done it ? What doubt has he elucidated,

or what fact has he established ?   Although I was but twelve years old and resident in another city when he died, I have taken some pains in my inquiries about him from persons of less vanity and less perverseness than his disciples.   He did not leave behind him any true philosopher among them ; any who followed his mode of argumentation, his subjects of disquisition, or his course of life ; any who would subdue the malignant passions or coerce the looser ; any who would abstain from calumny or from cavil ; any who would devote his days to the glory of his country, or, what is easier and perhaps wiser, to his own well-founded contentment and well-merited repose.   Xenophon, the best of them, offered up sacrifices, believed in oracles, consulted soothsayers, turned pale at a jay, and was dysenteric at a magpie.

PLATO. He [1] had then no courage ?   I was the first to suspect it.

DIOGENES. Which thou hadst never been if others had not praised him for it : but his courage was of so strange a quality, that he was ready, if jay or magpie did not cross him, to fight for Spartan or Persian.   Plato, whom thou esteemest much more, and knowest somewhat less, careth as little for portent and omen as doth Diogenes.   What he would have done for a Persian I can not say : certain I am that he would have no more fought for a Spartan than he would for his own father : yet he mortally hates the man who hath a kinder muse or a better milliner, or a seat nearer the minion of a king.   So much for the two disciples of Socrates who have acquired the greatest celebrity !

PLATO. Why [2] do you attribute to me invidiousness and malignity, rather than to the young philosopher who is coming prematurely forward into public notice, and who hath lately been invited by the King of Macedon to educate his son ?

DIOGENES. These very words of thine demonstrate to me, calm and expostulatory as they appear in utterance, that thou enviest in this young man, if not his abilities, his appointment.   And prythee now demonstrate to me as clearly, if thou canst, in what he is either a sycophant or a malignant.

PLATO. Willingly.

DIOGENES. I believe it.   But easily too ?

---

[1] 1st ed. reads : " He had courage at least.   DIOGENES. His courage was," etc.

[2] From " Why " to " Attica," p. 74, added in 2nd ed.

PLATO. I think so. Knowing the arrogance of Philip, and the signs of ambition which his boy (I forget the name) hath exhibited so early, he says, in the fourth book of his *Ethics* (already in the hands of several here at Athens, although in its present state unfit for publication), that " he who deems himself worthy of less than his due, is a man of pusillanimous and abject mind."

DIOGENES. His canine tooth, friend Plato, did not enter thy hare's fur here.

PLATO. No ; he sneered at Phocion, and flattered Philip. He adds, " whether that man's merits be great, or small, or middling." And he supports the position by sophistry.

DIOGENES. How could he act more consistently ? Such is the support it should rest on. If the man's merits were great, he could not be abject.

PLATO. Yet the author was so contented with his observation, that he expresses it again a hundred lines below.

DIOGENES. Then he was not contented with his observation ; for, had he been contented, he would have said no more about it. But, having seen lately his treatise, I remember that he varies the expression of the sentiment, and, after saying a very foolish thing, is resolved on saying one rather less inconsiderate : on the principle of the hunter on the snows of Pindus, who, when his fingers are frost-bitten, does not hold them instantly to the fire, but dips them first into cold water. Aristoteles says, in his second trial at the thesis, " *for* he who is of low and abject mind, strips himself of what is good about him, and is, to a certain degree, bad, because he thinks himself unworthy of the good."

Modesty and diffidence make a man unfit for public affairs : they also make him unfit for brothels : but do they therefore make him bad ? It is not often that your scholar is lost in this way, by following the echo of his own voice. His greatest fault is, that he so condenses his thoughts as to render it difficult to see through them : he inspissates his yellow into black. However, I see more and more in him the longer I look at him : in you I see less and less. Perhaps other men may have eyes of another construction, and filled with a subtler and more ethereal fluid.

PLATO. Acknowledge at least that it argues a poverty of thought to repeat the same sentiment.

DIOGENES. It may or it may not. Whatever of ingenuity or

72

invention be displayed in a remark, another may be added which surpasses it. If, after this and perhaps more, the author, in a different treatise, or in a different place of the same, throws upon it fresh materials, surely you must allow that he rather hath brought forward the evidence of plenteousness than of poverty. Much of invention may be exhibited in the variety of turns and aspects he makes his thesis assume. A poor friend may give me to-day a portion of yesterday's repast ; but a rich man is likelier to send me what is preferable, forgetting that he had sent me as much a day or two before. They who give us all we want, and beyond what we expected, may be pardoned if they happen to overlook the extent of their liberality. In this matter thou hast spoken inconsiderately and unwisely : but whether the remark of Aristoteles was intended as a slur on Phocion is uncertain. The repetition of it makes me incline to think it was ; for few writers repeat a kind sentiment, many an unkind one : and Aristoteles would have repeated a just observation rather than an unjust, unless he wished either to flatter or malign. The Gods rarely let us take good aim on these occasions, but dazzle or overcloud us. The perfumed oil of flattery, and the caustic spirit of malignity, spread over an equally wide surface. Here both are thrown out of their jars by the same pair of hands at the same moment ; the sweet (as usual) on the bad man, the unsweet (as universal) on the good. I never heard before that they had fallen on the hands of Phocion and of Philip. Thou hast furnished me with the suspicion, and I have furnished thee with the supports for it. Do not, however, hope to triumph over Aristoteles because he hath said one thoughtless thing : rather attempt to triumph *with* him on saying many wise ones. For a philosopher I think him very little of an impostor. He mingles too frequently the acute and dull ; and thou too frequently the sweet and vapid. Try to barter one with the other, amicably ; and not to twitch and carp. You may each be the better for some exchanges ; but neither for cheapening one another's wares. Do thou take my advice the first of the two ; for thou hast the most to gain by it. Let me tell thee also that it does him no dishonour to have accepted the invitation of Philip as future preceptor of his newly-born child. I would rather rear a lion's whelp and tame him, than see him run untamed about the city, especially if any tenement and cattle were at its outskirts. Let us hope that a soul once Attic can never become Macedonian; but rather Macedonian than Sicilian.

Aristoteles, and all the rest of you, must have the wadding of straw and saw-dust shaken out, and then we shall know pretty nearly your real weight and magnitude.

PLATO. A philosopher ought never to speak in such a manner of philosophers.

DIOGENES. None other ought, excepting now and then the beadle. However, the Gods have well protected thee, O Plato, against his worst violence. Was this raiment of thine the screen of an Egyptian temple? or merely the drapery of a thirty-cubit Isis? or per-adventure a holiday suit of Darius for a bevy of his younger con-cubines? Prythee do tarry with me, or return another day, that I may catch a flight of quails with it as they cross over this part of Attica.

PLATO. It hath always been the fate of the decorous to be calumniated for effeminacy by the sordid.

DIOGENES. Effeminacy! By my beard! he who could carry all this Milesian bravery on his shoulders, might, with the help of three more such able men, have tossed Typhöeus up to the teeth of Jupiter.

PLATO. We may serve our country, I hope, with clean faces.

DIOGENES. More serve her with clean faces than with clean hands: and some are extremely shy of her when they fancy she may want them.

PLATO. Although on some occasions I have left Athens, I can not be accused of deserting her in the hour of danger.

DIOGENES. Nor proved to have defended her: but better desert her on some occasions, or on all, than praise the tyrant Critias; the cruellest of the thirty who condemned thy master. In one hour, in the hour when that friend was dying, when young and old were weeping over him, where *then* wert thou?

PLATO. Sick at home.

DIOGENES. Sick! how long? of what malady? In such tor-ments, or in such debility, that it would have cost thee thy life to have been carried to the prison? or hadst thou no litter; no slaves to bear it; no footboy to inquire the way to the public prison, to the cell of Socrates? The medicine he took could never have made thy heart colder, or thy legs more inactive and torpid in their movement toward a friend. Shame upon thee ! scorn ! contempt ! everlasting reprobation and abhorrence !

PLATO. Little [1] did I ever suppose that, in being accused of hard-heartedness, Diogenes would exercise the office of accuser.

DIOGENES. Not to press the question, nor to avoid the recrimination, I will enter on the subject at large ; and rather as an appeal than as a disquisition. I am called hard-hearted ; Alcibiades is called tender-hearted. Speak I truly or falsely ?

PLATO. Truly.

DIOGENES. In both cases ?

PLATO. In both.

DIOGENES. Pray, in what doth hardness of heart consist ?

PLATO. There are many constituents and indications of it : want of sympathy with our species is one.

DIOGENES. I sympathise with the brave in their adversity and afflictions, because I feel in my own breast the flame that burns in theirs : and I do not sympathise with others, because with others my heart hath nothing of consanguinity. I no more sympathise with the generality of mankind than I do with fowls, fishes, and insects. We have indeed the same figure and the same flesh, but not the same soul and spirit. Yet, recall to thy memory, if thou canst, any action of mine bringing pain of body or mind to any rational creature. True indeed no despot or conqueror should exercise his authority a single hour if my arm or my exhortations could prevail against him. Nay, more : none should depart from the earth without flagellations, nor without brands, nor without exposure, day after day, in the market-place of the city where he governed. This is the only way I know of making men believe in the justice of their gods. And if they never were to believe in it at all, it is right that they should confide in the equity of their fellow-men. Even this were imperfect : for every despot and conqueror inflicts much greater misery than any one human body can suffer. Now then plainly thou seest the extent of what thou wouldst call my cruelty. We who have ragged beards are cruel by prescription and acclamation ; while they who have pumiced faces and perfumed hair, are called cruel only in the moments of tenderness, and in the pauses of irritation. Thy friend Alcibiades was extremely good-natured : yet, because the people of Melos, descendants from the

[1] From " Little " to " better " added in 2nd ed.

75

Lacedæmonians, stood neutral in the Peloponnesian war, and refused to fight against their fathers, the good-natured man, when he had vanquished and led them captive, induced the Athenians to slaughter all among them who were able to bear arms ; and we know that the survivors were kept in irons until the victorious Spartans set them free.

PLATO. I did not approve of this severity.

DIOGENES. Nor didst thou at any time disapprove of it. Of what value are all thy philosophy and all thy eloquence, if they fail to humanise a bosom-friend, or fear to encounter a misguided populace ?

PLATO. I thought I heard Diogenes say he had no sympathy with the mass of mankind : what could excite it so suddenly in behalf of an enemy ?

DIOGENES. Whoever is wronged is thereby my fellow-creature, although he were never so before. Scorn, contumely, chains, unite us.

PLATO. Take heed, O Diogenes ! lest the people of Athens hear you.

DIOGENES. Is Diogenes no greater than the people of Athens ? Friend Plato ! I take no heed about them. Somebody or something will demolish me sooner or later. An Athenian can but begin what an ant, or a beetle, or a worm will finish. Any one of the three would have the best of it. While I retain the use of my tongue, I will exercise it at my leisure and my option. I would not bite it off, even for the pleasure of spitting it in a tyrant's face, as that brave girl Egina did. But I would recommend that, in his wisdom, he should deign to take thine preferably, which, having always honey upon it, must suit his taste better.

PLATO. Diogenes ! if you must argue or discourse with me, I will endure your asperity for the sake of your acuteness : but it appears to me a more philosophical thing to avoid what is insulting and vexatious, than to breast and brave it.

DIOGENES. Thou hast spoken well.

PLATO. It belongs to the vulgar, not to us, to fly from a man's opinions to his actions, and to stab him in his own house for having received no wound in the school. One merit you will allow me : I always keep my temper ; which you seldom do.

DIOGENES. Is mine a good or a bad one ?

DIOGENES AND PLATO

PLATO. Now must I speak sincerely ?

DIOGENES. Dost thou, a philosopher, ask such a question of me, a philosopher ? Ay, sincerely or not at all.

PLATO. Sincerely as you could wish, I must declare then your temper is the worst in the world.

DIOGENES. I am much in the right, therefore, not to keep it. Embrace [1] me : I have spoken now in thy own manner. Because thou sayest the most malicious things the most placidly, thou thinkest or pretendest thou art sincere.

PLATO. Certainly those who are most the masters of their resentments, are likely to speak less erroneously than the passionate and morose.

DIOGENES. If they would, they might : but the moderate are not usually the most sincere : for the same circumspection which makes them moderate, makes them likewise retentive of what could give offence : they are also timid in regard to fortune and favour, and hazard little. There is no mass of sincerity in any place. What there is must be picked up patiently, a grain or two at a time ; and the season for it is after a storm, after the overflowing of banks, and bursting of mounds, and sweeping away of landmarks. Men will always hold something back : they must be shaken and loosened a little, to make them let go what is deepest in them, and weightiest and purest.

PLATO. Shaking and loosening as much about you as was requisite for the occasion, it became you to demonstrate where, and in what manner, I had made Socrates appear less sagacious and less eloquent than he was : it became you likewise to consider the great difficulty of finding new thoughts and new expressions for those who had more of them than any other men, and to represent them in all the brilliancy of their wit and in all the majesty of their genius. I do not assert that I have done it ; but if I have not, what man has ? what man has come so nigh to it ? He who could bring Socrates, or Solon, or Diogenes, through a dialogue, without disparagement, is much nearer in his intellectual powers to them, than any other is near to him.

DIOGENES. Let Diogenes alone, and Socrates, and Solon. None of the three ever occupied his hours in tinging and curling the tarnished plumes of prostitute Philosophy, or deemed anything

[1] From " Embrace " to " manner " added in 2nd ed.

worth his attention, care, or notice, that did not make men brave
and independent. As thou callest on me to show thee where and
in what manner thou hast misrepresented thy teacher, and as thou
seemest to set an equal value on eloquence and on reasoning, I
shall attend to thee awhile on each of these matters, first inquiring
of thee whether the axiom is Socratic, that it is never becoming
to get drunk,[1] *unless* in the solemnities of Bacchus ?

PLATO. This god was the discoverer of the vine and of its uses.

DIOGENES. Is drunkenness one of its uses, or the discovery of
a God ? If Pallas or Jupiter hath given us reason, we should
sacrifice our reason with more propriety to Jupiter or Pallas. To
Bacchus is due a libation of wine ; the same being his gift, as
thou preachest.

Another and a graver question.

Did Socrates teach thee that " slaves are to be scourged, and
by no means admonished as though they were the children of
the master " ?

PLATO. He did not argue upon government.

DIOGENES. He argued upon humanity, whereon all government
is founded : whatever is beside it is usurpation.

PLATO. Are slaves then never to be scourged, whatever be their
transgressions and enormities ?

DIOGENES. Whatever they be, they are less than his who reduced
them to their condition.

PLATO. What ! though they murder his whole family ?

DIOGENES. Ay, and poison the public fountain of the city.
What am I saying ? and to whom ? Horrible as is this crime,
and next in atrocity to parricide, thou deemest it a lighter one
than stealing a fig or grape. The stealer of these is scourged by
thee ; the sentence on the poisoner is to cleanse out the receptacle.[2]
There is, however, a kind of poisoning, which, to do thee justice,
comes before thee with all its horrors, and which thou wouldst
punish capitally, even in such a sacred personage as an aruspex
or diviner : I mean the poisoning by incantation. I, and my whole
family, my whole race, my whole city, may bite the dust in agony
from a truss of henbane in the well ; and little harm done forsooth !
Let an idle fool set an image of me in wax before the fire, and whistle
and caper to it, and purr and pray, and chant a hymn to Hecate

[1] Dialogue VI. on *The Laws*. [2] Dialogue VIII.

while it melts, intreating and imploring her that I may melt as easily ; and thou wouldst, in thy equity and holiness, strangle him at the first stave of his psalmody.

PLATO. If this is an absurdity, can you find another ?

DIOGENES. Truly, in reading thy book, I doubted at first, and for a long continuance, whether thou couldst have been serious ; and whether it were not rather a satire on those busy-bodies who are incessantly intermeddling in other people's affairs. It was only on the protestation of thy intimate friends that I believed thee to have written it in earnest. As for thy question, it is idle to stoop and pick out absurdities from a mass of inconsistency and injustice : but another and another I could throw in, and another and another afterward, from any page in the volume. Two bare staring falsehoods lift their beaks one upon the other, like spring frogs. Thou sayest that no punishment, decreed by the laws, tendeth to evil. What ! not if immoderate ? not if partial ? Why then repeal any penal statute while the subject of its animadversion exists ? In prisons the less criminal are placed among the more criminal, the inexperienced in vice together with the hardened in it. This is part of the punishment, though it precedes the sentence : nay, it is often inflicted on those whom the judges acquit : the law, by allowing it, does it.

The next is, that he who is punished by the laws is the better for it, however the less depraved. What ! if anteriorly to the sentence he lives and converses with worse men, some of whom console him by deadening the sense of shame, others by removing the apprehension of punishment ? Many laws as certainly make men bad, as bad men make many laws : yet under thy regimen they take us from the bosom of the nurse, turn the meat about upon the platter, pull the bedclothes off, make us sleep when we would wake, and wake when we would sleep, and never cease to rummage and twitch us, until they see us safe landed at the grave. We can do nothing (but be poisoned) with impunity. What is worst of all, we must marry certain relatives and connections, be they distorted, blear-eyed, toothless, carbuncled, with hair (if any) eclipsing the reddest torch of Hymen, and with a hide out-rivalling in colour and plaits his trimmest saffron robe. At the mention of this indeed, friend Plato ! even thou, although resolved to stand out of harm's way, beginnest to make a wry mouth, and findest it difficult to pucker and purse it up again, without an astringent store of moral sentences. Hymen [1] is truly no acquaintance of thine. We know the delicacies of love which thou wouldst reserve for the gluttony of heroes and the fastidiousness of philosophers. Heroes, like Gods, must have their own way : but against thee and thy confraternity of elders I would turn the closet-key, and your mouths might water over, but your tongues should never enter, those little pots of comfiture. Seriously, you who wear embroidered slippers ought to be very cautious of treading in the mire. Philosophers should not only live the simplest lives, but should also use the plainest language. Poets, in employing magnificent and sonorous words, teach philosophy the better by thus disarming suspicion that the finest poetry contains and conveys the finest philosophy. You will never let any man hold his right station : you would rank Solon with Homer for poetry. This is absurd. The only resemblance is, in both being eminently wise. Pindar too makes even the cadences of his dithyrambics keep time to the flute of Reason. My tub, which holds fifty-fold thy wisdom, would crack at the reverberation of thy voice.

PLATO. Farewell.

DIOGENES. Not [2] quite yet. I must physic thee a little with law again before we part ; answer me one more question. In punishing a robbery, wouldst thou punish him who steals everything from one who wants everything, less severely than him who steals little from one who wants nothing ?

PLATO. No : in this place the iniquity is manifest : not a problem in geometry is plainer.

DIOGENES. Thou liedst then — in thy sleep perhaps — but thou liedst. Differing in one page from what was laid down by thee in another,[3] thou wouldst punish what is called *sacrilege* with death. The magistrates ought to provide that the temples be watched so well, and guarded so effectually, as never to be liable to thefts. The Gods, we must suppose, can not do it by themselves ; for, to admit the contrary, we must admit their indifference to the possession of goods and chattels : an impiety so great, that sacrilege

---

[1] From " Hymen " to " voice " added in 2nd ed.
[2] From " Not " to " part " absent in 1st ed., which reads : " Ha ! ha ! thou hast cried wolf till thou hearest him."
[3] Books IX. and X.

itself drops into atoms under it. He, however, who robs from the Gods, be the amount what it may, robs from the rich ; robs from those who can want nothing, although, like the other rich, they are mightily vindictive against petty plunderers. But he who steals from a poor widow a loaf of bread, may deprive her of everything she has in the world ; perhaps, if she be bedridden or paralytic, of life itself.

I am weary of this digression on the inequality of punishments ; let us come up to the object of them. It is not, O Plato ! an absurdity of thine alone, but of all who write and of all who converse on them, to assert that they both are and ought to be inflicted publicly, for the sake of deterring from offence. The only effect of public punishment is to show the rabble how bravely it can be borne, and that everyone who hath lost a toe-nail hath suffered worse. The virtuous man, as a reward and a privilege, should be permitted to see how calm and satisfied a virtuous man departs. The criminal should be kept in the dark about the departure of his fellows, which is oftentimes as unreluctant ; for to him, if indeed no reward or privilege, it would be a corroborative and a cordial. Such things ought to be taken from him, no less carefully than the instruments of destruction or evasion. Secrecy and mystery should be the attendants of punishment, and the sole persons present should be the injured, or two of his relatives, and a functionary delegated by each tribe, to witness and register the execution of justice.

Trials, on the contrary, should be public in every case. It being presumable that the sense of shame and honour is not hitherto quite extinguished in the defendant, this, if he be guilty, is the worst part of his punishment : if innocent, the best of his release. From the hour of trial until the hour of return to society (or the dust) there should be privacy, there should be solitude.

PLATO. It occurs to me, O Diogenes, that you agree with Aristoteles on the doctrine of necessity.

DIOGENES. I do.

PLATO. How then can you punish, by any heavier chastisement than coercion, the heaviest offences ? Everything being brought about, as you hold, by fate and predestination——

DIOGENES. Stay ! Those terms are puerile, and imply a petition of a principle : keep to the term *necessity*. Thou art silent. Here then, O Plato, will I acknowledge to thee, I wonder it should have escaped thy perspicacity that *free-will* itself is nothing else than a part and effluence of *necessity*. If everything proceeds from some other thing, every impulse from some other impulse, that which impels to choice or will must act among the rest.

PLATO. Every impulse from some other (I must so take it) under God, or the first cause.

DIOGENES. Be it so : I meddle not at present with infinity or eternity : when I can comprehend them I will talk about them. You metaphysicians kill the flower-bearing and fruit-bearing glebe with delving and turning over and sifting, and never bring up any solid and malleable mass from the dark profundity in which you labor. The intellectual world, like the physical, is inapplicable to profit and incapable of cultivation a little way below the surface— of which there is more to manage, and more to know, than any of you will undertake.

PLATO. It happens that we do not see the stars at even-tide, sometimes because there are clouds intervening, but oftener because there are glimmerings of light : thus many truths escape us from the obscurity we stand in ; and many more from that crepuscular state of mind, which induceth us to sit down satisfied with our imaginations and unsuspicious of our knowledge.

DIOGENES. Keep [1] always to the point, or with an eye upon it, and instead of saying things to make people stare and wonder, say what will withhold them hereafter from wondering and staring. This is philosophy ; to make remote things tangible, common things extensively useful, useful things extensively common, and to leave the least necessary for the last. I have always a suspicion of sonorous sentences. The full shell sounds little, but shows by that little what is within. A bladder swells out more with wind than with oil.

PLATO. I would not neglect politics nor morals, nor indeed even manners : these however are mutable and evanescent : the human understanding is immovable and for ever the same in its principles and its constitution, and no study is so important or so inviting.

DIOGENES. Your sect hath done little in it. You are singularly fond of those disquisitions in which few can detect your failures

[1] From " Keep " to " within " added in 2nd ed.

and your fallacies, and in which, if you stumble or err, you may find some countenance in those who lost their way before you.

Is not this school-room of mine, which holdeth but one scholar, preferable to that out of which have proceeded so many impetuous in passion, refractory in discipline, unprincipled in adventure, and (worst of all) proud in slavery? Poor creatures who run after a jaded mule or palfrey, to pick up what he drops along the road, may be certain of a cabbage the larger and the sooner for it; while those who are equally assiduous at the heel of kings and princes, hunger and thirst for more, and usually gather less. Their attendance is neither so certain of reward nor so honest; their patience is scantier, their industry weaker, their complaints louder. What shall we say of their philosophy? what of their virtue? What shall we· say of the greatness whereon their feeders plume themselves? not caring they indeed for the humbler character of virtue or philosophy. We never call children the greater or the better for wanting others to support them: why then do we call men, so for it? I[1] would be servant of any helpless man for hours together: but sooner shall a king be the slave of Diogenes than Diogenes a king's.

PLATO. Companionship, O Sinopean, is not slavery.

DIOGENES. Are the best of them worthy to be my companions? Have they ever made you wiser? have you ever made them so? Prythee, what is companionship where nothing that improves the intellect is communicated, and where the larger heart contracts itself to the model and dimension of the smaller? 'Tis a dire calamity to *have* a slave; 'tis an inexpiable curse to *be* one. When it befalls a man through violence he must be pitied: but where is pity, where is pardon, for the wretch who solicits it, or bends his head under it through invitation? Thy hardness of heart toward slaves, O Plato, is just as unnatural as hardness of heart toward dogs would be in me.

PLATO. You would have none perhaps in that condition.

DIOGENES. None should be made slaves, excepting those who have attempted to make others so, or who spontaneously have become the instruments of unjust and unruly men. Even these ought not to be scourged every day perhaps[2]: for their skin is

---

[1] From " I " to " invitation " added in 2nd ed.
[2] " Every day perhaps " added in 2nd ed.

the only sensitive part of them, and such castigation might shorten their lives.

PLATO. Which, in your tenderness and mercy, you would not do.

DIOGENES. Longevity is desirable in them ; that they may be exposed in coops to the derision of the populace on holidays ; and that few may serve the purpose.

PLATO. We will pass over this wild and thorny theory, into the field of civilisation in which we live ; and here I must remark the evil consequences that would ensue, if our domestics could listen to you about the hardships they are enduring.

DIOGENES. And is it no evil that truth and beneficence should be shut out at once from so large a portion of mankind ? Is it none when things are so perverted, that an act of beneficence might lead to a thousand acts of cruelty, and that one accent of truth should be more pernicious than all the falsehoods that have been accumulated, since the formation of language, since the gift of speech ? I have taken thy view of the matter ; take thou mine. Hercules was called just and glorious, and worshiped as a deity, because he redressed the grievances of others : is it unjust, is it inglorious, to redress one's own ? If that man rises high in the favour of the people, high in the estimation of the valiant and the wise, high before God, by the assertion and vindication of his holiest law, who punishes with death such as would reduce him or his fellow-citizens to slavery, how much higher rises he, who, being a slave, springs up indignantly from his low estate, and thrusts away the living load that intercepts from him, what even the reptiles and insects, what even the bushes and brambles of the roadside, enjoy !

PLATO. We began with definitions : I rejoice, O Diogenes, that you are warmed into rhetoric, in which you will find me a most willing auditor : for I am curious to collect a specimen of your prowess, where you have not yet established any part of your celebrity.

DIOGENES. I am idle enough for it : but I have other things yet for thy curiosity, other things yet for thy castigation.

Thou wouldst separate the military from the citizens, from artizans and from agriculturists. A small body of soldiers, who never could be anything else, would in a short time subdue and subjugate the industrious and the wealthy. They would begin by demanding an increase of pay ; then they would insist on admission to magistracies ; and presently their general would assume the sovranty, and create new offices of trust and profit for the strength and security of his usurpation. Soldiers, in a free state, should be enrolled from those principally who are most interested in the conservation of order and property ; chiefly the sons of tradesmen in towns : first, because there is the less detriment done to agriculture ; the main thing to be considered in all countries : secondly, because such people are pronest to sedition, from the two opposite sides of enrichment and poverty : and lastly, because their families are always at hand, responsible for their fidelity, and where shame would befall them thickly in case of cowardice, or any misconduct. Those governments are the most flourishing and stabile, which have the fewest idle youths about the streets and theatres : it is only with the sword that they can cut the halter.

Thy faults arise from two causes principally : first, a fondness for playing tricks with argument and with fancy : secondly, swallowing from others what thou hast not taken time enough nor exercise enough to digest.

PLATO. Lay before me the particular things you accuse me of drawing from others.

DIOGENES. Thy opinions on numbers are distorted from those of the Chaldeans, Babylonians, and Syrians ; who believe that numbers, and letters too, have peculiar powers, independent of what is represented by them on the surface.

PLATO. I have said more, and often differently.

DIOGENES. Thou hast indeed. Neither they nor Pythagoras ever taught, as thou hast done, that the basis of the earth is an equilateral triangle, and the basis of water a rectangular. We are then informed by thy sagacity, that " the world has no need of eyes, because nothing is left to be looked at out of it ; nor of ears, because nothing can be heard beyond it ; nor of any parts for the reception, concoction, and voidance, of nutriment ; because there can be no secretion nor accretion." [1]

This indeed is very providential. If things were otherwise, foul might befall your genii, who are always on active service : a world would not bespatter them so lightly as we mortals are bespattered by a swallow. Whatever is asserted on things tangible, should

[1] *Timæus.*

be asserted from experiment only. Thou shouldst have defended better that which thou hast stolen : a thief should not only have impudence, but courage.

PLATO. What do you mean ?

DIOGENES. I mean that every one of thy whimsies hath been picked up somewhere by thee in thy travels ; and each of them hath been rendered more weak and puny by its place of concealment in thy closet. What thou hast written on the immortality of the soul, goes rather to prove the immortality of the body ; and applies as well to the body of a weazel or an eel as to the fairer one of Agathon or of Aster. Why not at once introduce a new religion * ? since religions keep and are relished in proportion as they are salted with absurdity, inside and out ; and all of them must have one great crystal of it for the centre ; but Philosophy pines and dies unless she drinks limpid water. When Pherecydes and Pythagoras felt in themselves the majesty of contemplation, they spurned the idea that flesh and bones and arteries should confer it ; and that what comprehends the past and the future, should sink in a moment and be annihilated for ever. No, cried they, the power of thinking is no more in the brain than in the hair, although the brain may be the instrument on which it plays. It is not corporeal, it is not of this world ; its existence is eternity, its residence is infinity. I forbear to discuss the rationality of their belief, and pass on straight-way to thine ; if indeed I am to consider as one, belief and doctrine.

PLATO. As you will.

DIOGENES. I should rather then regard these things as mere ornaments ; just as many decorate their apartments with lyres and harps, which they themselves look at from the couch, supinely complacent, and leave for visitors to admire and play on.

PLATO. I foresee not how you can disprove my argument on the immortality of the soul, which, being contained in the best of my dialogues, and being often asked for among my friends, I carry with me.

DIOGENES. At this time ?

PLATO. Even so.

DIOGENES. Give me then a certain part of it for my perusal.

PLATO. Willingly.

* He alludes to the various worships of Egypt, and to what Plato had learned there.—W. S. L.

DIOGENES AND PLATO

DIOGENES. Hermes and Pallas! I wanted but a cubit of it, or at most a fathom, and thou art pulling it out by the plethron.

PLATO. This is the place in question.

DIOGENES. Read it.

PLATO (reads). " Sayest thou not that death is the opposite of life, and that they spring the one from the other ? " " *Yes.*" " What springs then from the living ? " " *The dead.*" " And what from the dead ? " " *The living.*" " Then all things alive spring from the dead." [1]

DIOGENES. Why that repetition ? but go on.

PLATO (reads). " Souls therefore exist after death in the infernal regions."

DIOGENES. Where is the *therefore ?* where is it even as to *existence ?* As to the *infernal regions*, there is nothing that points toward a proof, or promises an indication. Death neither springs from life, nor life from death. Although death is the inevitable consequence of life, if the observation and experience of ages go for anything, yet nothing shows us, or ever hath signified, that life comes from death. Thou mightest as well say that a barley-corn dies before the germ of another barley-corn grows up from it : than which nothing is more untrue : for it is only the protecting part of the germ that perishes, when its protection is no longer necessary. The consequence, that souls exist after death, can not be drawn from the corruption of the body, even if it were demonstrable that out of this corruption a live one could rise up. Thou hast not said that the soul is among those dead things which living things must spring from : thou hast not said that a living soul produces a dead soul, or that a dead soul produces a living one.

PLATO. No indeed.

DIOGENES. On my faith, thou hast said however things no less inconsiderate, no less inconsequent, no less unwise ; and this very thing must be said and proved, to make thy argument of any value. Do dead men beget children ?

PLATO. I have not said it.

DIOGENES. Thy argument implies it.

PLATO. These are high mysteries, and to be approached with reverence.

DIOGENES. Whatever we can not account for, is in the same

[1] *Phædo,* 71.

predicament. We may be gainers by being ignorant if we can be thought mysterious. It is better to shake our heads and to let nothing out of them, than to be plain and explicit in matters of difficulty. I do not mean in confessing our ignorance or our imperfect knowledge of them, but in clearing them up perspicuously : for, if we answer with ease, we may haply be thought good-natured, quick, communicative ; never deep, never sagacious ; not very defective possibly in our intellectual faculties, yet unequal and chinky, and liable to the probation of every clown's knuckle.

PLATO. The brightest of stars appear the most unsteady and tremulous in their light ; not from any quality inherent in themselves, but from the vapours that float below, and from the imperfection of vision in the surveyor.

DIOGENES. To the stars again ! Draw thy robe round thee ; let the folds fall gracefully, and look majestic. That sentence is an admirable one ; but not for me. I want sense, not stars. What then ? Do no vapours float below the others ? and is there no imperfection in the vision of those who look at *them*, if they are the same men, and look the next moment ? We must move on : I shall follow the dead bodies, and the benighted driver of their fantastic bier, close and keen as any hyena.

PLATO. Certainly, O Diogenes, you excell me in elucidations and similes : mine was less obvious. Lycaon [1] became against his will, what you become from pure humanity.

DIOGENES. When Humanity is averse to Truth, a fig for her.

PLATO. Many, who profess themselves her votaries, have made her a less costly offering.

DIOGENES. Thou hast said well, and I will treat thee gently for it.

PLATO. I may venture then in defence of my compositions, to argue that neither simple metaphysics nor strict logic would be endured long together in a dialogue.

DIOGENES. Few people can endure them anywhere : but whatever is contradictory to either is intolerable. The business of a good writer is to make them pervade his works, without obstruction to his force or impediment to his facility ; to divest them of their forms, and to mingle their potency in every particle. I must

---

[1] In 1st ed. this passage runs : " Lycaon became against his will what you become from pure humanity and condescension. DIOGENES. I hate those foolish old stories ; I hate condescension ; a fig for humanity."

acknowledge that, in matters of love, thy knowledge is twice as extensive as mine is : yet nothing I ever heard is so whimsical and silly as thy description of its effects upon the soul, under the influence of beauty. The *wings* of the soul, thou tellest us, are *bedewed ;* and certain *germs* of theirs expand from every part of it.

The only thing I know about the soul is, that it makes the ground slippery under us when we discourse on it, by virtue (I presume) of this *bedewing ;* and beauty does not assist us materially in rendering our steps the steadier.

PLATO. Diogenes ! you are the only man that admires not the dignity and stateliness of my expressions.

DIOGENES. Thou [1] hast many admirers ; but either they never have read thee, or do not understand thee, or are fond of fallacies, or are incapable of detecting them. I would rather hear the murmur of insects in the grass than the clatter and trilling of cymbals and timbrels over-head. The tiny animals I watch with composure, and guess their business : the brass awakes me only to weary me : I wish it under-ground again, and the parchment on the sheep's back.

PLATO. My sentences, it is acknowledged by all good judges, are well constructed and harmonious.

DIOGENES. I admit it : I have also heard it said that thou art eloquent.

PLATO. If style, without elocution, can be.

DIOGENES. Neither without nor with elocution is there eloquence, where there is no ardour, no impulse, no energy, no concentration. Eloquence raises the whole man : thou raisest our eyebrows only. We wonder, we applaud, we walk away, and we forget. Thy eggs are very prettily speckled ; but those which men use for their sustenance are plain white ones. People do not every day put on their smartest dresses ; they are not always in trim for dancing, nor are they practising their steps in all places. I profess to be no weaver of fine words, no dealer in the plumes of phraseology, yet every man and every woman I speak to understands me.

PLATO. Which would not always be the case if the occulter operations of the human mind were the subject.

DIOGENES. If what is occult must be occult for ever, why throw away words about it ? Employ on every occasion the simplest and

[1] From " Thou " to " one of Diogenes," p. 91, added in 2nd ed.

easiest, and range them in the most natural order. Thus they will serve thee faithfully, bringing thee many hearers and readers from the intellectual and uncorrupted. All popular orators, victorious commanders, crowned historians, and poets above crowning, have done it. Homer, for the glory of whose birth-place none but the greatest cities dared contend, is alike the highest and the easiest in poetry. Herodotus, who brought into Greece more knowledge of distant countries than any or indeed than all before him, is the plainest and gracefulest in prose. Aristoteles, thy scholar, is possessor of a long and lofty treasury, with many windings and many vaults at the sides of them, abstruse and dark. He is unambitious of displaying his wealth ; and few are strong-wristed enough to turn the key of his iron chests. Whenever he presents to his reader one full-blown thought, there are several buds about it which are to open in the cool of the study ; and he makes you learn more than he teaches.

PLATO. I can never say that I admire his language.

DIOGENES. Thou wilt never say it ; but thou dost. His language, where he wishes it to be harmonious, is highly so : and there are many figures of speech exquisitely beautiful, but simple and unobtrusive. You see what a fine head of hair he might have if he would not cut it so short. Is there as much true poetry in all thy works, prose and verse, as in that *Scolion* of his on Virtue ?

PLATO. I am less invidious than he is.

DIOGENES. He may indeed have caught the infection of malignity, which all who live in the crowd, whether of a court or a school, are liable to contract. We had dismissed that question : we had buried the mortal and corruptible part of him, and were looking into the litter which contains his true and everlasting effigy : and this effigy the strongest and noblest minds will carry by relays to interminable generations. We were speaking of his thoughts and what conveys them. His language then, in good truth, differs as much from that which we find in thy dialogues, as wine in the goblet differs from wine spilt upon the table. With thy leave, I would rather drink than lap.

PLATO. Methinks such preference is contrary to your nature.

DIOGENES. Ah Plato ! I ought to be jealous of thee, finding that two in this audience can smile at thy wit, and not one at mine.

PLATO. I would rather be serious, but that my seriousness is provocative of your moroseness. Detract from me as much as can be detracted by the most hostile to my philosophy, still it is beyond the power of any man to suppress or to conceal from the admiration of the world the amplitude and grandeur of my language.

DIOGENES. Thou remindest me of a cavern I once entered. The mouth was spacious ; and many dangling weeds and rampant briers caught me by the hair above, and by the beard below, and flapped my face on each side. I found it in some places flat and sandy ; in some rather miry ; in others I bruised my shins against little pointed pinnacles, or larger and smoother round stones. Many were the windings, and deep the darkness. Several men came forward with long poles and lighted torches on them, promising to show innumerable gems, on the roof and along the sides, to some ingenuous youths whom they conducted. I thought I was lucky, and went on among them. Most of the gems turned out to be drops of water ; but some were a little more solid. These however in general gave way and crumbled under the touch ; and most of the remainder lost all their brightness by the smoke of the torches underneath. The farther I went in, the fouler grew the air and the dimmer the torchlight. Leaving it, and the youths, and the guides and the long poles, I stood a moment in wonder at the vast number of names and verses graven at the opening, and forebore to insert the ignoble one of Diogenes.

The vulgar indeed and the fashionable do call such language as thine the noblest and most magnificent : the scholastic bend over it in paleness, and with the right hand upon the breast, at its unfathomable depth : but what would a man of plain simple sound understanding say upon it ? what would a metaphysician ? what would a logician ? what would Pericles ? Truly, he had taken thee by the arm, and kissed that broad well-perfumed forehead, for filling up with light (as thou wouldst say) the dimple in the cheek of Aspasia, and for throwing such a gadfly in the current of her conversation. She was of a different sect from thee both in religion and in love, and both her language and her dress were plainer.

PLATO. She,[1] like yourself, worshiped no deity in public : and probably both she and Aristoteles find the more favour with you from the laxity of their opinions in regard to the powers above.

---

[1] From " She " to " words " added in 2nd ed.

The indifference of Aristoteles to religion may perhaps be the reason why King Philip bespoke him so early for the tuition of his successor ; on whom, destined as he is to pursue the conquests of the father, moral and religious obligations might be incommodious.

DIOGENES. Kings who kiss the toes of the most Gods, and the most zealously, never find any such incommodiousness. In courts, religious ceremonies cover with their embroidery moral obligations ; and the most dishonest and the most libidinous and the most sanguinary kings (to say nothing of private men) have usually been the most punctual worshipers.

PLATO. There may be truth in these words. We however know your contempt for religious acts and ceremonies, which, if you do not comply with them, you should at least respect, by way of an example.

DIOGENES. What ! if a man lies to me, should I respect the lie for the sake of an example ! Should I be guilty of duplicity for the sake of an example ! Did I ever omit to attend the Thesmophoria ? the [1] only religious rite worthy of a wise man's attendance. It displays the union of industry and law. Here is no fraud, no fallacy, no filching : the Gods are worshiped for their best gifts, and do not stand with open palms for ours. I neither laugh nor wonder at anyone's folly. To laugh at it, is childish or inhumane, according to its nature ; and to wonder at it, would be a greater folly than itself, whatever it may be.

Must [2] I go on with incoherencies and inconsistencies ?

PLATO. I am not urgent with you.

DIOGENES. Then I will reward thee the rather.

Thou makest poor Socrates tell us that a beautiful vase is inferior to a beautiful horse ; and as a beautiful horse is inferior to a beautiful maiden, in like manner a beautiful maiden is inferior in beauty to the immortal Gods.

PLATO. No doubt, O Diogenes !

DIOGENES. Thou hast whimsical ideas of beauty : but, understanding the word as all Athenians and all inhabitants of Hellas understand it, there is no analogy between a horse and a vase.

---

[1] 1st ed. reads : " the only religious rite that ever was invented or ever will be," etc. The Thesmophoria being a woman's festival, Diogenes could have taken no part in it.

[2] From " Must " to " advantage," p. 94, added in 2nd ed.

DIOGENES AND PLATO

Understanding it as thou perhaps mayest choose to do on the occasion, understanding it as applicable to the service and utility of man and Gods, the vase may be applied to more frequent and more noble purposes than the horse. It may delight men in health; it may administer to them in sickness; it may pour out before the protectors of families and of cities the wine of sacrifice. But if it is the quality and essence of beauty to gratify the sight, there are certainly more persons who can receive gratification from the appearance of a beautiful vase than of a beautiful horse. Xerxes brought into Hellas with him thousands of beautiful horses and many beautiful vases. Supposing now that all the horses which were beautiful seemed so to all good judges of their symmetry, it is probable that scarcely one man in fifty would fix his eyes attentively on one horse in fifty; but undoubtedly there were vases in the tents of Xerxes which would have attracted all the eyes in the army and have filled them with admiration. I say nothing of the women, who in Asiatic armies are as numerous as the men, and who would every one admire the vases, while few admired the horses. Yet women are as good judges of what is beautiful as thou art, and for the most part on the same principles. But, repeating that there is no analogy between the two objects, I must insist that there can be no just comparison: and I trust I have clearly demonstrated that the postulate is not to be conceded. We will nevertheless carry on the argument and examination: for " the beautiful virgin is inferior in beauty to the immortal Gods." Is not Vulcan an immortal God? are not the Furies and Discord immortal Goddesses? Ay, by my troth are they; and there never was any city and scarcely any family on earth to which they were long invisible. Wouldst thou prefer them to a golden cup, or even to a cup from the potter's? Would it require one with a dance of bacchanals under the pouting rim? would it require one foretasted by Agathon? Let us descend from the deities to the horses. Thy dress is as well adapted to horsemanship as thy words are in general to discourse. Such as thou art would run out of the horse's way; and such as know thee best would put the vase out of thine.

PLATO. So then, I am a thief, it appears, not only of men's notions, but of their vases!

DIOGENES. Nay, nay, my good Plato! Thou hast however the

frailty of concupiscence for things tangible and intangible, and thou likest well-turned vases no less than well-turned sentences : therefore they who know thee would leave no temptation in thy way, to the disturbance and detriment of thy soul. Away with the horse and vase ! we will come together to the quarters of the virgin. Faith ! my friend, if we find her only just as beautiful as some of the Goddesses we were naming, her virginity will be as immortal as their divinity.

PLATO. I have given a reason for my supposition.

DIOGENES. What is it ?

PLATO. Because there is a beauty incorruptible, and for ever he same.

DIOGENES. Visible beauty ? beauty cognisable in the same sense as of vases and of horses ? beauty that in degree and in quality can be compared with theirs ? Is there any positive proof that the gods possess it ? and all of them ? and all equally ? Are there any points of resemblance between Jupiter and the daughter of Acrisius ? any between Hatè and Hebe ? whose sex being the same brings them somewhat nearer. In like manner thou confoundest the harmony of music with symmetry in what is visible and tangible : and thou teachest the stars how to dance to their own compositions, enlivened by fugues and variations from thy master-hand. This, in the opinion of thy boy scholars, is sublimity ! Truly it is the sublimity which he attains who is hurled into the air from a ballista. Changing my ground, and perhaps to thy advantage, in the name of Socrates I come forth against thee ; not for using him as a wide-mouthed mask, stuffed with gibes and quibbles ; not for making him the most sophistical of sophists, or (as thou hast done frequently) the most improvident of statesmen and the worst of citizens ; my accusation and indictment is, for representing him, who had distinguished himself on the field of battle above the bravest and most experienced of the Athenian leaders (particularly at Delion and Potidea), as more ignorant of warfare than the worst-fledged crane that fought against the Pygmies.

PLATO. I am not conscious of having done it.

DIOGENES. I believe thee ; but done it thou hast. The language of Socrates was Attic and simple : he hated the verbosity and refinement of wranglers and rhetoricians ; and never would he have attributed to Aspasia, who thought and spoke like Pericles, and

94

whose elegance and judgment thou thyself hast commended, the chaff and litter thou hast tossed about with so much wind and wantonness, in thy dialogue of *Menexenus*. Now, to omit the other fooleries in it, Aspasia would have laughed to scorn the most ignorant of her tire-women, who should have related to her the story thou tellest in her name, about the march of the Persians round the territory of Eretria. This narrative seems to thee so happy an attempt at history, that thou betrayest no small fear lest the reader should take thee at thy word, and lest Aspasia should in reality rob thee or Socrates of the glory due for it.

PLATO. Where lies the fault ?

DIOGENES. If the Persians had marched, as thou describest them forming a circle, and from sea to sea, with their hands joined together, fourscore shepherds with their dogs, their rams, and their bell-wethers, might have killed them all, coming against them from points well-chosen. As, however, great part of the Persians were horsemen, which thou appearest to have quite forgotten, how could they go in single line with their hands joined, unless they lay flat upon their backs along the backs of their horses, and unless the horses themselves went tail to tail, one pulling on the other ? Even then the line would be interrupted, and only two could join hands. A pretty piece of net-work is here ! and the only defect I can find in it is, that it would help the fish to catch the fisherman.

PLATO. This is an abuse of wit, if there be any wit in it.

DIOGENES. I doubt whether there is any; for the only man that hears it does not smile. We will be serious then. Such nonsense, delivered in a school of philosophy, might be the less derided ; but it is given us as an oration, held before an Athenian army, to the honour of those who fell in battle. The beginning of the speech is cold and languid : the remainder is worse ; it is learned and scholastic.

PLATO. Is learning worse in oratory than languor ?

DIOGENES. Incomparably, in the praises of the dead who died bravely, played off before those who had just been fighting in the same ranks. What we most want in this business is sincerity ; what we want least are things remote from the action. Men may be cold by nature, and languid from exhaustion, from grief itself, from watchfulness, from pity ; but they can not be idling and wandering about other times and nations, when their brothers and sons and bosom-friends are brought lifeless into the city, and the least inquisitive, the least sensitive, are hanging immovably over their recent wounds. Then burst forth their names from the full heart ; their fathers' names come next, hallowed with lauds and benedictions that flow over upon their whole tribe ; then are lifted their helmets and turned round to the spectators ; for the grass is fastened to them by their blood, and it is befitting to show the people how they must have struggled to rise up, and to fight afresh for their country. Without [1] the virtues of courage and patriotism, the seeds of such morality as is fruitful and substantial spring up thinly, languidly, and ineffectually. The images of great men should be stationed throughout the works of great historians.

PLATO. According to your numeration, the great men are scanty : and pray, O Diogenes ! are they always at hand ?

DIOGENES. Prominent men always are. Catch them and hold them fast, when thou canst find none better. Whoever hath influenced the downfall or decline of a commonwealth, whoever hath altered in any degree its social state, should be brought before the high tribunal of History.

PLATO. Very mean intellects have accomplished these things. Not only battering-rams have loosened the walls of cities, but foxes and rabbits have done the same. Vulgar and vile men have been elevated to power by circumstances : would you introduce the vulgar and vile into the pages you expect to be immortal ?

DIOGENES. They never can blow out immortality. Criminals do not deform by their presence the strong and stately edifices in which they are incarcerated. I look above them and see the image of Justice : I rest my arm against the plinth where the protectress of cities raises her spear by the judgment-seat. Thou art not silent on the vile ; but delightest in bringing them out before us, and in reducing their betters to the same condition.

PLATO. I am no writer of history.

DIOGENES. Every great writer is a writer of history, let him treat on almost what subject he may. He carries with him for thousands of years a portion of his times : and indeed if only his own effigy were there, it would be greatly more than a fragment of his country.

In all thy writings I can discover no mention of Epaminondas,

[1] From " Without " to " people," p. 98, added in 2nd ed.

who vanquished thy enslavers the Lacedæmonians ; nor of Thrasybulus, who expelled the murderers of thy preceptor. Whenever thou again displayest a specimen of thy historical researches, do not utterly overlook the fact that these excellent men were living in thy days ; that they fought against thy enemies ; that they rescued thee from slavery ; that thou art indebted to them for the whole estate of this interminable robe, with its valleys and hills and wastes ; for these perfumes that overpower all mine ; and moreover for thy house, thy grove, thy auditors, thy admirers and thy admired.

PLATO. Thrasybulus, with many noble qualities, had great faults.

DIOGENES. Great men too often have greater faults than little men can find room for.

PLATO. Epaminondas was undoubtedly a momentous man, and formidable to Lacedæmon, but Pelopidas shared his glory.

DIOGENES. How ready we all are with our praises when a cake is to be divided ; if it is not ours !

PLATO. I acknowledge his magnanimity, his integrity, his political skill, his military services, and, above all, his philosophical turn of mind : but since his countrymen, who knew him best, have until recently been silent on the transcendency of his merits, I think I may escape from obloquy in leaving them unnoticed. His glorious death appears to have excited more enthusiastic acclamation than his patriotic heroism.

DIOGENES. The sun colours the sky most deeply and most diffusely when he hath sunk below the horizon ; and they who never said, " How beneficently he shines ! " say at last, " How brightly he set ! " They who believe that their praise gives immortality, and who know that it gives celebrity and distinction, are iniquitous and flagitious in withdrawing it from such exemplary men, such self-devoted citizens, as Epaminondas and Thrasybulus.

Great writers are gifted with that golden wand which neither ages can corrode nor violence rend asunder, and are commanded to point with it toward the head (be it lofty or low) which nations are to contemplate and to revere.

PLATO. I should rather have conceived from you that the wand ought to designate those who merit the hatred of their species.

DIOGENES. This too is another of its offices, no less obligatory and sacred.

PLATO. Not only have I particularised such faults as I could investigate and detect, but in that historical fragment, which I acknowledge to be mine (although I left it in abeyance between Socrates and Aspasia), I have lauded the courage and conduct of our people.

DIOGENES. Thou recountest the glorious deeds of the Athenians by sea and land, staidly and circumstantially, as if the Athenians themselves, or any nation of the universe, could doubt them. Let orators do this when some other shall have rivalled them, which, as it never hath happened in the myriads of generations that have passed away, is never likely to happen in the myriads that will follow. From Asia, from Africa,[1] fifty nations came forward in a body, and assailed the citizens of one scanty city : fifty nations fled from before them. All the wealth and power of the world, all the civilisation, all the barbarism, were leagued against Athens ; the ocean was covered with their pride and spoils ; the earth trembled ; mountains were severed, distant coasts united : Athens gave to Nature her own again : and equal laws were the unalienable dowry brought by Liberty, to the only men capable of her defence or her enjoyment. Did Pericles, did Aspasia, did Socrates foresee, that the descendants of those whose heroes and gods were at best but like them should enter into the service of Persian satraps, and become the parasites of Sicilian kings ?

PLATO. Pythagoras, the most temperate and retired of mortals, entered the courts of princes.

DIOGENES. True ; he entered them and cleansed them : his breath was lustration ; his touch purified. He persuaded the princes of Italy to renounce their self-constituted and unlawful authority : in effecting which purpose, thou must acknowledge, O Plato, that either he was more eloquent than thou art, or that he was juster. If, being in the confidence of a usurper, which in itself is among the most heinous of crimes, since they virtually are outlaws, thou never gavest him such counsel at thy ease and leisure as Pythagoras gave at the peril of his life, thou in this likewise wert wanting to thy duty as an Athenian, a republican, a philosopher. If thou offeredst it, and it was rejected, and after the rejection thou yet tarriedst with him, then wert thou, friend Plato, an importunate sycophant and self-bound slave.

[1] 1st ed. inserts : " from the remotest parts of Europe and from the nearest."

DIOGENES AND PLATO

PLATO. I never heard that you blamed Euripides in this manner for frequenting the court of Archeläus.

DIOGENES. I have heard *thee* blame him for it; and this brings down on thee my indignation. Poets, by the constitution of their minds, are neither acute reasoners nor firmly-minded. Their vocation was allied to sycophancy from the beginning: they sang at the tables of the rich: and he who could not make a hero could not make a dinner. Those who are possessed of enthusiasm are fond of everything that excites it; hence poets are fond of festivals, of wine, of beauty, and of glory. They can not always make their selection; and generally they are little disposed to make it, from indolence of character. Theirs partakes less than others of the philosophical and the heroic. What wonder if Euripides hated those who deprived him of his right, in adjudging the prize of tragedy to his competitor? From hating the arbitrators who committed the injustice, he proceeded to hate the people who countenanced it. The whole frame of government is bad to those who have suffered under any part. Archeläus praised Euripides's poetry: he therefore liked Archeläus: the Athenians bantered his poetry: therefore he disliked the Athenians. Beside, he could not love those who killed his friend and teacher: if thou canst, I hope thy love may be for ever without a rival.

PLATO. He might surely have found, in some republic of Greece, the friend who would have sympathized with him.

DIOGENES. He might: nor have I any more inclination to commend his choice than thou hast right to condemn it. Terpander and Thales and Pherecydes were at Sparta with Lycurgus: and thou too, Plato, mightst have found in Greece a wealthy wise man ready to receive thee, or (where words are more acceptable) an unwise wealthy one. Why dost thou redden and bite thy lip? Wouldst thou rather give instruction, or not give it?

PLATO. I would rather give it, where I could.

DIOGENES. Wouldst thou rather give it to those who have it already, and do not need it, or to those who have it not, and do need it?

PLATO. To these latter.

DIOGENES. Impart it then to the unwise; and to those who are wealthy in preference to the rest, as they require it most, and can do most good with it.

99

IMAGINARY CONVERSATIONS : GREEK

PLATO. Is not this a contradiction to your own precepts, O Diogenes ? Have you not been censuring me, I need not say how severely, for my intercourse with Dionysius ? and yet surely he was wealthy, surely he required the advice of a philosopher, surely he could have done much good with it.

DIOGENES. An Athenian is more degraded by becoming the counsellor of a king, than a king is degraded by becoming the schoolmaster of paupers in a free city. Such people as Dionysius are to be approached by the brave and honest from two motives only : to convince them of their inutility, or to slay them for their iniquity. Our fathers and ourselves have witnessed in more than one country the curses of kingly power.[1] All nations, all cities, all communities, should enter into one great hunt, like that of the Scythians at the approach of winter, and should follow it up unrelentingly to its perdition. The diadem [2] should designate the victim : all who wear it, all who offer it, all who bow to it, should perish. The smallest, the poorest, the least accessible village, whose cottages are indistinguishable from the rocks around, should offer a reward for the heads of these monsters, as for the wolf's, the kite's, and the viper's.

Thou tellest us, in thy fourth book on *Polity*, that it matters but little whether a state be governed by many or one, if the one is obedient to the laws. Why hast not thou likewise told us, that it little matters whether the sun bring us heat or cold, if he ripens the fruits of the earth by cold as perfectly as by heat ? Demonstrate that he does it, and I subscribe to the proposition. Demonstrate that kings, by their nature and education, are obedient to the laws ; bear them patiently ; deem them no impediment to their wishes, designs, lusts, violences ; that a whole series of monarchs hath been of this character and condition, wherever a whole series hath been permitted to continue ; that under them independence of spirit, dignity of mind, rectitude of conduct, energy of character, truth of expression, and even lower and lighter things, eloquence, poetry, sculpture, painting, have flourished more exuberantly than among the free. On the contrary, some of the best princes have rescinded the laws they themselves introduced and sanctioned.

---

[1] Note on " power " in 1st ed. : " Speaking in the language of the Athenians by *kingly* power Diogenes means *despotic*."

[2] Note on " diadem " in 1st ed. : " Darius then threatened Greece."

DIOGENES AND PLATO

Impatient of restraint and order are even the quiet and inert of the species.

PLATO. There is a restlessness in activity : we must find occupation for kings.

DIOGENES. Open the fold to them and they will find it themselves : there will be plenty of heads and shanks on the morrow. I do not see why those who, directly or indirectly, would promote a kingly government, should escape the penalty of death, whenever it can be inflicted, any more than those who decoy men into slave-ships.

PLATO. Supposing me to have done it, I have used no deception.

DIOGENES. What ! it is no deception to call people out of their homes, to offer them a good supper and good beds if they will go along with thee ; to take the key out of the house-door, that they may not have the trouble of bearing the weight of it ; to show them plainly through the window the hot supper and comfortable bed, to which indeed the cook and chamberlain do beckon and invite them, but inform them however on entering, it is only on condition that they never stir a foot beyond the supper-room and bed-room ; to be conscious, as thou must be, when they desire to have rather their own key again, eat their own lentils, sleep on their own pallet, that thy friends the cook and chamberlain have forged the title-deeds, mortgaged the house and homestead, given the lentils to the groom, made a horse-cloth of the coverlet and a manger of the pallet ; that, on the first complaint against such an apparent injury (for at present they think and call it one), the said cook and chamberlain seize them by the hair, strip, scourge, imprison, and gag them, showing them through the grating what capital dishes are on the table for the more deserving, what an appetite the fumes stir up, and how sensible men fold their arms upon the breast contentedly, and slumber soundly after the carousal.

PLATO. People may exercise their judgment.

DIOGENES. People may spend their money. All people have not much money ; all people have not much judgment. It is cruel to prey or impose on those who have little of either. There is nothing so absurd that the ignorant have not believed : they have believed, and will believe for ever, what thou wouldst teach : namely, that others who never saw them, never are likely to see them, will care more about them than they should care about themselves. This pernicious fraud begins with perverting the intellect, and proceeds with seducing and corrupting the affections, which it transfers from the nearest to the most remote, from the dearest to the most indifferent. It enthrals the freedom both of mind and body; it annihilates not only political and moral, but, what nothing else however monstrous can do, even arithmetical proportions, making a unit more than a million. Odious is it in a parent to murder or sell a child, even in time of famine : but to sell him in the midst of plenty, to lay his throat at the mercy of a wild and riotous despot, to whet and kiss and present the knife that immolates him, and to ask the same favour of being immolated for the whole family in perpetuity, is not this an abomination ten thousand times more execrable ?

Let Falsehood be eternally the enemy of Truth, but not eternally her mistress : let Power be eternally the despiser of Weakness, but not eternally her oppressor : let Genius be eternally in the train or in the trammels of Wealth, but not eternally his sycophant and his pander.

PLATO. What a land is Attica ! in which the kings themselves were the mildest and best citizens, and resigned the sceptre ; deeming none other worthy of supremacy than the wisest and most warlike of the immortal Gods. In Attica the olive and corn were first cultivated.

DIOGENES. Like other Athenians, thou art idly fond of dwelling on the antiquity of the people, and wouldst fain persuade thyself, not only that the first corn and olive, but even that the first man, sprang from Attica. I rather think that what historians call the emigration of the Pelasgians under Danaüs was the emigration of those " *shepherds*," as they continued to be denominated, who, having long kept possession of Egypt, were besieged in the city of Aoudris, by Thoutmosis, and retired by capitulation. These probably were of Chaldaic origin. Danaüs, like every wise legislator, introduced such religious rites as were adapted to the country in which he settled. The ancient being once relaxed, admission was made gradually for honouring the brave and beneficent, who in successive generations extended the boundary of the colonists, and defended them against the resentment and reprisal of the native chieftains.

PLATO. This may be ; but evidence is wanting.

DIOGENES AND PLATO

DIOGENES. Indeed it is not quite so strong and satisfactory as in that piece of history, where thou maintainest that "*each of us is the half of a man.*" * By Neptune! a vile man, too, or the computation were overcharged.

PLATO. We copy these things from old traditions.

DIOGENES. Copy rather the manners of antiquity than the fables; or copy those fables only which convey the manners. That one man was cut off another, is a tradition little meriting preservation. Any old woman who drinks and dozes, could recite to us more interesting dreams, and worthier of the Divinity.

Surely thy effrontery is of the calmest and most philosophical kind, that thou remarkest to me a want of historic evidence, when I offered a suggestion; and when thou thyself hast attributed to Solon the most improbable falsehoods on the antiquity and the exploits of your ancestors, telling us that time had "*obliterated*" these "*memorable*" annals. What is obliterated at home, Solon picks up fresh and vivid in Egypt. An Egyptian priest, the oldest and wisest of the body, informs him that Athens was built a thousand years before Sais, by the goddess Neithes, as they call her, but as we, Athenè, who received the *seed* of the city from the Earth and Vulcan. The records of Athens are lost, and those of Sais mount up no higher than eight thousand years. Enough to make her talk like an old woman.

I have, in other places and on other occasions, remarked to those about me many, if not equal and similar, yet gross absurdities in thy writings.

PLATO. Gently! I know it. Several of these, supposing them to be what you denominate them, are originally from others, and from the gravest men.

DIOGENES. Gross absurdities are usually of that parentage: the

* In the *Banquet*. No two qualities are more dissimilar than the imagination of Plato and the imagination of Shakespeare. The *Androgyne* was probably of higher antiquity than Grecian fable. Whencesoever it originated, we can not but wonder how Shakespeare met with it. In his *King John*, the citizen of Angiers says of the Lady Blanche and of the Dauphin,

> "He is the half-part of a blessed man,
> Left to be finished by such a *she;*
> And *she* a fair divided excellence
> Whose fullness of perfection lies in him."

What is beautiful in poetry may be infantine in philosophy, and monstrous in physics.—W. S. L.

103

idle and weak produce but petty ones, and such as gambol at theatres and fairs. Thine are good for nothing : men are too old, and children too young, to laugh at them. There is no room for excuse or apology in the adoption of another's foolery. Imagination may heat a writer to such a degree, that he feels not what drops from him or clings to him of his own : another's is taken up deliberately, and trimmed at leisure. I [1] will now proceed with thee. I have heard it affirmed (but, as philosophers are the affirmers, the assertion may be questioned) that there is not a notion or idea, in the wide compass of thy works, originally thy own.

PLATO. I have made them all mine by my manner of treating them.

DIOGENES. If I throw my cloak over a fugitive slave to steal him, it is so short and strait, so threadbare and chinky, that he would be recognised by the idlest observer who had seen him seven years ago in the market-place : but if thou hadst enveloped him in thy versicoloured and cloudlike vestiary, puffed and effuse, rustling and rolling, nobody could guess well what animal was under it, much less what man. And such a tissue would conceal a gang of them, as easily as it would a parsley-bed, or the study yonder of young Demosthenes. Therefore, I no more wonder that thou art tempted to run in chase of butterflies, and catchest many, than I am at discovering that thou breakest their wings and legs by the weight of the web thou throwest over them ; and that we find the head of one indented into the body of another, and never an individual retaining the colour or character of any species. Thou hast indeed, I am inclined to believe, some ideas of thy own : for instance, when thou tellest us that a well-governed city ought to let her walls go to sleep along the ground. Pallas forbid that any city should do it where thou art, for thou wouldst surely deflower her, before the soldiers of the enemy could break in on the same errand. The poets are bad enough : they every now and then want a check upon them : but there must be an eternal vigilance against philosophers. Yet I would not drive you all out of the city-gates, because I fain would keep the country parts from pollution.

PLATO. Certainly, O Diogenes, I can not retort on you the accusation of employing any language or any sentiments but your own, unquestionably the purest and most genuine Sinopean.

[1] From " I " to " boast," p. 105, added in 2nd ed.

DIOGENES AND PLATO

DIOGENES. Welcome to another draught of it, my courteous guest! By thy own confession, or rather thy own boast, thou stolest every idea thy voluminous books convey; and therefore thou wouldst persuade us that all other ideas must have an archetype; and that God himself, the demiurgos, would blunder and botch without one. Now can not God, by thy good leave, gentle Plato! quite as easily form a thing as conceive it? and execute it as readily at once as at twice? Or hath he rather, in some slight degree, less of plastic power than of mental? Seriously, if thou hast received these fooleries from the Egyptian priests, prythee, for want of articles more valuable to bring among us, take them back on thy next voyage, and change them against the husk of a pistachio dropped from the pouch of a sacred ape.

Thy God is like thyself, as most men's gods are : he throws together a vast quantity of stuff, and leaves his workpeople to cut it out and tack it together, after their own fashion and fancy. These demons or genii are mischievous and fantastical imps : it would have been better if they had always sitten with their hands before them, or played and toyed with one another, like the young folks in the garden of Academus. As thou hast modified the ideas of those who went before thee, so those who follow thee will modify thine. The wiser of them will believe, and reasonably enough, that it is time for the demiurgos to lay his head upon his pillow, after heating his brains with so many false conceptions, and to let the world go on its own way, without any anxiety or concern.

Beside, would not thy dialogues be much better and more interesting, if thou hadst given more variety to the characters, and hadst introduced them conversing on a greater variety of topics? Thyself and Prodicus, if thou wouldst not disdain to meet him, might illustrate the nature of allegory, might explain to your audience where it can enter gracefully, and where it must be excluded : we should learn from you, perhaps, under whose guidance it first came into Greece : whether anyone has mentioned the existence of it in the poems of Orpheus and Musæus (now so lost that we possess no traces of them), or whether it was introduced by Homer, and derived from the tales and mythology of the East. Certainly he has given us for deities such personages as were never worshipped in our country; some he found, I suspect, in the chrysalis state of metaphors, and hatched them by the warmth of his genius into allegories, giving them a strength of wing by which they were carried to the summit of Olympus. Euripides and Aristophanes might discourse upon comedy and tragedy, and upon that species of poetry which, though the earliest and most universal, was cultivated in Attica with little success until the time of Sophocles.

PLATO. You mean the Ode.

DIOGENES. I do. There was hardly a corner of Greece, hardly an islet, where the children of Pallas were not called to school and challenged by choristers.

PLATO. These disquisitions entered into no portion of my plan.

DIOGENES. Rather say, ill-suited thy genius ; having laid down no plan whatever for a series of dialogues. School-exercises, or, if thou pleasest to call them so, *disquisitions*, require no such form as thou hast given to them, and they block up the inlets and outlets of conversation, which, to seem natural, should not adhere too closely to one subject. The most delightful parts both of philosophy and of fiction might have opened and expanded before us, if thou hadst selected some fifty or sixty of the wisest, most eloquent, and most facetious, and hadst made them exert their abilities on what was most at their command.

PLATO. I am not certain that I could have given to Aristophanes all his gaiety and humour.

DIOGENES. Art thou certain thou hast given to Socrates all his irony and perspicacity, or even all his virtue ?

PLATO. His virtue I think I have given him fully.

DIOGENES. Few can comprehend the whole of it, or see where it is separated from wisdom. Being a philosopher, he must have known that marriage would render him less contemplative and less happy, though he had chosen the most beautiful, the most quiet, the most obedient, and most affectionate woman in the world ; yet he preferred what he considered his duty as a citizen to his peace of mind.

PLATO. He might hope to beget children in sagacity like himself.

DIOGENES. He can never have hoped it at all, or thought about it as became him. He must have observed that the sons of meditative men are usually dull and stupid ; and he might foresee that those philosophers or magistrates whom their father had excelled would be, openly or covertly, their enemies.

PLATO. Here then is no proof of his prudence or his virtue. True [1] indeed is your remark on the children of the contemplative ; and we have usually found them rejected from the higher offices, to punish them for the celebrity of their fathers.

DIOGENES. Why didst not thou introduce thy preceptor arguing fairly and fully on some of these topics ? Wert thou afraid of disclosing his inconsistencies ? A man to be quite consistent must live quite alone. I know not whether Socrates would have succeeded in the attempt ; I only know I have failed.

PLATO. I hope, most excellent Diogenes, I shall not be accused of obstructing much longer so desirable an experiment.

DIOGENES. I will bear with thee some time yet. The earth is an obstruction to the growth of seed ; but the seed can not grow well without it. When I have done with thee, I will dismiss thee with my usual courtesy.

There are many who marry from utter indigence of thought, captivated by the playfulness of youth, as if a kitten were never to be a cat ! Socrates was an unlikely man to have been under so sorrowful an illusion. Those among you who tell us that he married the too handy Xantippe for the purpose of exercising his patience, turn him from a philosopher into a fool. We should be at least as moderate in the indulgence of those matters which bring our patience into play, as in the indulgence of any other. It is better to be sound than hard, and better to be hard than callous.

PLATO. Do you say that, Diogenes ?

DIOGENES. I do say it ; and I confess to thee that I am grown harder than is well for me. Thou wilt not so easily confess that an opposite course of life hath rendered thee callous. Frugality and severity must act upon us long and uninterruptedly before they produce this effect : pleasure and selfishness soon produce the other. The red-hot iron is but one moment in sending up its fumes from the puddle it is turned into, and in losing its brightness and its flexibility.

PLATO. I [2] have admitted your definitions, and now I accede to

[1] From " True " to " fathers " added in 2nd ed.
[2] From " I " to " and " added in 2nd ed.

your illustrations. But illustrations are pleasant merely; and definitions are easier than discoveries.

DIOGENES. The easiest things in the world when they are made : nevertheless thou hast given us some dozens, and there is hardly a complete or a just one on the list; hardly one that any wench, watching her bees and spinning on Hymettus, might not have corrected.

PLATO. As you did, no doubt, when you threw into my school the cock you had stripped of its feathers.

DIOGENES. Even to the present day, neither thou nor any of thy scholars have detected the fallacy.

PLATO. We could not dissemble that our definition was inexact.

DIOGENES. I do not mean that.

PLATO. What then ?

DIOGENES. I would remark that neither thou nor thy disciples found me out.

PLATO. We saw you plainly enough : we heard you too, crying, *Behold Plato's man !*

DIOGENES. It was not only a reproof of thy temerity in definitions, but a trial of the facility with which a light and unjust ridicule of them would be received.

PLATO. Unjust perhaps not, but certainly rude and vulgar.

DIOGENES. Unjust, I repeat it : because thy definition was of man as nature formed him : and the cock, when I threw it on the floor, was no longer as nature had formed it. Thou art accustomed to lay down as peculiarities the attributes that belong, equally or nearly, to several things or persons.

PLATO. The characteristic is not always the definition, nor meant to be accepted for it. I have called tragedy $\delta\eta\mu o\tau\epsilon\rho\pi\acute{\epsilon}\sigma\tau a\tau o\nu$, " most delightful to the people," and $\psi v\chi a\gamma\omega\gamma\iota\kappa\acute{\omega}\tau a\tau o\nu$, " most agitating to the soul " : no person can accuse me of laying down these terms as the *definition* of tragedy. The former is often as applicable to rat-catching, and the latter to cold-bathing. I have called the dog $\phi\iota\lambda o\mu a\theta\acute{\epsilon}s$, " fond of acquiring information," and $\phi\iota\lambda\acute{o}\sigma o\phi o\nu$, " fond of wisdom " ; but I never have denied that man is equally or more.

DIOGENES. Deny it then instantly. Every dog has that property ; every man has not : I mean the $\phi\iota\lambda o\mu a\theta\acute{\epsilon}s$. The $\phi\iota\lambda\acute{o}\sigma o\phi o\nu$ is false in both cases : for words must be taken as they pass current in our days, and not according to any ancient acceptation. The author of the *Margites* says,

Τόνδ' οὔτ' αὖ σκαπτῆρα θεοὶ θέσαν οὔτ' ἀροτῆρα
Οὔτ' ἄλλως τι σοφόν.

Here certainly the σοφός has no reference to the higher and intellectual powers, as with us, since he is placed by the poet among delvers and ploughmen. The compound word φιλόσοφος did not exist when the author of *Margites* wrote ; and the lover of wisdom, in his days, was the lover of the country. Her aspirants, in ours, are quarrelling and fighting in the streets about her ; and nevertheless, while they rustle their Asiatic robes around them, leave her as destitute, as naked, and as hungry as they found her.

PLATO. Did your featherless cock render her any service ?

DIOGENES. Yes.

PLATO. I corrected and enlarged the definition without your assistance.

DIOGENES. Not without it : the best assistance is the first, and the first was the detection of insufficiency and error. Thy addition was, " that man has broad nails " : now art thou certain that all monkeys have sharp and round ones ? I have heard the contrary ; and [1] I know that the mole has them broad and flat.

PLATO. What wouldst thou say man is, and other animals are not ?

DIOGENES. I would say, *lying* and *malicious*.

PLATO. Because he alone can speak ; he alone can reflect.

DIOGENES. Excellent reason ! If speech be the communication of what is felt, made by means of the voice, thinkest thou other creatures are mute ? All that have legs, I am inclined to believe, have voices : whether fishes have, I know not. Thou wouldst hardly wish me to take the trouble of demonstrating that men lie, both before their metamorphosis into philosophers and after : yet perhaps thou mayst wish to hear wherefore, if other animals reason and reflect (which is proved in them by apprehending mischief and avoiding it, and likewise by the exertion of memory), they are not also malicious.

PLATO. Having kept in their memory an evil received, many of them evince their malice, by attacking long afterward those who did it.

---

[1] From " and " to " flat " added in 2nd ed.

DIOGENES. This is not malice, in man or beast. Malice is ill-will without just cause, and desire to injure without any hope of benefiting from it. Tigers and serpents seize on the unwary, and inflict deadly wounds : tigers from sport or hunger, serpents from fear or hurt : neither of them from malice, neither of them from hatred. Dogs indeed and horses do acquire hatred in their domestic state : they had none originally : they must sleep under man's roof before they share with him his high feeling ; that high feeling which renders him the destroyer of his own kind, and the devourer of his own heart. We are willing to consider both revenge and envy as much worse blemishes in the character than malice. Yet for one who is invidious there are six or seven who are malicious, and for one who is revengeful there are fifty. In revenge there must be something of energy, however short-breathed and indeterminate. Many are exempt from it because they are idle and forgetful ; more, because they are circumspect and timid ; but nothing hinders the same people from being malicious. Envy, abominable as we call her, and as she is, often stands upon a richly-figured base, and is to be recognised only by the sadness with which she leans over the emblems of power and genius. The contracted heart of Malice can never swell to sadness. Seeing nothing that she holds desirable, she covets nothing ; she would rather the extinction than the possession of what is amiable ; she hates high and low, bad and good, coldly pertinacious and lazily morose.

Thou Plato, who hast cause to be invidious of not many, art of nearly all : and thy wit pays the fine, being rendered thereby the poorest I know in any Athenian ambitious of it.

PLATO. If the fact be thus, the reason is different.

DIOGENES. What is it then ?

PLATO. That every witticism is an inexact thought : that what is perfectly true is imperfectly witty : and that I have attended more sedulously and more successfully to verity.

DIOGENES. Why not bring the simplicity of truth into the paths of life ? why not try whether it would look as becomingly in actions as in words ; in the wardrobe and at table as in deductions and syllogisms ? why not demonstrate to the youth of Athens that thou in good earnest canst be contented with a little ?

PLATO. So I could, if the times required it.

DIOGENES AND PLATO

DIOGENES. They will soon ; and we should at least be taught our rudiments, before a hard lesson is put into our hands.

PLATO. This makes me think again that your grammatical knowledge, O Diogenes, is extensive. The plain and only sense of the second verse——

DIOGENES. What second verse ? Were we talking of any such things ?

PLATO. Yes, just now.

DIOGENES. I had forgotten it.

PLATO. How ! forgotten the *Margites?* The meaning of the words is, " nor fit for anything else."

Homer in like manner uses εἶδος very frequently, to indicate mere manual skill. The spirit of inquiry, the φιλομαθές, we take upon ourselves with the canine attributes : we talk of *indagating*, of *investigating*, of *questing*.

DIOGENES. I know the respect thou bearest to the dogly character, and can attribute to nothing else the complacency with which thou hast listened to me since I released thy cloak. If ever the Athenians, in their inconstancy, should issue a decree to deprive me of the appellation they have conferred on me, rise up, I pray thee, in my defence, and protest that I have not merited so severe a mulct. Something I do deserve at thy hands ; having supplied thee, first with a store of patience, when thou wert going without any about thee, although it is the readiest viaticum and the heartiest sustenance of human life ; and then with weapons from this tub, wherewith to drive the importunate cock before thee out of doors again.[1]

PLATO. My presence then may, after so generous and long a hospitality, be excused.

DIOGENES. Wait a little yet, to accept a few gifts and gratuities at parting. The *Defence of Socrates* comes out somewhat late. The style pleases me greatly more than in any of thy dialogues : truth is the chief thing wanting in it.

PLATO. In what part ? For surely the main is well remembered by all the city.

DIOGENES. Socrates, I am credibly informed, never called Meletus a strange man, as thou recordest, for accusing him of thinking the sun stone, the moon earth, instead of Gods ; telling him before

---

[1] In 1st ed. the Conversation ends here.

the judges that such an accusation ought rather to have been brought against Anaxagoras, whose treatise to this purport was sold at the theatre for a drachma. Never did Socrates say that he might fairly be laughed to scorn if he ever had countenanced so absurd a doctrine. Now, Plato, although in thy work on the Laws thou art explicit in thy declaration that the sun and moon are deities, Anaxagoras denied the fact, and Socrates never asserted it. In this misrepresentation of thine, regarding the friend of Pericles, there was little harm beyond the falsehood : for Anaxagoras was dead ; and hemlock might be growing on his grave, but could not reach his heart or even his extremities. When I was a youngster I often tried to throw a stone over the moon, unsuspicious that it was a Goddess : had it been, she must be the best tempered of all in heaven, or she would have sent the stone back on my head for my impiety. My wonder was, that, although I clearly saw the stone ascend as high as the moon, and somewhat higher, it always fell on this side. The moon seemed only to laugh at me ; and so did the girls who were reaping. Had they been philosophers, with any true religion about them, they would have made an Orpheus of me, and have torn me to pieces. But being of Sinopè, not of Athens, they thought about nothing else than merriment at an idle pelter of the moon.

PLATO. We may know more hereafter in relation to these matters.

DIOGENES. Not if philosophers are agreed that it is impious to inquire into them, which, as thou relatest, was the opinion of Socrates. Without sun and moon we have more Gods than we know what to do with. If the greater are unable to manage us and keep us in order, sun and moon can help them but little. It is long before men apply to any good the things that lie before them. Air, fire, water, have been applied to new purposes from age to age : poets have seen dimly some of them : philosophers would extinguish the little lamps they carry ; but not such philosophers as Anaxagoras. Common things, which at present are brought into little or no use, will hereafter be applied to many ; above other common things, common sense. Socrates calls that forbidden which, piling up syllogism on syllogism, and exerting the whole length of his tongue, he was unable to reach. Pythagoras, as wise a man, Anaxagoras a wiser, were invited by Nature to investigate her secrets : when they were advancing too boldly, she gently pushed them back, but never threw the door abruptly in their faces; it stands wide open still. Socrates denounced as impious all physical speculations; these the religious man, the only true philosopher, might find manifested to him through oracles and omens. If thy master, among his many acquirements, had acquired the faculty of speaking plainly, he would have spoken like Anaxagoras, whom, at least it must be conceded, he never had, as thou representest, the folly, the disingenuousness, the impudence to decry.

PLATO. Did not the priestess of Apollo declare him to be the wisest of mankind?

DIOGENES. The priestess was an old woman, and the fumes were potent. I have never been able to find out on what occasion this oracle was delivered. Oracles are consulted by those who are the most interested. Surely not even a philosopher would be so impudent as to ask a God whether he was the wisest man upon earth. Nor are such the matters on which oracles are pronounced; but future results of arduous undertakings. The story carries a falsehood on the face of it.

PLATO. You are the first that ever doubted the fact, whatever may have been the occasion: there is a cloud of witnesses to its universal belief.

DIOGENES. I never could see my way through a cloud of witnesses, especially in temples. Lies are as communicative as fleas; and truth is as difficult to lay hold upon as air.

PLATO. I feel the acuteness of the former simile; and I wish I could controvert the latter.

DIOGENES. Consider well the probability of such a declaration from Delphi. Would the people of Athens, religious as they are, ever have ventured to accuse of impiety, and to condemn to death for it, the very man whom an infallible God had so signalised? If fifty ages and fifty nations had taken up this fable, I would reduce it to dust under my feet.

PLATO. I dare not listen to such discourse.

DIOGENES. Thou shalt; were it only for variety.

PLATO. I limited my discourse to the defence of Socrates: with such as Anaxagoras and Democritus we have nothing in common. But censuring Socrates as you do, you must surely want your usual modesty, O citizen of Sinopè!

DIOGENES. Praise me then ; since, wanting it, I never took anyone's away.

PLATO. Little should I now wonder to hear you call yourself as wise as he was.

DIOGENES. Could he keep at home as I do ? Could he abstain from questioning and quibbling, to win the applause of boys and pedants ? Am I not contented in my own house here, over whose roof, standing on level ground, I cast my shadow. I pretend not to know the secrets of the lower regions or the upper : I let the gods sit quiet, and they do the same by me. Hearing that there are three Furies, I have taken the word of the wise for it, and never have carried a link down below in search of a fourth. He found her up here. I neither envy him his discovery, nor wonder at the tranquillity of his death. Wisdom is tripartite ; saying, doing, avoiding.

PLATO. Mine, I must acknowledge, has been insufficient in the latter quality : but I hope to correct my fault in future.

DIOGENES. On this particular I am not incredulous. Thou owest me too much ever to let me smell thy beard again. From this humble and frugal house of mine thou shalt carry home whole truths, and none mutilated ; intelligible truths, and none ambiguous. Probably I know not a quarter of thy writings ; but, in the number I do know, I find more incongruous scraps of philosophy and religion, sweet, sour, and savoury, thrown into one stewing-pan, and simmering and bubbling, than my stomach can digest or my fingers separate.

PLATO. Too encomiastic ! If I may judge by the fumes of the garlic, the stomach is surely strong : and, if another sense is equally faithful, the fingers are armed at all points.

DIOGENES. Well spoken and truly. I have improved thee already, go thy way, and carry thy whole robe safe back.[1]

Diogenes Laertius, biographer of the Cynic, is among the most inelegant and injudicious writers of antiquity ; yet his book is highly valuable for the anecdotes it preserves. No philosopher or other man more abounded in shrewd wit than the philosopher of Sinopè, whose opinions have been somewhat misunderstood, and whose memory hath suffered much injustice. One Diocles, and

---

[1] For Landor's late and imperfect study of Plato, see his *Letter to Emerson*: "Resolved to find out what there was in this remarkable philosopher, I went daily for several weeks to the Maglabechian library at Florence, and thus refreshing my neglected Greek," etc.

DIOGENES AND PLATO

afterward Eubulides, mention him (it appears) as having been expelled from Sinopè for counterfeiting money : and his biographer tells us that he has recorded it of himself. His words led astray these authors. He says that he *marked* false money : for an equivoke was ever the darling of Diogenes, and, by the marking of false money, he means only that he exposed the fallacies of pretenders to virtue and philosophy. Had he been exiled for the crime of forgery, Alexander of Macedon, we may well suppose, would not have visited him, would not have desired him to ask any favour he chose, would not have declared that if he were not Alexander, he would fain have been Diogenes. He did not visit him from an idle curiosity, for he had seen him before in his father's camp on his first invasion of Greece, where he was apprehended as a spy, and, being brought before the king, exclaimed, " I am indeed a spy ; a spy of thy temerity and cupidity, who hazardest on the cast of a die thy throne and life." This is related by Plutarch in his *Ethics*. Some men may think forgery no very heinous crime, but all must think it an act of dishonesty ; and kings (whose moral scale is nowhere an exact one) would be likely to hold it in greater reprobation than anything but treason and insurrection. Had the accusation been true, or credited, or made at the time, the Athenians would not have tolerated so long his residence among them, severe as he was on their manners, and peculiarly contemptuous and contumelious toward the orators and philosophers ; Plato for instance, and afterward Demosthenes. Here however we may animadvert on the inaccuracy of attributing to him the reply, when somebody asked him what he thought of Socrates as having seen him, " *that he thought him a madman.*" Diogenes was but twelve years old at the death of Socrates, and did not leave Sinopè till long after. The answer, we may conceive, originated from the description that Plato in many of his dialogues had given of his master. Among the faults of Plato he ridiculed his affectation of new words unnecessary and inelegant ; for instance his coinage of $\tau\rho\alpha\pi\epsilon\zeta\acute{o}\tau\eta s$ and $\kappa\upsilon\alpha\theta\acute{o}\tau\eta s$, which Plato defended very frigidly, telling him that, although he had eyes to see a cup and a table, he had not understanding for *cuppeity* and *tableity* ; and it indeed must be an uncommon one. Plato himself, the most invidious of the Greek writers, says that he was another Socrates, but a mad one ; meaning (no doubt) that he was a Socrates when he spoke generally, a mad one when he spoke of *him*. Among his hearers was Phocion : a fact which alone would set aside the tale of his adversaries, a thousand times repeated by their readers, about his public indulgence in certain immoralities which no magistrature would tolerate.

Late in life he was taken by pirates, and sold to Xeniades the Corinthian, whose children he educated, and who declared that a good genius had entered his house in Diogenes. Here he died. A contest arose, to whom among his intimates and disciples should be allowed the distinction of supplying the expenses of his funeral : nor was it settled till the fathers of his auditors and the leaders of the people met together, and agreed to bury him at the public charge at the gate of the Isthmus : the most remarkable spot in Greece, by the assemblage of whose bravest inhabitants it was made glorious, and sacred by the games in honour of her Gods.—W. S. L.

VIII. XENOPHON AND CYRUS THE YOUNGER

401 B.C.

(Imag. Convers., iii., 1828 ; *Wks.*, i., 1846 ; *Imag. Convers. Gk. and Rom.*, 1853 ;
Wks., ii., 1876.)

CYRUS. Xenophon, I have longed for an opportunity of conversing with thee alone, on matters in which thou excitest my admiration. According to report thou wert the disciple of Socrates the mage, whom the Athenians condemned to drink hemlock, because he had a genius of his own.

XENOPHON. It is true, O Cyrus, I was.[1]

CYRUS. Verily, O wonderful man, thou must be the best farrier and hunter in Greece ; and, thinking on thee, I have oftentimes wished in my heart that so deserving a country as thy Attica, which is not destitute of wolves, polecats, and foxes, had, for every one of them, a leopard, a lion, and a tiger.

XENOPHON. O son of Darius, king of kings ! the Gods do not bestow all their gifts upon one country ; or, having bestowed them, it seemeth good unto their divine majesties that mortals should counteract their beneficence. We no longer have those valiant creatures among us ; to which privation I attribute it chiefly that we possess more eloquence indeed and learning than those who have them, but less bodily activity and strength.

CYRUS. There are other and better reasons, O Xenophon, for these things. You are unbelievers in the true religion, and have sunk through [2] your idleness on the bosom of false Gods : you clasp graven images, falling at the feet of such as have any.

XENOPHON. O Cyrus, I have observed that the authors of good make men very bad as often as they talk much about them ; whether it be to punish us for our presumption, or merely to laugh at us, I do not know ; nor have I ever heard my master Socrates discourse upon the question. Certain it appears to me from whatever I have read,[3]

---

[1] 1st ed. adds : " so." [2] 1st ed. reads : " thro." [3] 1st ed. reads : " redd."

that the powerful and the wise lose both their power and their wisdom the moment they enter into this dim and sacred inclosure ; just as, on entering the apartment of the women in your country, you lay aside both slipper and turban, and cover the head with only the extremity of the robe.

CYRUS. We will try to keep ourselves no less cool and orderly on our argument, if thou wilt come into it with me. And now inform me, O most excellent, on what difference in religion or government you Greeks denominate all other nations, and among the rest even us, barbarians ?

XENOPHON. If, O Cyrus, I may (as I believe I may) rely on thy wisdom, thy modesty and moderation, I will answer the question to the best of my abilities.

CYRUS. I, who aspire to the throne of my ancestors, can not be angry at the voice of truth, nor offended that a guest should execute my wishes.

XENOPHON. Courtesy and gentleness distinguish the Persians from other mortals. They are less subject to cruelty than any race among men, unless sceptres lie across their path.[1] Now, Cyrus, those things must surely be the worst of things which render the most humane of men the most inhumane. I deviate a little way from the main question, like my teacher, for the purpose of asking a preparatory one, which may lead me back again, and enable me to conduct thee smoothly and pleasantly. Pray inform me, O Cyrus, since I am about to be a leader in thy army, what are thy orders if I should happen to intercept the concubines of any hostile satrap ?

CYRUS. O Xenophon, keep thy hands, thy eyes, thy desires, away from them, as becomes thy gravity of wisdom and purity of heart, expressed in a countenance where we discern and venerate the beauty of seriousness and reserve.

XENOPHON. O Cyrus, I am a hunter, and, being so, a deviser of stratagems, and may perchance take others than concubines. I dare not utter what labours in my bosom : in vain fidelity excites and urges me.

CYRUS. Speak, O best Xenophon !

XENOPHON. If then Destiny should cast down before me the

---

[1] 1st ed., here ignored by Crump, reads : " unless brothers and sceptres cross their path."

horse of thy brother Artaxerxes, and the chances of war, or Mars, after due sacrifice, should place him in my power, what is my duty ?

CYRUS. Canst not thou, having in turn with others of thy countrymen the command of ten thousand Greeks, do thy duty without consulting me, in cases which, being unforeseen, are discretionary ?

XENOPHON. The fall of a king is terrible.

CYRUS. The rebound is worse. When your Saturn fell from heaven, did any God or mortal lend a hand to raise him up again ?

XENOPHON. It were impiety to contend against Jupiter.

CYRUS. It were madness to contend against Destiny. According to your fables, Saturn came first ; then came Jupiter.[1] The same divine right of expelling and occupying will be asserted as occasion may require. But Destiny saw the order of things rise, and sees it continue : and Gods before her are almost as little and weak as we are : she teaches them to repeat her words and obliges them to execute her will. If thou hast any wisdom, as thou surely hast, O disciple of Socrates the mage, never ask me another question on such a contingency : but answer me now, I entreat thee, about the strange word *barbarian*, at which (I hear) there are satraps and royalets[2] who take offence when you apply it to them.

XENOPHON. Attribute not the invention of the word to us, O Cyrus ! I have been as studious to know the derivation of it, as thou art ; for it is not Greek. On the return of Plato (of whom perhaps thou hast heard some mention) from Egypt, I learned from him * that the expression was habitual with the priests of that country, whence we, who have borrowed much knowledge from the Egyptians, borrowed also this term. They apply it as we do, to all strangers indiscriminately : but originally it signified those only who live nearest to them, and whom on that account, as is customary with every nation in the world, they hated most. The Africans to the

[1] 1st ed. has no break between this and the following sentence ; there is a colon instead of a period.

[2] A word used again, as Mr. Stephen Wheeler reminds me, in " Epicurus, Leontion, and Ternissa."

* Plato says nothing on the subject : it seems probable that in this manner the expression came first among the Greeks, who would otherwise, we may suppose, have taken the name of some nearer and more ferocious tribe.—W. S. L.

1st ed. adds : " In fact none suited them for excellent contempt but one perpetually governed by hereditary kings."

westward are called by themselves *ber-ber*, a generic name, and probably of honourable import.

CYRUS. O Xenophon, thou art indeed a treasury of wisdom : and in addition to it, I pray thee, do the Gods, as I have heard, manifest to thee future events in dreams ?

XENOPHON. Some they have truly laid open unto me.

CYRUS. Couldst not thou, O most wonderful, pray to them (not telling them that I said anything about the matter) to give thee one about the success of my arms ? For [1] our own pure religion does not allow us to expect or to pray for such an intervention.[2]

XENOPHON. If we had an oracle near, I would consult it. For dreams usually are confined to the eventual good or evil of the dreamer ; although there are instances to the contrary,[3] but in these instances the dreams fall upon minds peculiarly gifted, and properly fitted for their reception.

CYRUS. I have asked the Sun several times for counsel ; and yet I never could collect out of his radiance any certain sign or token. Only once it was attended by a lark, suddenly

> " Springing from crystal step to crystal step
> In the bright air, where none can follow her."

Thus one of our old poets, in a volume laid up at Persepolis, describes her. The lark herself, and the recollection of the lines, comforted and animated me greatly ; first the bird, merry and daring ; then the brightness of the air ; and lastly, but principally, the words " that she was rising where none could follow her." This must certainly mean myself : for who can suppose that Artaxerxes at that moment saw another lark doing the like, or remembered the same verses, which came upon me like a voice inspired ?

XENOPHON. Although larks are not strictly birds of augury, like eagles and vultures, and swans and herons, and owls and chickens, yet in this country, and against the Sun, and upon such an occasion, the appearance hath its weight with me, O Cyrus ! However I would not neglect to sharpen the scimitar,[4] and to see that the horses be well exercised and have plenty of oats and barley in the manger, and that their manes be carefully combed, lest the adversary think

---

[1] 1st ed. has no break here, reading " arms ? for our," etc.
[2] 1st ed. reads : " any such intervention."
[3] 1st ed. has a colon.   [4] 1st ed. reads : " scymetar."

us disorderly and unprovided, and inclined to flight. For the immortal Gods have often changed their minds upon finding us too confident and secure, or too negligent and idle, and have enlightened ours, to our cost, with a new and contrary interpretation of sentences uttered by their oracles.

CYRUS. On reflecting a little, I think these oracles in general are foolish things.

XENOPHON. I wish, O blameless Cyrus, that such a word had never overflown the enclosure of thy teeth, as the divine Homer says.

CYRUS. I wonder, O most intelligent and thoughtful Xenophon, that you Greeks, so few as there are of you, should worship such a number of Gods.

XENOPHON. And I, O Cyrus, that you who have occasion for so many, and particularly just at present, should adore but one. The Sun (I would speak it without offence) is nothing but an orb of fire ; although, as some say, of a prodigious magnitude,[1] hardly less than the Peloponnese.

CYRUS. I once heard from a slave, a scholar of Democritus, that it is many hundred times greater than the earth.

XENOPHON. I seldom laugh, and ought never at insanity, and least of all at this. Alas, poor Greek ! when he lost his freedom he lost his senses. O immortal gods ! may my countrymen at no time be reduced to that calamity, which nothing but this can mitigate.

CYRUS. He added that, immense as is the glorious orb, it is only a dewdrop on the finger of God, shining from it under the light of his countenance, as he waves his paternal blessing over the many-peopled world.

XENOPHON. This is poetry, but oriental. Strange absurdity ! when Jupiter is barely a foot taller than I am ; as may be well imagined by his intermingling with our women, and without inconvenience on either side : at least I have heard of none recorded by the priests. He has indeed a prodigious power of limb, and his expansion at need is proportionate to his compactness.

CYRUS. Give me thy sentiments, freely and entirely.

XENOPHON. I can not but marvel then, O Cyrus, at the blindness of the Persians. There is no other great nation, at all known to us, that does not acknowledge a plurality and variety of gods ;

[1] Anaxagoras was the author of this estimate. The 1st ed. reads: " Peloponnesus."

and this consent, so nearly universal, ought to convince the ingenuous and unprejudiced. I see the worst consequences to a government in countenancing the adoration of a single one, to the exclusion and mortification of the rest.

CYRUS. Perhaps to such a loose fabric as a republic.

XENOPHON. In a monarchy no less. Power hath here too its gradations ; the monarch, the mages, and the satraps.

CYRUS. Do not you see at once the beauty of this form ? No government is harmonious or rational without three estates ; none decorous or stabile. The throne must have legs ; but the legs must never stand uppermost : the king bears upon the mages, they bear upon the floor, or people. The king reserves to himself omnipotence ; he grants to his mages omniscience ; to his people, in the body, omnipresence. In this manner he divides himself ; but all is one. Where power is so well poised, in case of urgency we might impose taxes to the amount of nearly a tenth, and rarely hear a murmur in the land. If you, the magistrates of free Greeks, were to demand a fifteenth of the property in Attica for the purposes of government, the people would stone you. Now unquestionably that regimen is the best, which hath constantly the most power over them ; as that is the best riding by which the horse is managed the most easily and quietly, in even places and uneven. Nothing is truer or plainer. If we had as many gods and temples as you have, and if our deities and priests had as good appetites, our armies must be smaller, our horses leaner, and there would be more malignity and discord in the provinces.[1] For all sects, all favourers I mean of particular Gods and Goddesses, are united in one sentiment, that their deities are equally fond of picking bones and breaking them.

XENOPHON. Our religion is most beautiful.

CYRUS. Extremely so on the outside. In this external beauty, as in that of women when it is extreme, there is little expression, little sense. Our ritual is the best that can be devised for any hot climate. In order to adore the Sun at his rising, we must (it is needless to say) rise early. This is the time of day when the mind and body are most active, and most labour can be performed both by men and cattle. Hence agriculture flourishes among us. Cleanliness, the consequence of our ablutions, is another spring of activity

---

[1] 1st ed. reads: " provinces : for all sects," etc., and has a semicolon after " sentiment."

and health. We possess large sandy plains, which never would be cultivated unless they produced myrrh, benzoin, lavender, and other odours ; the only sacrifices we make to God. The [1] earth offers them to her Creator where she hath nothing else to offer ; and he receives with a paternal smile, in these silent downs, remote from groves, from cities and from temples, her innocent oblations, her solitary endearments, her pure breath. I do not complain that the Bœotians kill a bull for the same purpose ; but a bull is that to which others beside Gods and priests could sit down at table : and the richer plains of Bœotia would be cultivated whether Jupiter ate his roast beef or not.

XENOPHON. There are many reasons, O Cyrus, politically speaking, for your religion ; but it is not founded on immutable truth, nor supported by indubitable miracles.

CYRUS. What things are those ?

XENOPHON. I could mention several, attested by thousands. Those of Bacchus, who traversed your country, are remembered still among you : but as Apollo is the God from whom at this crisis we may hope a favourable oracle, I would represent to you his infancy, his flight in the arms of Latona, and his victory over the serpent : all as evident as that he sits above us arrayed in light, and is worshipped by you, O Cyrus, although in ignorance of his Godhead.

CYRUS. I have heard about these things : and since perhaps we may consult his oracle, I will not question his power or deity until that is over. About the event I have more curiosity than inquietude, knowing the force of legitimacy on the minds of men.

Why dost thou sigh, my friend ? do I appear to thee light, irresolute, inconstant ?

XENOPHON. Not thou, O Cyrus ; but thy evil station. Nothing is so restless as royalty : not air, nor ocean, nor fire : nothing can content or hold it. Certainties are uninteresting and sating to it ; uncertainties are solicitous and sad. In its weakness it ruins many, in its strength more. Thou, O Cyrus, art the most intelligent of kings, and wilt be (let me augur it) the most potent. Think that the immortal Gods have placed thee on thy eminence only as their sentinel, whose watch is long and wide, stationing thee at the principal gate in the encampment of mankind. Great is the good or evil that is about to flow far and near under thee.

[1] From " The " to " breath " added in 2nd ed.

XENOPHON AND CYRUS

CYRUS. *Far and near!* These words, I think, are rather ill placed, by one who was the disciple of Socrates the mage. They have however their meaning, their propriety, and, in thy eyes, their right order. Thou, O Xenophon, I perceive, wouldst wish to penetrate into my thoughts relating to the Athenians : I have already penetrated into theirs. I know that in sound policy you never should let an ally whom you have served be greater than yourselves, if you can prevent it ; and that those whom you assist, like those whom you attack, should come off the worse for it in the end. Individuals whom you succour in private life may sometimes be grateful ; kings never are. They will become of an unfriendly temper toward you, were it only to prove to others, and to persuade themselves, that they were powerful and flourishing enough to have done without you.

If the victory should be mine, as can not be doubted—I being born the son of a king, Artaxerxes not—there is no danger that so small a people as the Athenians should attempt to divide the kingdom, or to compromise it in any way between us : nor would I suffer it : but Policy is my voucher that I will assist you against your enemies : in such a manner however as to provide that you shall always have some, and dangerous enough at least to attract your notice. I say these words to you in pure confidence. To a friend here speaks a friend ; to a wise man here speaks no simple one.

XENOPHON. If you would worship, O Cyrus, the Gods of Greece, I should be the more confident of success.

CYRUS. I have indeed at times, to a certain degree, a faith in auguries, in which I know the Greeks are expert : but although your religion is in her youth, your Gods are as avaricious as old age could make them. Every religion that starts up, beyond Persia,[1] takes only as much truth to stand upon as will raise her safely to men's purses. The Egyptian priests have extensive lands : Attica is poorer in soil : there it is requisite to have oracles too and sacrifices, gold and cattle, oil and milk, wax and honey. If this religion should be succeeded by another, as it must be when the fraud is laid open, the populace will follow those enthusiasts who threw down the images of the Gods, and will help them the next morning to raise

---

[1] " Beyond Persia " added in 2nd ed., where the next sentence reads : " Our mages and likewise the Egyptian priests had their lands : Attica," etc.

up others in the same places, or even those elsewhere, differing but in name. Pride will at first put on the garment of Humility; and soon afterward will Humility raise up her sordid baldness out of Pride's. Change in rituals is made purely for lucre, and, under the name of Reformation, comes only to break up a virgin turf or to pierce into an unexplored mine. Religion with you began in veneration for those who delivered you from robbers: it will end in the discovery that your temples have been ever the dens of them. But in our hopes we catch at straws; the movement of a feather shakes us; the promise of a priest confirms us.

Let us now go to the stables: I have intelligence of a noble tiger, scarcely three days' hard riding from us. The peasant who found the creature shall be exalted in honour, and receive the government of a province.

XENOPHON. Is the beast a male or female, to the best of his knowledge?

CYRUS. A female: she was giving milk to her young ones. On perceiving the countryman, she drew up her feet gently, and squared her mouth, and rounded her eyes, slumberous with content; and they looked, he says, like sea-grottoes, obscurely green, interminably deep, at once awakening fear and stilling and compressing it.

XENOPHON. Fortunate he escaped her! We might have lost a fine day's hunting in ignorance of her lair.

CYRUS. He passed away gently, as if he had seen nothing; and she lay still, panting. Come, thou shalt take thy choice, O wonderful Xenophon, of my spears.

IX. ALCIBIADES AND XENOPHON

(*Athenæum*, 1852; *Imag. Convers. Gk. and Rom.*, 1853; *Wks.*, ii., 1876.)

XENOPHON. Hail, O Alcibiades [1]! Welcome art thou to the Athenian who hath retired from the contentions and turmoils of Athens, to spend his latter days among these hills and woodlands.

ALCIBIADES. Hail also, in return, O Xenophon, to thee! Long life, and sound health for the enjoyment of it! Thou wast always a lover of the chase, of which there is none within our Attic territory; and of whatever else is manly, of which there is but little.

XENOPHON. My old pursuits are indeed not wanting here. We are, as thou discernest, under the ridges of Taygetos; which are reflected at this eventime with more than their own grandeur on the broad Eurotas.

ALCIBIADES. Graciously and hospitably am I received by the most illustrious of the Athenians, under whose command it would have been my glory to have fought. But, pardon my interrogation when I diffidently ask thee, in the name of all the Gods and Demigods, why thou withdrewest thy right-hand so suddenly and abruptly.

XENOPHON. Wait, O Alcibiades, until the servants have brought the salt water.

ALCIBIADES. Infinite and immortal thanks, O most considerate of mankind! but I never drink it salt.

XENOPHON. Of a certainty no such beverage is proposed to thee. Chian wine is far preferable. But, unless I see thee duly lustrated, I dare not touch thy hand.

ALCIBIADES. Thine own, O Xenophon, hath done bolder things repeatedly. It would have prostrated the monarch of the Medes and Persians, the king of kings.

XENOPHON. Surely, had the Gods so willed it. But behold, here comes the vase of water; here also the salt, gift of Poseidon to the human race, and virgin oil, strengthener and purifier, gift of the virgin Goddess.

---

[1] Anachronism: Alcibiades was assassinated before Cyrus started on his expedition against Artaxerxes; death of Socrates; Philip of Macedon.

ALCIBIADES. Pleasant to the hand, after holding the bridle so many hours in the heat of the day, are truly all these appliances ; excepting the salt perhaps.

XENOPHON. Precisely the one thing needful.—Remember, O Alcibiades, the statues of Hermes, which it is believed, but believed (I hope) erroneously, were disfigured by thee. If it be true (and pardon my fears) lustration in this fortunate house may be accepted in some sort as expiatory.—Grant it, ye Gods! and especially thou, O son of Maia, grant it, I beseech thee! Methinks the dogs are howling ominously in the courtyard. Whether it portend good or evil, will perhaps be manifested unto me in my dreams this night. Meanwhile, let me propitiate the Blessed by a libation.— And now, O Alcibiades, the divine thing having been performed, tell me, are the girls and the youths and the philosophers as fond of thee as ever ? Do they play as formerly with thy crisp glossy curls, so delicate and umbrageous ? Do they attempt to make thee angry by applying the odious flute to thy lips, and threatening a worse infliction on thy refusal to blow it ?—O cruel Summer that absorbest Spring ! thou deservest that Autumn should wither all thy flowers.—Youth is a precious thing, O Alcibiades, and I would rather be the possessor of it than of nearly all my dogs and half my farms.

ALCIBIADES. Our teacher Socrates was entirely of the same opinion in regard to its value ; but then indeed he had no land wherewith to make the barter ; and no such an inmate and confidant as that grave, sagacious old hound, that soothsayer in the courtyard, whose language methinks is unambiguous and impressive.

XENOPHON. Thou mockest inconsiderately, I am loth to say impiously, the admonitions sent us from above through the brute creation. The wisest men that ever existed upon earth have implicitly believed in them. If birds foretell us events, and guide us by their voices and their flight, surely those animals may as reasonably be listened to which have spent their lives with us, and know our habitudes and tempers, our desires and imperfections. But, alas ! there are men in the present times who doubt whether an image of Pallas ever brandished a spear ; whether Aphroditè ever smiled on her worshiper ; whether Herè ever frowned with indignation on the wife who had violated her vows : whether Apollo

126

flayed Marsyas for impious presumption; whether the marble brow of Zeus or Poseidon ever sweated.

ALCIBIADES. Incredulous men indeed! sheer atheists! I myself have known miscalled philosophers, who doubted, or pretended to doubt, whether Pallas sprang in full growth and complete armature from the forehead of Zeus.

XENOPHON. Possibly this may be allegorical: I would neither say nor deny it; nor willingly entertain the question. Hesitation and awe become us in the presence of the gods; resolution and courage in presence of mortal men.—Cavillers! they might even object to the recorded fact, that Bacchus was inclosed in the thigh of his father for safety, and cut out from it in due season.

ALCIBIADES. His father would have afforded him a residence more commodious to both parties, had he recollected his own, at nearly the same age, among the Nymphs of Crete. Readily do I believe that both Zeus and Poseidon sweated: Zeus, when the Titans were almost as bad toward him as if they had been, one and all, his own fathers; and Poseidon, when the flaming car of Apollo was within a hair's-breadth of his beard. But possibly it was only the statues that were in question, and not the Gods personally.

XENOPHON. Verily, O Alcibiades, in the truly religious mind there is no difference whatsoever. Zeus is omnipresent, but more particularly existent within his image. And, when his votaries have knelt before him, he sometimes hath nodded affirmatively, sometimes negatively. Aphroditè herself, who listens in general more complacently, hath been known to turn quite round.

ALCIBIADES. What did she refuse by this extraordinary tergiversation?

XENOPHON. To listen.

ALCIBIADES. I have always found that Aphroditè is best disposed toward those who are least importunate. Her ears were as nigh to the supplicant as before. Neither would I have left her until I had found her placable.

XENOPHON. Thou speakest now discreetly and devoutly, as becomes the scholar of Socrates.

ALCIBIADES. There are some, I grieve to say it, who doubt his discretion; many, his devotion.

XENOPHON. His last command ought to have given those sceptics the most complete satisfaction in that matter. The cock, I hope and trust, was duly sacrificed : otherwise, ye may expect ere long another plague within your city.

ALCIBIADES. Certainly the offence would deserve it.

XENOPHON. Asclepius is among the most beneficent of the immortals, yet he demands his dues.

ALCIBIADES. Our teacher was accused of impiety, and of corrupting the youth of Athens. Pious men have lately turned the tide, and stand ready and alert to take all the youth into their own hands and all their little sins into their own bosoms. They come with authority, they tell us.

XENOPHON. With whose ?

ALCIBIADES. A priest's, whom they have chosen and appointed from their own body.

XENOPHON. So ! they give the authority first and then receive it ?

ALCIBIADES. It seems so. But they say that a God always guides them in their choice.

XENOPHON. Then the object of their choice must always be pure, beneficent, and consistent. But is it possible that a mortal, who believes in the existence of any God, should assume that God's nature and exercise his authority ? The worst atheists are not those who deny the existence of a deity, but those who arrogate to themselves the attributes. Every man must be conscious of his daily wants and weaknesses, common alike to him and to all his fellow-creatures. And if it were in the nature of things that his vanity should render him blind to them, or that his presumption should impel him to seize with avidity what the imbecile or the wicked may offer, yet there are hours of repentance and of remorse ; there are lights brought by invisible hands into the midnight chamber ; and there is an account-book laid by them on his breast, of insufferable weight until he rises to open it, and even less tolerable when he peruses its contents.

ALCIBIADES. The world is occupied, O Xenophon, and occupied almost exclusively, by knaves who deceive and by fools who are deceived. Our nurses lull us to sleep by their cant; other old women take us out of their arms and prolong it by their incantations.

XENOPHON. Whether in these there be efficacy, or none, I would not here inquire. But supposing a hierophant such as thou hast represented to me, with power unlimited and divine, and equal benevolence, he must be able and willing to compose all the differences of mankind, and to diffuse universal peace and goodwill. Do those under him preach such doctrine ?

ALCIBIADES. Some of them do. Indeed I believe it is to be found in the holy books, which all of them profess to read and to be guided by. However, the universal goodwill is confined to their own peculiar sect's universality. Benevolent as they profess themselves to be, they have been known to shut up young persons in the dark, as we shut up quails, and to keep them all their lifetime in such a situation. The refractory or incredulous they lash and famish. Those who only laugh at them, or refuse to be handled by them, or recalcitrate at their caresses, they threaten with Tartarus and Cerberus and Phlegethon and the Furies.

XENOPHON. Comminations such as these are against the laws. Intimidation is not for men, but for children ; and the parent is the only judge in the court. Religious men show us the way to the Gods, but never drag us by the throat to them, nor fire us as we do horses to correct the bad humours and to increase the speed. But who and whence, O Alcibiades, are these priests ?

ALCIBIADES. Egyptian mostly. Even Athenians are beginning to inculcate their dogmas, together with other oriental superstitions, pretending that, as they are the most ancient, they are also for this reason the most venerable, and that our own religion is only a cutting or slip from theirs, much withered and dwarfed by transplantation. Isis is striding up rapidly to the Parthenon ; and some sagacious ones smell the sludge of the Nile, and dream of its inundating the Ilyssus.

XENOPHON. O saviour Zeus ! O protectress Pallas ! avert this dire calamity ! Return ye also, twin sons of Leda, from your beneficent and warning stars ; stand again on the confines of your country and defend her ! If Athens falls, Sparta falls too. Civilisation and manliness are carried down the same torrent, and courage makes vain efforts in the dark. Incredible ! that men deriding the sophist, denouncing the philosopher, contemning the institutions of our city, defying its enactments, should embrace the most humiliating and emasculating of Egyptian superstitions !

ALCIBIADES. Many have gone over into Egypt, and have thought themselves as wise as Pythagoras, or Herodotus, or Plato, for having made the same voyage. Some indeed have found such favour with the priesthood of that country, as to have received a scale of a crocodile, a tail of an ichneumon, or a feather of an ibis. Few of them however are disposed to shave their crowns until the hair is thinner and greyer, apprehensive that they might be less efficient in bringing over the flexible sex to embrace their tenets.

XENOPHON. Where priests have much influence, the Gods have little ; and where they are numerous and wealthy, the population is scanty and miserably poor. War may be, and certainly is, destructive ; but war, as thou well knowest, if it cuts off boughs and branches, yet withers not the trunk. Priests, like ants, corrode and corrupt whatever they enter. Consider how potent was Egypt in the reign of her king Sesostris, when the military, for ever in action, kept the priesthood to its own duties and subordinate. Consider what she afterward became when the helmet was less honoured than the tonsure. Cambyses overran her fertile regions, throwing down the images of Gods and heroes, under which, it is probable, Menelaüs, holding the hand of Helen, stood in amazement at their majesty and antiquity. Unconscious that he was about to meet another Memnon on the banks of the Scamander, he gazed intently on the tranquil features of the hero who had held his station for ages by the Pyramid. No long period before the invasion of Greece, which ended with such disaster and shame to the barbarian, the monuments of Egypt, too solid to be overthrown, were mutilated and effaced ; even the records of her ancient glory were obliterated. The season of peace is indeed a happy season ; and sorrowful is it to see a mother and her daughters in the field all day without a stronger arm to help them in their labour. Yes, happy is the season of peace even to men ; but it is only when strenuous toil hath preceded a harvest which without industry and forethought must be unproductive. Whatever nation supposes that peace is the greatest of blessings, will enjoy none ; and peace itself will remain with it more uncertainly and precariously than any. What hath rendered Sparta powerful and prosperous ? Not her priests, nor even the dioscuri (with reverence be it spoken !) her patrons and protectors, but prudent kings, valiant citizens, disciplined soldiers, dutiful wives, virtuous mothers and maidens, who breathe courage into the heart before it beats to love.

ALCIBIADES. Religions that blunt the sword and emasculate the soldier level the road for despotism. When I hear the sound of drum and trumpet let it not be Cybèlè's.

XENOPHON. Powerful as is Cybèlè, and mother of the Gods, the manlier Greeks erect no temples and offer no sacrifices or prayers to her : enough of honour to be mother of the Gods. Pallas and Arès we supplicate.

ALCIBIADES. Believe me, those importations from Egypt will presently bring toward our market-place no welcome customers from Macedon.

XENOPHON. Philip, king of that country, is politic and warlike.

ALCIBIADES. He is reported to be given to drunkenness.

XENOPHON. Drunken men often imagine vain things, and sometimes dreadful ones. Martial order I have seen among them, such, my friend, as we soberer could with difficulty extinguish. Although the Macedonians are addicted to conviviality and indulge somewhat largely in wine, do not fancy that they are in the daily habitude of such excesses. They rise early, which habitual drunkards never do : and many hours of every day are spent in the habitual exercise of arms, not always singly, nor by twos and threes, but oftener in divisions of the phalanx. Sometimes the whole phalanx is ranged, in order, performs its evolutions, and remains in the field the greater part of the morning. Moreover the king of Macedon hath archers and slingers from among his tributaries and allies. Variety of arms hath frequently been disastrous to armies well disciplined, but ill prepared to encounter them. We may despise the barbarians at a distance ; but there are places and occurrences where they are far from despicable. Be sure the faces of the Macedonians are not always turned northward. The fountain of Dircè may tremble and dry up under the hoof of the Thessalian charger ; and he may stamp and paw, to make it sufficiently turbid for his draught, the clear Ismenos. Sorrow and shame and indignation seize and agitate me when I think it possible (O ye Gods avert it !) that in our very birthplace, in the city of Theseus, of Codrus, and of Solon, Pallas may lower her spear, and he who shakes the earth may drop his trident. And shall these locusts from Egypt settle in the holy places where they stood ?

ALCIBIADES. Nothing more likely. The schools of Pythagoras, no longer modest, no longer taciturn, are sending over to us from the middle of Italy thriftless though busy swarms.

IMAGINARY CONVERSATIONS : GREEK

XENOPHON. Religion and irreligion seem to prevail by turns. Better an empty cup than a cup of poison.

ALCIBIADES. It appears to me, O Xenophon, who indeed have thought but little and incuriously about the varieties of religion, that whichever is the least intrusive and dogmatical is the best. All are ancient; as ancient as man's fears and wishes: the Gods would all be kind enough if nations would not call upon them to scatter and exterminate their enemies. Hitherto it has been our privilege to worship them in our own way, whether in the temple or round the domestic hearth; grateful to those of our family who taught us how best to propitiate them, but indignant at any impudent intruder from Samothrace or from Taurida who exacted bloody sacrifices. And indeed at the present day we are not highly pleased at the near prospect of strangers, less ferocious but more perfidious, raising up their altar on our olive-grounds or tinkling their brass to attract the bees from our gardens.

XENOPHON. Let every man hive his own bees in his own garden; let every man worship his own God in his own house.

ALCIBIADES. Be those who assume to themselves the right of controlling it, driven out with scourges from the precincts of the city.

XENOPHON. Now, O Alcibiades, come into another room, and, this being the supper hour, partake with me, complacently and benignly, of our Spartan fare.

132

X. DEMOSTHENES AND EUBULIDES *

Circa 338 B.C.

(*Imag. Convers.*, i., 1824 ; i., 1826 ; *Wks.*, i., 1846 ; *Imag. Convers.
Gk. and Rom.*, 1853 ; *Wks.*, ii., 1876.)

EUBULIDES. You have always convinced me, O Demosthenes,
while you were speaking ; but I had afterward need to be convinced again ; and I acknowledge that I do not yet believe in the
necessity, or indeed in the utility, of a war with Philip.

DEMOSTHENES. He is too powerful.

EUBULIDES. This is my principal reason for recommending that
we should abstain from hostilities.   When you have said that he [1]
is too powerful, you have admitted that we are too weak : we [1]
are still bleeding from the Spartan.

DEMOSTHENES. Whatever [2] I could offer in reply, O Eubulides,
I have already spoken in public, and I would rather not enlarge
at present on it.   Come, tell me freely what you think of my
speech.

EUBULIDES. In your language, O Demosthenes, there is, I think,
a resemblance to the Kephisos,[3] whose waters, as you must have
observed, are in most seasons pure and limpid and equable
in their course, yet abounding in depths of which, when we
discern the bottom, we wonder that we discern it so clearly : the
same river at every storm swells into a torrent, without ford or
boundary, and is the stronger and the more impetuous from
resistance.

DEMOSTHENES. Language is part of a man's character.

EUBULIDES. It often is artificial.

DEMOSTHENES. Often both are.[4]   I speak [5] not of such language

* A philosopher of Miletus and a dramatic poet : Demosthenes is said to have
been his scholar.—W. S. L.
[1] 1st ed. italics.   [2] 1st ed. reads : " All," etc.
[3] 1st and 2nd eds. read : " Ilissus."   [4] 1st ed. reads : " are so."
[5] 1st ed. reads : " spoke."

as that of Gorgias and Isocrates and other rhetoricians, but of that which belongs to eloquence, of that which enters the heart however closed against it, of that which pierces like the sword of Perseus, of that which carries us [1] aloft and easily as Medea her children, and holds the world below in the same suspense.[2]

EUBULIDES.[3] When I had repeated in the morning to Cynobalanos part of a conversation I held with you the evening before, word for word, my memory being very exact, as you know, and especially in retaining your phrases, he looked at me with a smile on his countenance, and said, " Pardon me, O Eubulides, but this surely is not the language of Demosthenes." In reality, you had then, as you often do when we are alone together, given way to your genius, and had hazarded an exuberance of thought, imagination, and expression, which delighted and transported me. For there was nothing idle, nothing incorrect, but much both solid and ornamental ; as those vases and tripods are which the wealthy and powerful offer to the Gods.

DEMOSTHENES. Cynobalanos is a sensible man, and conversant in style ; but Cynobalanos never has remarked that I do not wear among my friends at table the same short dress I put on for the bema. A more sweeping train would be trodden down, and the wearer not listened to, but laughed at. Look into the field before you. See those anemones, white, pink, and purple, fluttering in the breeze ; and those other flowers, whatever they are, with close-knotted spiral blossoms, in the form of a thyrsus. Some of both species rise above the young barley, and are very pretty ; but the farmer will root them out as a blemish to his cultivation, and unprofitable in sustaining his family. In such a manner must we treat the undergrowth of our thoughts, pleasing as they may be at their first appearance in the spring of life. One fellow thinks himself like Demosthenes,[4] because he employs the same movement of the arms and body : another, for no better reason than because he is vituperative, acrid, and insolent, and, before he was hissed and hooted from the Agora, had excited the populace by the vehemence of his harangues. But you, who know the face and features of Demosthenes, his joints and muscles and whole con-

---

[1] 1st and 2nd eds. read : " away upon its point." [2] 1st ed. reads : " and terror."
[3] From " EUBULIDES " to " do " added in 3rd ed.
[4] Demosthenes, apparently Burke ; his imitator, Sheridan.

formation, know that nature hath separated this imitative animal most widely from him.

EUBULIDES. Mischievous as an ape, noisy as a lap-dog, and restless as a squirrel, he runs along to the extremity of every twig, leaps over from party to party, and, shaken off from all, creeps under the throne at Pella.

DEMOSTHENES. Philip is the fittest ruler for his own people, but he is better for anyone else to dine with than to act or think with. His conversation is far above the kingly : it is that of an urbane companion, of a scholar, I was going to say of a philosopher, I will say more, of a sound unwrangling reasoner, of a plain, intelligent, and intelligible man. But those qualities, not being glaring, do not attract to him the insects from without. Even [1] the wise become as the unwise in the enchanted chambers of Power, whose lamps make every face of the same colour. Royalty is fed incessantly by the fuel of slavish desires, blown by fulsome breath and fanned by cringing follies. It melts mankind into one inert mass, carrying off and confounding all beneath it, like a torrent of Ætnean lava, bright amid the darkness, and dark again amid the light.

EUBULIDES. O for Cynobalanos ! how would he stare and lift up his shoulders at this torrent.

DEMOSTHENES. He never can have seen me but in the Agora ; and I do not carry a full purse into the crowd. Thither I go with a tight girdle round my body : in the country I walk and wander about discinct. How I became what I am, you know as well as I do.[2] I was [3] to form a manner, with great models on one side of me, and nature on the other. Had I imitated Plato (the writer then most admired) I must have fallen short of his amplitude [4] ; and his sentences are seldom such as could be admitted into a popular harangue. Xenophon is elegant, but unimpassioned, and not entirely free, I think, from affectation. Herodotus is[5] exempt from it : what simplicity ! what sweetness ! what harmony ! not to mention his sagacity of inquiry and his accuracy of description. He could not however form an orator for the times in which we

---

[1] Taken, with slight changes, from the earlier version of the Conversation of Washington and Franklin.
[2] End of the passage added in 3rd ed.   [3] 1st ed. reads : " had," etc.
[4] 1st ed. reads : " and dignity."
[5] 1st ed. reads : " the most faultless and perhaps the most excellent of all."

live; nor [1] indeed is vigour a characteristic or a constituent of his style. I profited more from Isæus, from the study of whose writings, and attendance on whose pleadings, I acquired greater strength, compression, and concentration. Aristoteles and Thucydides were before me : I trembled lest they should lead me where I might raise a recollection of Pericles, whose plainness and conciseness and gravity they imitated, not always with success. Laying down these qualities as the foundation, I have ventured on more solemnity, more passion : [2] I have also been studious to bring the powers of action into play, that great instrument in exciting the affections which Pericles disdained. He and Jupiter could strike any head with their thunderbolts, and stand serene and immovable [3] ; I could not.

EUBULIDES. Your opinion of Pericles hath always been the same, but I have formerly heard you mention Plato with much less esteem than to-day.

DEMOSTHENES. When we talk diversely of the same person or thing we do not of necessity talk inconsistently. There is much in Plato which a wise man will commend ; there is more that will captivate an unwise one. The irony in his Dialogues has amused me frequently and greatly, and the more because in others I have rarely found it accompanied with fancy and imagination. If I however were to become a writer of dialogues, I should be afraid of using it constantly, often as I am obliged to do it [4] in my orations. Woe betide those who force us into it by injustice and presumption ! Do they dare to censure us ? they who are themselves the dust that sullies the wing of genius. Had I formed my opinion of Socrates from Plato, I should call Socrates a sophist. Who would imagine on reading Plato, that his master, instead of questioning and quibbling, had occupied his time in teaching [5] the uses and offices of philosophy ? There is as wide a difference between the imputed and the real character of this man, as there is between him who first discovered corn growing, and him who first instructed us how to grind [6] and cleanse and prepare it for our sustenance. We [7] are ashamed to give a false character of a slave, and not at all

---

[1] From " nor " to " concentration " added in 3rd ed.
[2] Colon substituted for semicolon of 1st ed. after " passion."
[3] 1st ed. reads : " motionless."
[4] 1st ed. reads : " so."   [5] 1st ed. reads : " shewing."
[6] 1st ed. reads : " it and purify it."   [7] " We " to " opponents " not in 1st ed.

to give a falser of our betters. In this predicament stands Plato, regarding his master, his scholars, and his opponents.

EUBULIDES. Before him Pythagoras and Democritus and, earlier still, Pherecydes,[1] taught important truths, and, what is rarer, separated them from pernicious falsehoods. Pythagoras, who preceded Plato in Egypt, and from whom many of his fancies are taken, must have been a true lover of wisdom,[2] to have travelled so far into countries known hardly by name in Greece.

DEMOSTHENES. Perhaps he sought some congenial soul ; for if two great men are existing at the extremities of the earth, they will seek each other.

EUBULIDES.[3] Their greatness then must be of a different form and texture from what mankind hath usually admired. Greatness, as we daily see it, is unsociable.

DEMOSTHENES. The [4] perfect loves what generates it, what proceeds from it, what partakes its essence. If you have formed an idea of greatness, O Eubulides, which corresponds not with this description, efface it and cast it out. Pythagoras adapted his institutions to the people he would enlighten and direct. What portion of the world was ever so happy, so peaceable, so well-governed, as the cities of southern Italy [5] ? While they retained his manners they were free and powerful : some have since declined, others are declining, and perhaps at a future and not a distant time they may yield themselves up to despotism. In a few ages more, those flourishing towns, those inexpugnable citadels, those temples which you might [6] deem eternal, will be hunted for in their wildernesses like the boars and stags. Already there are philosophers who would remedy what they call popular commotions by hereditary despotism,

---

[1] 1st ed. reads: "Pherecydes . . . DEMOSTHENES. Of the latter " (2nd ed. " former ") " our accounts are contradictory. I entertain no doubt that the knowledge, the prudence, the authority of Pythagoras were greater than those of any man who, under the guidance of the Gods, hath enlightened the regions of Europa. EUBULIDES. He must have been," etc.

[2] 1st and 2nd eds. insert here : " as he modestly called himself," etc.

[3] 1st ed. reads : " EUBULIDES. Greatness is unsociable. DEMOSTHENES," etc.

[4] 1st ed. reads : " It loves what generates it. . . . If you have formed any idea of greatness which . . . cast it out. I admire in Pythagoras a disdain and contempt of dogmatism, amidst the plenitude of power. He adapted," etc.

[5] 1st and 2nd eds. read : " Magna Græcia."

[6] 1st ed. reads : " which one would."

and who think it as natural and reasonable as that children who cry should be compelled to sleep : and there likewise are honest citizens who, when they have chewed their fig and swallowed it, say, " Yes, 'twere well." What a [1] eulogy on the human understanding ! to assert that it is dangerous to choose a succession of administrators from the wisest of mankind, and advisable to derive it from the weakest ! There have been free Greeks within our memory who would have entered into [2] alliance with the most iniquitous and most insolent of usurpers, Alexander of Pherai, a territory in which Thebè, who murdered her husband, is praised above [3] others of both sexes. O Juno ! may such marriages be frequent in such countries !

Look at history : where do you find in continuation three hereditary kings, of whom one at [4] least was not inhuman in disposition or weak in intellect ? Either of these qualities may subvert a state, exposing it first to many sufferings. In our Athenian constitution, if we are weakly or indiscreetly governed, or capriciously, which hardly can happen, the mischief is transitory and reparable : one year closes it : and the people, both for its satisfaction and its admonition, sees that no corruption, no transgression, in its magistrates, is unregarded or unchastised. This of all advantages is the greatest, the most corroborative of power, the most tutelary of morals. I know that there are many in Thrace, and some in Sicily, who would recall my wanderings with perfect good-humour and complacency. Demosthenes has not lived, has not reasoned, has not agitated his soul, for these [5] : he leaves them in the quiet possession of all their moulten arguments, and in the persuasive hope of all their bright reversions. Pythagoras could have had little or no influence on such men [6] : he raised up higher, who kept them down. It is easier to make an impression upon sand than upon marble : but it is easier to make a just one upon marble than upon sand. Uncivilised as were the Gauls, he with his moderation and prudence hath softened the ferocity of their religion, and hath made it so contradictory and inconsistent, that the first of them [7] who reasons will subvert it. He did not say, " You shall no longer

---

[1] 1st ed. reads : " an eulogy."
[2] 1st ed. reads : " an holy alliance."
[3] 1st ed. reads : " all others."
[4] 1st ed. reads : " at the least."
[5] 1st ed. reads : " for them."
[6] 1st ed. reads : " men like these."
[7] 1st ed. reads : " amongst them."

sacrifice your fellow-creatures " : he said, " Sacrifice the criminal."
Other nations do the same : often wantonly, always vindictively :
the Gauls appease by it, as they imagine, both society and the
Gods. He did not say, " After a certain time even this outrage
on Nature must cease " : but he said, " We have souls which pass
into other creatures." [1] A belief in the transmigration of souls
would abolish by degrees our inhumanity.

EUBULIDES. But what absurdity !

DEMOSTHENES. Religion, when it is intended for the uncivilised,
must contain things marvellous, things quite absurd to the wiser.
But I discover no absurdity in making men gentler and kinder ;
and I would rather worship an onion or a crust of bread, than a
God who requires me to immolate [2] an ox or kid to appease him.
The idea, not of having lost her daughter, but of having lost her
by a sacrifice, fixed the dagger in the grasp of Clytemnestra. Let
us observe, O Eubulides, the religion of our country, be it what it
may, unless it command us to be cruel or unjust. In religion, if
we are right, we do not know we are ; if we are wrong, we would not.
Above all, let us do nothing and say nothing which may abolish or
diminish in the hearts of the vulgar the sentiments of love and awe [3] :
on the contrary, let us perpetually give them fresh excitement and
activity, by baring them to the heavens. On the modifications of
love it is unnecessary to expatiate ; but I am aware that you may
demand of me what excitement is required to fear. Among its
modifications or dependencies are veneration and obedience, against
the weakening of which we ought to provide, [4] particularly in what
relates to our magisterial and military chiefs.

EUBULIDES. I do not conceive that Pythagoras has left behind
him in Gaul, unless at Massilia, the remembrance of his doctrines
or of his name.

DEMOSTHENES. We hear little of the Gauls. It appears however

---

[1] 1st ed. reads : " creatures : our dreams prove it : if they are not reminiscences of what has happened or been represented in our actual life, they must be
of what passed before : for from a confusion of brain, to which some attribute
them, there can arise nothing so regular and beautiful as many of these visions
which you have all experienced. A belief in . . . degrees all inhumanity. I
know nothing else that can : in other words I know nothing else that is worthy
to be called religion. EUBULIDES. But what absurdity ! DEMOSTHENES. I
discover no," etc.

[2] 1st ed. reads : " to kill."   [3] 1st ed. reads : " fear."
[4] 1st ed. reads : " provide and guard."

that [1] they have not forgotten the wisdom or the services of Pythagoras. The man of Samos was to some extent their teacher. It is remarkable that they should have preserved the appellation. He [2] was too prudent, I suspect, to trust himself many paces beyond the newly-built walls of Massilia ; for the ignorant and barbarous priests would be loth to pardon him the crime of withdrawing a dependant in a proselyte.

EUBULIDES. The Druids, the most ferocious and ignorant of all the priests our countrymen have anywhere discovered, fell back farther into their woods and wilderness at seeing the white stones of the citadel rise higher than their altars. Even these rude altars were not of their construction, but were the work of a much earlier race. The Phocæans and other Ionians were sufficiently well versed in policy to leave the natives unmolested in their religion. Already does that lively and imitative people prefer a worship in which the song and the dance and geniality warm the blood, to one which exacts it in the windy downs and gloomy woodlands, and spills it on the channelled stone, and catches it dropping from the suspended wicker. Young men crowned with flowers are likelier to be objects of aversion to the ancient priests than to the most timorous and shy of their disciples. The religion of blood, like the beasts of prey, will continue to trend northward. Worshipers of Apollo, and followers of Bromius and the nymphs, would perish in the sunless oak forests ; and the Druid has no inheritance in the country of the vine. But it becomes the quiet religion and placid wisdom of the Greeks, to leave inviolate all the institutions of the circumjacent people, and especially of those who wish to live among them. By degrees they will acknowledge a superiority which they could contend against were it asserted.

DEMOSTHENES. Pythagoras is said to have been vigorous in enforcing his doctrines.

EUBULIDES. In his school ; not beyond. They are such indeed

[1] 1st ed. reads : " that this most capricious and most cruel of nations is building cities and establishing communities. The most arrogant, the most ungrateful, the most unthinking of mankind have not forgotten . . . Pythagoras. Ask them who was their legislator . . . they answer you Samotes : ask them who was Samotes, they reply *A wise man who came amongst us long ago from beyond the sea :* for barbarians have little notion of times, and run wildly into far antiquity. The man of Samos was in fact their legislator, or rather their teacher, and it is remarkable that they should have preserved the name in such integrity."

[2] From " He " to " reply " added in 3rd ed.

as we would little wish to see established in a free state, but none ever were better adapted to prepare the road for civilisation. We find it difficult to believe in the metempsychosis. In fact, as other things grow easy, belief is apt to grow difficult.

DEMOSTHENES. Where there is mysticism we may pause and listen ; where there is argument we may contend and reply.[1] Democritus, whom you often mention,[2] certainly no mystic, often contradicts our senses. He tells us that colours have no colour : but his arguments are so strong, his language so clear, his pretensions so modest and becoming, I place more confidence in him than in others : future philosophers may demonstrate to calmer minds what we have not the patience to investigate.*

EUBULIDES. Plato hath not mentioned him.

DEMOSTHENES. O greatness ! what art thou, and where is thy foundation ! I speak not, Eubulides, of that which the vulgar call greatness, a phantom stalking forward from a salt-marsh in Bœotia, or from a crevice in some rock of Sunion or of Taxos † ; but the highest, the most illustrious, the most solid among men, what is it ! Philosophy gives us arms against others, not against ourselves, not against those domestic traitors, those homestead incendiaries, the malignant passions ; arms that are brilliant on the exercise-ground, but brittle in the fight, when the most dangerous of enemies is pressing us. Early love was never so jealous in anyone as philosophy in Plato. He resembles his own idea of God, whose pleasure in the solitudes of eternity is the contemplation of himself.

EUBULIDES. Jealousy [3] is not quite excluded from the school opposite. Aristoteles,[4] it has been suggested to me, when he remarks that by the elongation of the last member in a sentence a dignity is added to composition, looked toward you, who, as you have [5] heard the rhetoricians say, are sometimes inattentive or indifferent to nobility of expression.

DEMOSTHENES. When Aristoteles gives an opinion upon eloquence I listen with earnestness and respect : so wise a man can say nothing

---

[1] End of the passage added in 3rd ed.   [2] 1st ed. reads : " mentioned."

* Newton has elucidated the theory of colours first proposed by Democritus, the loss of whose voluminous works is the greatest that philosophy has sustained.—W. S. L.   † Taxos was rich in silver mines.—W. S. L.

[3] From " Jealousy " to " opposite " added in 3rd ed.

[4] 1st ed. reads : " It has been . . . that Aristoteles," etc.

[5] 1st ed. reads : " as you have often heard."

inconsiderately. His own style on every occasion is exactly what it should be : his sentences, in which there are no cracks or inequalities, have always their proper tone : for whatever is rightly said, sounds rightly.

Ought I to speak nobly, as you call it, of base matters and base men ? ought my pauses to be invariably the same ? would Aristoteles wish that a coat of mail should be as flowing as his gown ? Let peace be perfect peace, war decisive war ; but let Eloquence move upon earth with all the facilities of change that belong to the Gods themselves ; only let her never be idle, never be vain, never be ostentatious ; for these are indications of debility. We, who have habituated ourselves from early youth to the composition of sonorous periods, know that it requires more skill to finger and stop our instrument than to blow it. When we have gained over the ear to our party, we have other work to do, and sterner and rougher. Then comes forward action, not unaccompanied by vehemence. Pericles, you have heard, used none, but kept his arm wrapped up within his vest. Pericles was in the enjoyment of that power which his virtues and his abilities [1] well deserved. If he had carried in his bosom the fire that burns in mine, he would have kept his hand outside. By the contemplation of men like me, Aristoteles is what he is ; and, instead of undervaluing, I love him the better for it. Do we not see with greater partiality and fondness those who have been educated and fed upon our farms, than those who come from Orchomenos or Mantinea ? If he were now among us in Athens, what would he think of two or three haranguers, who deal forth [2] metaphysics by the pailful in their addresses to the people ?

EUBULIDES. I heard one, a little [3] time since, who believed he was doing it, ignorant that the business of metaphysics is rather to analyse than to involve. He avoided [4] plain matter, he rejected idiom ; he [5] filtered the language of the people and made them drink through a sieve.

DEMOSTHENES. What an admirable definition have you given, unintentionally, of the worst public speaker possible, and, I will add with equal confidence, of the worst writer. If I send to Hymettos

---

[1] 1st ed. reads : " so well."   [2] 1st ed. reads : " his metaphysics."
[3] 1st ed. reads : " some time."   [4] 1st ed. reads : " all plain ... all idiom."
[5] From " he " to " sieve " added in 3rd ed.

for a hare, I expect to distinguish it at dinner by its flavour as readily as before dinner by its ears and feet. The people you describe to me soak out all the juices of our dialect. Nothing [1] is so amusing to me as to hear them talk on eloquence. No disciple at the footstool is so silent and ductile as I am at the lessons I receive ; none attends with such composure, none departs with such hilarity.

I have been careful to retain as much idiom as I could, often at the peril of being called ordinary and vulgar. Nations in a state of decay lose their idiom, which loss is always precursory to that of freedom. What your father and your grandfather used as an elegance in conversation, is now abandoned to the populace, and every day we miss a little of our own, and collect a little from strangers : this prepares us for a more intimate union with them, in which we merge at last altogether. Every good writer has much idiom ; it is the life and spirit of language ; and none such ever entertained a fear or apprehension that strength and sublimity were to be lowered and weakened by it. Speaking to the people, I use the people's phraseology : I temper my metal according to the uses I intend it for. In fact no language is very weak in its natural course, until it runs too far ; and then the poorest and the richest are ineffectual equally. The habitude of pleasing by flattery makes a language soft ; the fear of offending by truth makes it circuitous and conventional. Free governments, where such necessity can not exist, will always produce true eloquence.

EUBULIDES. We have in Athens young orators from the schools, who inform us that no determinate and masculine peculiarities of manner should appear in public : they would dance without displaying their muscles, they would sing without discomposing their lips.

DEMOSTHENES. I will drag them, so help me Jupiter ! back again to their fathers and mothers : I will grasp their wrists so tightly, the most perverse of them shall not break away from me. Tempestuous times are coming. Another month, or two at farthest, and I will throw such animation into their features and their gestures, you shall imagine they have been singing to the drum and horn, and

---

[1] From "Nothing" to "hilarity" added in 2nd ed. 1st ed. inserts : "EUBULIDES. They could do nothing better. To come again with you into the kitchen, if they can only give us tripe let them give it clean. DEMOSTHENES. I," etc.

dancing to dithyrambics. The dustbox of metaphysics shall be emptied no more from the schoolroom into the council.

I[1] suspect I have heard the chatterer you mentioned. The other day in the market-place, I saw a vulgar and shuffling man lifted on a honey-barrel by some grocers and slave-merchants, and the crowd was so dense around me I could not walk away. A fresh-looking citizen, next me, nodded and winked in my face at the close of every sentence. Dissembling as well as I could my impatience at his importunity, " Friend," said I, " do believe me, I understand not a syllable of the discourse."

" Ah Demosthenes ! " whispered he, " your time is fairly gone by : we have orators now whom even you, with all your acuteness and capacity,[2] can not comprehend."

" Whom will they convince ? " said [3] I.

" Convince ! " cried [4] my narrator ; " who has ever wished to be persuaded against the grain in any matter of importance or utility ? A child, if you tell him a horrible or a pathetic story, is anxious to be persuaded it is true ; men and women, if you tell them one injurious to the respectability of a neighbour. Desire of persuasion rests and dies here. We listen to those whom we know to be of the same opinion as ourselves, and we call them wise for being of it ; but we avoid such as differ from us ; we pronounce them rash before we have heard them, and still more afterward, lest we should be thought at any time to have erred. We come already convinced : we want surprise, as at our theaters ; astonishment, as at the mysteries of Eleusis."

" But what astonishes, what surprises you ? "

" To hear an Athenian talk two hours together, hold us [5] silent and immovable as the figures of Hermes before our doors, and find not a single one among us that can carry home with him a thought or an expression."

" Thou art right," I exclaimed ; " he is greater than Triptolemos ; he not only gives you a plentiful meal out of chaff and husks, but he persuades you that it is a savoury repast."

---

[1] 1st ed. reads : " I suspect that I also have heard . . . a vulgar and clumsy man lifted . . . crowd was so dense that I," etc.
[2] 1st ed. inserts : " as you yourself have acknowledged to me."
[3] 1st ed. reads : " cried I."
[4] From " cried " to " erred " added in 2nd ed.
[5] 1st ed. reads : " hold us all silent," etc.

DEMOSTHENES AND EUBULIDES

" By Jupiter ! " swore aloud my [1] friend, " he persuades us no such thing : but everyone is ashamed of being the first to acknowledge that he never was master of a particle out of what [2] he had listened to and applauded."

I had the curiosity to inquire who the speaker was.

" What ! do you not know Anædestatos [3] ? " said he, making a mark of interrogation upon my ribs, with a sharper elbow than from his countenance I could have imagined had belonged to him ; " the clever Anædestatos, who came into notice as a youth by the celebration in verse of a pebble at the bottom of the Ilyssos.[4] He forthwith was presented to Anytos,[5] who experienced a hearty pleasure in seducing him away from his guardians. Anytos on his deathbed (for the Gods allowed him one) recommended the young Anædestatos warmly to his friends : such men have always many, and those the powerful. Fortunate had it been for our country if he had pilfered only the verses he pronounced. His new patrons connived at his withdrawing from the treasury no less than six hundred talents."

" Impossible ! six hundred talents are sufficient for the annual stipend of all our civil magistrates, from the highest to the lowest, and of all the generals in our republic and its dependencies."

" It was before you came forward into public life, O Demosthenes ! but my father can prove the exactness of my statement. The last little sip from the reservoir was seventy talents * for a voyage to Lesbos,[6] and a residence there of about three months, to settle the

---

[1] 1st ed. reads : " disenchanted friend."　　[2] 1st ed. reads : " all he had," etc.

[3] Anædestatos—Canning ; see Landor, *Wks.*, and *Poemata et Inscriptiones,* p. 291.

> "Et Caninius uno verso memoratus est ; nec suo:
> Lactea purpureos interfluit unda lapillos."

For Canning's verse on a pebble see *Poemata Præmiis Cancellarii academicis donata et in theatro Sheldoniano recitata*, Oxonii, 1810, ii. p. 1.

Iter ad Meccam Religionis causa susceptum, by Canning ex Æde Christi, 1789, v. p. 13.

> "Alta domus lautæque epulæ, et madentia fusis
> Vina favis ; trepido miscens ibi murmura lapsu
> Lactea purpureos interstrepit unda lapillos.'

[4] 1st ed. reads : " Cephisus."　　　　　　[5] 1st ed. reads : " Anglus."
* 14,000 pounds.—W. S. L.

[6] Canning, in 1816, was appointed Minister Extraordinary at Lisbon to receive the King of Portugal on his return from Brazil, whither he had fled during the French invasion. The Minister's salary was fixed at £14,000 a year, and when in the end the King refused to return at all the transaction provoked criticism.

value of forty skins of wine, owing to the Lesbians in the time of Thrasybulos. This, I know not by what oversight, is legible among the accounts."

Indignant at what I heard, I threatened to call him before the people.

"Let him alone," said slowly in an undervoice my prudent friend : " he has those about him who will swear, and adduce the proofs, that you are holding a traitorous correspondence with Philip or Artaxerxes."

I began to gaze in [1] indignation on his florid and calm countenance ; he winked again, again accosted me with his elbow, and withdrew.

EUBULIDES. Happy Athenians ! who have so many great men of so many kinds, peculiar to yourselves, and can make one even out of Anædestatos.

SECOND CONVERSATION

B.C. 336

(*Imag. Convers.*, iii., 1828 ; *Wks.*, i., 1846 ; *Imag. Convers. Gk. and Rom.*, 1853 ; *Wks.*, ii., 1876.)

EUBULIDES.[2] It was nearly in this place that we met once before ; but not so early in the day ; for then the western sun had withdrawn from the plain, and was throwing its last rays among the columns of the Parthenon.

DEMOSTHENES. I think it was about the time when the question was agitated of war or peace with the king of Macedon.

EUBULIDES. It was. Why do you look so cheerful on a sudden ? Soon afterward followed the disastrous battle at Cheronæa.

DEMOSTHENES. Certainly, I derive no cheerfulness out of that.

EUBULIDES. Well, I believe there is little reason at the present hour why we should be melancholy.

DEMOSTHENES. If there is, I hope it lies not on the side of the Agora.

[1] 1st ed. reads : " some indignation."
[2] " EUBULIDES " to " same " added in 2nd ed.

DEMOSTHENES AND EUBULIDES

EUBULIDES. You have composed your features again, and seem to be listening : but rather (I suspect) at your own internal thoughts than in the expectation of mine.

DEMOSTHENES. Let us avoid, I entreat you, my dear Eubulides, those thorny questions which we can not so well avoid within the walls. Our opinions in matters of state are different : let us walk together where our pursuits are similar or the same.

EUBULIDES. Demosthenes ! it is seldom that we have conversed on politics, sad refuge of restless minds, averse from business and from study.

DEMOSTHENES. Say worse against them, Eubulides ! and I, who am tossed on the summit of the wave, will cry out to you to curse them deeplier.[1] There are few men who have not been witnesses that, on some slight divergence of incondite and unsound opinions, they have rolled away the stone from the cavern-mouth of the worst passions, and have evoked them up between two friends. I, of all men, am the least inclined to make them the subject of conversation ; and particularly when I meet a literary man as you are, from whom I can receive, and often have received, some useful information, some philosophical thought, some generous sentiment, or some pleasant image. Beside, wishing to make an impression on the public mind, I must not let my ideas run off in every channel that lies before me : I must not hear the words, " Demosthenes will say this or this to-day." People ought to come toward me in expectation, and not carrying my sentiments, crude and broken, walleted before them.

EUBULIDES. There however are occasions when even politics are delightful ; when they rejoice and exult as a stripling, or breathe softly as an infant.

DEMOSTHENES. Then we can not do better than sit quiet and regard them in silence : for it is such a silence as the good citizen and good father of a family would be unwilling to disturb. Why do you smile and shake your head, Eubulides ?

EUBULIDES. Answer me first ; had you no morning dream, Demosthenes, a few hours ago ; which dreams (they tell us) are sure to be accomplished, or show us things that are already so ?

DEMOSTHENES. I dream seldom.

EUBULIDES. Were you awakened by no voices ?

[1] 1st ed. reads : " deeper."

147

DEMOSTHENES. I sleep soundly. Come, do not fall from philosophy to divination. We usually have conversed on eloquence. I am not reminding you of this, from the recollection that you once, and indeed more than once, have commended me. I took many lessons in the art from you ; and will take more, if you please, as we walk along.

EUBULIDES. Be contented : none surpasses you.

DEMOSTHENES. Many speak differently upon that subject, lying to the public, and to their own hearts, which I agitate as violently as those incited by me to bleed in the service of our country. If [1] among our literary men I have an enemy so rash and impudent as to decry my writings, or to compare them with the evanescences of the day, I desire for him no severer punishment than the record of his sentence. The cross will be more durable than the malefactor.

EUBULIDES. In proportion as men approach you, they applaud you. To those far distant and far below, you seem as little as they seem to you. Fellows who can not come near enough to reverence you, think they are only a stone's throw distant ; and they throw it. Unfortunate men ! Choked by their criticisms ! which others expectorate [2] so easily !

DEMOSTHENES. Commiserate them more still : ignorant or regardless, as they are, that they have indented and incorporated a mark of ignominy in their names. Ay, by the *dog!* (as Socrates used to swear) and such too as no anger of mine could have heated for them, no ability of mine impressed.[3]

EUBULIDES. There [4] are few among the ignorant, and especially if they are pompous and inflated, who, if we attend to them patiently, may not amuse us by the clumsy display of some rash opinion. I was present a few nights ago at a company where you were mentioned——

DEMOSTHENES. My master in rhetoric ! dear Eubulides ! do we correctly say " present *at* a company " ?

---

[1] From " If among " to " throw it " added in 2nd ed.
[2] 1st ed. reads for " expectorate," " spit out or bring up again."
[3] 1st ed. adds : " Laying their hands upon me they have touched the idle waters of immortality ; and will mourn for it like Thetis, and as bitterly and as vainly."
[4] From " There " to " justice " added in 2nd ed., possibly to meet a criticism made by Forster on these two Conversations. He had suggested that Demosthenes' language was too figurative.

DEMOSTHENES AND EUBULIDES

EUBULIDES. You and I do. We are present at many companies ; we form a part of few.

DEMOSTHENES. Continue the narrative : the objection is overcome.

EUBULIDES. Willingly do I continue it, for it reminds me of an evening in which your spirits had all their play, and soared above the city-walls, and beyond the confines of Attica. Men whose brains are like eggs boiled hard, thought your ideas or your speech exuberant ; and very different was indeed your diction from its usual economy and frugality. This conversation of yours was repeated, the reciter employing the many metaphors you had used. Halmuros sat next me, kicking my legs now and then, in his impatience to express that ill-humour which urges him on all occasions to querulousness and contradiction. At last he sprang up, and wiping the corners of his mouth, declared that your mind was not rich enough for all those metaphors which an injudicious friend had quoted as yours. I replied to him calmly, that it was natural he should be ignorant of the fact, and certain that he must remain so, since Demosthenes only used such language when it was excited by the wit or the wisdom or the geniality of his friends ; and I consoled him with the assurance that a warier man might have fallen into the same pit, without the same help of extrication. Although he saw how friendly I had been to him, he was not pacified, but protested that many doubts remained upon his mind. He appealed to Cliniades who sate opposite. " I have been present," said Cliniades, " at my father's and in other places, when Demosthenes hath scattered among us all the ornaments of diction ; it would puzzle me to recount, and you to remember, the names of them." " That is a modest youth," said Halmuros in my ear, " but rather too zealous in partisanship."

DEMOSTHENES. Inconsiderate and silly is the criticism of Halmuros. Must a pugilist, because he is a pugilist, always clench his fist ? may he not relax it at dinner, at wine, at the reception of a friend ? Is it necessary to display the strength of my muscles when I have no assailant to vanquish or intimidate ? When we are wrestling we do not display the same attitudes as when we are dancing. On the sand and in the circle we contend for the crown ; amid the modulations of flute and lyre, of tabor and symbal, we wear it. And it is there, among our friends and favourites, among

149

the elegant and refined, we draw attention to the brightness and the copiousness and the pliancy of its constituent parts. It is permitted me, I trust, O Eubulides, to indulge in a flowery and flowing robe when I descend from the bema, and relax my limbs in the cool retirement at home. If I did it in public I should be powerless ; for there is paralysis in derision. Plainness and somewhat of austerity ought to be habitual with the orator. If he relinquishes them rarely, when he *does* relinquish them he gains the affections of his audience by his heartiness, warmth, and condescension. But sentences well measured and well moulded are never thrown away on the meanest of the Athenians : and many of them perhaps are as sensible of the variety I give to mine as the most delicate of the critics, and are readier to do me justice.

EUBULIDES. It appears to be among the laws of Nature that the mighty of intellect should be pursued and carped by the little, as [1] the solitary flight of one great bird is followed by the twittering petulance of many smaller.

DEMOSTHENES. The higher and richer bank is corroded by the stream, which is gentle to the flat and barren sand : and philosophers tell us that mountains are shaken by the vilest of the minerals below them.

EUBULIDES. Here, O Demosthenes, let the parallel be broken. And now, can not I draw from you the avowal, that you have heard the news from Pella, brought by the messager at sun-rise? Your derision has not deterred the people from asking " Is Philip dead ? "

DEMOSTHENES. The messager came first to my house, knowing my habitude of early rising. My order as magistrate was, that he keep secret this visit of his to me, threatening him with the displeasure and censure of the more ancient, if ever they should discover that the intelligence reached them after. My thoughts crowded upon me so fast and turbulently, that, no sooner had I reached the monument of Antiope, than I stopped from exhaustion, and sate down beneath it. Happy as I always am to meet you, my good Eubulides, I acknowledge I never was less so than on this occasion. For it is my practice, and ever has been, to walk quite alone. In my walks I collect my arguments, arrange my sentences, and utter them aloud. Eloquence with me can do little

---

[1] From "as " to " smaller " added in 2nd ed.

else in the city, than put on her bracelets, tighten her sandals, and show herself to the people. Her health, and vigour, and beauty, if she has any, are the fruits of the open fields. The slowness or celerity of my steps is now regulated and impelled by the gravity and precision, now by the enthusiasm and agitation of my mind : and the presence of anyone, however dear and intimate, is a check and impediment to the free agency of these emotions. Thousands, I know, had I remained in the city, would have come running up to me with congratulations and embraces ; as if danger could befall us only from the hand of Philip ! another Jove, who alone upon earth can vibrate the thunder.

EUBULIDES. One hour afterward I passed through them hastily, and saw and heard them wandering and buzzing along the streets in every direction.

DEMOSTHENES. Leaving to us the country and fresh air, and, what itself is the least tranquil thing in Nature, but is the most potent tranquilliser of an excited soul, the sea. To-day I avoid the swarm : to-morrow I strike my brass and collect it.

How soon, O Eubulides, may this ancient hive be subverted, and these busy creatures lie under it extinct !

EUBULIDES.[1] That greatest and most fortunate event, the death of Philip, seems at one moment in the course of our conversation to have given you more than your ordinary vigour, and at another (as now again) to have almost torpefied you.

DEMOSTHENES. Inattention and taciturnity are not always proofs of incivility and disrespect. I was revolving in my mind what I might utter as we went along, less unworthy of your approbation than many things I have spoken in public, and with great anxiety that they should be well received.

There is then one truth, O Eubulides, far more important than every other ; far more conducive to the duration of states, to the glory of citizens, to the adornment of social life, to the encouragement of arts and sciences, to the extension of the commerce and intercourse of nations, to the foundation and growth of colonies, to the exaltation and dominion of genius, and indeed to whatever is desirable to the well-educated and the free.

EUBULIDES. Enounce it.

DEMOSTHENES. There is, I repeat it, one truth above all the rest ;

[1] From " EUBULIDES " to " dead " added in 2nd ed.

above all promulgated by the wisdom of legislators, the zeal of orators, the enthusiasm of poets, or the revelation of Gods : a truth whose brightness and magnitude are almost lost to view by its stupendous highth. If I never have pointed it out, knowing it as I do, let the forbearance be assigned not to timidity but to prudence.

EUBULIDES. May I hope at last to hear it ?

DEMOSTHENES. I must conduct you circuitously, and interrogate you beforehand, as those do who lead us to the mysteries.

You have many sheep and goats upon the mountain, which were lately bequeathed to you by your nephew Timocles. Do you think it the most advantageous to let some mastiff, with nobody's chain or collar about his neck, run among them and devour them one after another, or to prepare a halter and lay poison and a trap for him ?

EUBULIDES. Certainly here, O Demosthenes, you are not leading me into any mysteries. The answer is plain : the poison, trap, and halter, are ready.

DEMOSTHENES. Well spoken. You have several children and grandchildren : you study economy in their behalf : would you rather spend twenty drachmas for fuel, than three for the same quantity of the same material ?

EUBULIDES. Nay, nay, Demosthenes, if this is not mystery, it is worse. You are like a teacher to whom a studious man goes to learn the meaning of a sentence, and who, instead of opening the volume that contains it, asks him gravely whether he has learnt his alphabet. Prythee do not banter me.

DEMOSTHENES. Tell me, then, which you would rather ; make one drunken man sober for ever, or ten thousand men drunk for many years ?

EUBULIDES. By all the Gods ! abstain from such idle questions.

DEMOSTHENES. The solution of this, idle as you call it, may save you much more than the twenty drachmas. O Eubulides ! we have seen, to our sorrow and ignominy, the plain of Cheronæa bestrewn with the bodies of our bravest citizens ; had one barbarian fallen, they had not. Rapine and licentiousness are the precursors and the followers of even the most righteous war. A single blow against the worst of mortals may prevent them. Many years and much treasure are usually required for an uncertain issue, beside the stagnation of traffic, the prostration of industry, and innumerable maladies arising from towns besieged and regions depopulated. A

152

moment is sufficient to avert all these calamities. No usurper, no invader, should be permitted to exist on earth. And on whom can the vengeance of the Gods be expected to descend, if it descend not on that guilty wretch, who would rather that ten thousand innocent, ten thousand virtuous citizens should perish, than that one iniquitous and atrocious despot should be without his daily bath of blood. A single brave man might have followed the late tyrant into Scythia and have given his carcass to the vulture ; by which heroic deed we should have been spared the spectacle of Greece in mourning. What columns, what processions, would have been decreed to this deliverer, out of the treasure we may soon be condemned to pay, whether as tribute or subsidy, to our enslaver.

EUBULIDES. No, no. Praises to the immortals ! he is dead.

DEMOSTHENES. Philip has left the world. But regard not, O my friend, the mutual congratulations, the intemperate and in tempestive joy of the Athenians, with any other sentiment than pity ; for while Alexander lives, or Alexander's successor, while any king whatever breathes on any of our confines, Philip is not dead.

EUBULIDES. Raise up thy brow, O Demosthenes ! raise up again that arm, hanging down before thee as if a flame from heaven had blasted it. Have we not seen it in its godlike strength, terrible even in beneficence, like Neptune's, when the horse sprang from under his trident ? Take courage ! give it ! Inspire it in a breath from the inner and outer Keramicus to the Parthenon, from the temple of the Eumenides to the gates of the Piræus. What is the successor of Philip ? a mad youth.

DEMOSTHENES. Does much mischief require much wisdom ? Is a firebrand sensible ; is a tempest prudent ? It is a very indifferent rat or weazel that hath not as much courage as Alexander, and more prudence : I say nothing of temperance, in which even inferior beasts, if there be any such, are his betters. We know this : the knowledge of it does not ensure our quiet, but rather is a reason, at least the latter part of it, why we can trust in him for none.

If men considered the happiness of others, or their own ; in fewer words, if they were rational or provident, no state would be depopulated, no city pillaged, not a village would be laid in ashes, not a farm deserted. But there always have been, and always will be, men about the despot, who persuade him that terror is better than esteem ; that no one knows whether he is reverenced or not, but that he who is dreaded has indubitable proofs of it, and is regarded by mortals as a God. By pampering this foible in the prince, they are admitted to come closer and closer to him ; and from the indulgence of his corrupted humours they derive their wealth and influence. Every man in the world would be a republican, if he did not hope from fortune and favour more than from industry and desert ; in short, if he did not expect to carry off sooner or later, from under another system, what never could belong to him rightfully, and what can not (he thinks) accrue to him from this. To suppose the contrary, would be the same as to suppose that he would rather have a master in his house, than friend, brother, or son ; and that he has both more confidence and more pleasure in an alien's management of it, than in his own, or in any person's selected by his experience and deputed by his choice.

EUBULIDES. Insanity to imagine it !

DEMOSTHENES. In religions and governments, O Eubulides, there are things on which few men reason, and at which those who do reason, shrink and shudder. The worthless cling upon these lofty follies, and use them as the watchtowers of Ambition. We too are reproved by them in turn for like propensities : and truly I wish it could be said that every human motive were ingenuous and pure. We can not say anything similar. Come, let us own the worst ; we are ambitious. But is it not evident of us orators in a republic, that our ambition and the scope of it must drop together when we no longer can benefit or forewarn our citizens ? In kingdoms the men are most commended and most elevated who serve the fewest, and who, serving the fewest, injure the most ; in republics, those who serve the many, and injure none. The loss of this privilege is the greatest loss humanity can sustain. To you, because I ponder and meditate, I appear dejected. Clearly do I see indeed how much may soon cease to be within my power ; but I possess the confidence of strength within me, and the consciousness of having exerted it for the glory of my country and the utility of mankind. Look at that olive before us. Seasons and iron have searched deeply into its heart ; yet it shakes its berries in the air, promising you sustenance and light. In olives it is common to see remaining just enough of the body to support the bark ; and this is often so perforated, that, if near the ground, a dog or sheep may pass

DEMOSTHENES AND EUBULIDES

through. Neither the vitality nor the fecundity of the tree appears in the least to suffer by it. While I remember what I have been, I never can be less. External power affects those only who have none intrinsically. I have seen the day, Eubulides, when the most august of cities had but one voice within her walls ; and when the stranger on entering them stopped at the silence of the gateway, and said, " Demosthenes is speaking in the assembly of the people."

This is an ambition which no other can supplant or reach. The image of it stands eternally between me and kings, and separates me by an immeasurable interval from their courts and satraps. I swear against them, in the name of our country, in the name of Pallas Athenè and of all the Gods, amid the victims that have fallen by them and are about to fall, everlasting hatred.

Go now to the city, Eubulides, and report my oath. Add, that you left me contemplating in solitude the posture of our affairs, reluctant to lay before the Athenians any plan or project until I have viewed it long and measured it correctly ; and to deliver any words to them, whether of counsel or comfort or congratulation, unworthy of so sedate and circumspect a people.

EUBULIDES. How gravely and seriously you speak ! do you think of them so highly ?

DEMOSTHENES. I have said it ; go ; repeat it.

XI. ÆSCHINES AND PHOCION

Circa 338 B.C.

(*Imag. Convers.*, i., 1824 ; i., 1826 ; *Wks.*, i., 1846 ; *Imag. Convers. Gk. and Rom.*, 1853 ; *Wks.*, ii., 1876.)

ÆSCHINES. O Phocion, again I kiss the hand that hath ever raised up the unfortunate.

PHOCION. I know not, Æschines, to what your discourse would tend.

ÆSCHINES. Yesterday, when the malice of Demosthenes would have turned against me the vengeance of the people ; by pointing me out as him whom the priestess of Apollo had designated, in declaring the Athenians were [1] unanimous, one excepted ; did you not cry aloud, *I am the* [2] *man ; I approve of nothing you do ?* That I see you again, that I can express to you my gratitude, these are your gifts.

PHOCION. And does Æschines then suppose that I should not have performed my duty, whether he were alive or dead ? To have removed from the envy of an ungenerous rival, and from the resentment of an inconsiderate populace, the citizen who possesses my confidence, the orator who defends my country, and the soldier who has fought by my side, was among those actions which are always well repaid. The line is drawn across the account : let us close it.

ÆSCHINES. I am not insensible, nor have ever been, to the afflicted ; my compassion hath [3] been excited in the city and in the field ; but when have I been moved, as I am now, to weeping ? Your generosity is more pathetic than pity [4] ; and at your eloquence, stern as it is, O Phocion, my tears gush like those warm fountains which burst forth suddenly from some convulsion of the earth.

Immortal Gods ! that Demades and Polyeuctus and Demosthenes

---

[1] 1st ed. reads : " all unanimous."
[2] 1st ed. reads : " that man."
[3] 1st ed. reads : " has."
[4] 1st ed. adds : " or than pain."

should prevail in the council over Phocion ! that even their projects
for a campaign should be adopted, in preference to that general's
who hath defeated Philip in every encounter, and should precipitate
the war against the advice of a politician, by whose presages, and
his only, the Athenians have never been deceived.

PHOCION. It is true, I am not popular.

ÆSCHINES. Become so.

PHOCION. It has been frequently [1] and with impunity in my
power to commit base actions ; and I abstained : would my friend
advise me at last to commit the basest of all ? to court the suffrages [2]
of people I despise !

ÆSCHINES. You court not even those who love and honour you.
Thirty times and oftener have you been chosen to lead our armies,
and never once were present at the election.[3] Unparalleled glory !
when have the Gods shown anything similar among men ! Not
Aristides nor Epaminondas, the most virtuous of mortals, not
Miltiades nor Cimon, the most glorious in their exploits,[4] enjoyed the
favour of Heaven so uninterruptedly. No presents, no solicitations,
no flatteries, no concessions : you never even asked a vote, however
duly, customarily, and gravely.[5]

PHOCION. The highest price we can pay for anything is, to ask it :
and to solicit a vote appears to me as unworthy an action as to
solicit a place in a will : it is not ours, and might have been another's.

ÆSCHINES.[6] A question unconnected with my visit now obtrudes
itself ; and indeed, Phocion, I have remarked heretofore that an
observation from you hath made Athenians, on several occasions,
forget their own business and debates, and fix themselves upon it.
What is your opinion on the right and expediency of making wills ?

PHOCION. That it is neither expedient nor just to make them ;
and that the prohibition would obviate and remove (to say nothing
of duplicity and servility) much injustice and discontent ; the two
things against which every legislator should provide the most
cautiously. General and positive laws should secure the order of

---

[1] From " frequently " to " impunity " not in 1st ed.
[2] 1st ed. reads : " the favour of men I abominate and despise."
[3] 1st ed. reads : " assembly which elected you."
[4] 2nd ed. adds : " not Codrus, great enough to redeem from contempt the
name of King." 1st ed. : " Codrus, so great as to," etc.
[5] 1st ed. reads : " customarily and legitimately."
[6] From " ÆSCHINES " to " public affairs " added in 2nd ed.

succession, as far as unto the grandchildren of brother and sister : beyond and out of these, property of every kind should devolve to the commonwealth. Thousands have remained unmarried, that, by giving hopes of legacies, they may obtain votes for public offices ; thus being dishonest, and making others so, defrauding the community of many citizens by their celibacy, and deteriorating many by their ambition. Luxury and irregular love have produced in thousands the same effect. They care neither about offspring nor about offices, but gratify the most sordid passions at their country's most ruinous expense. If these two descriptions of citizens were prohibited from appointing heirs at their option, and obliged to indemnify the republic for their inutility and nullity, at least by so insensible a fine as that which is levied on them after death, the members would shortly be reduced to few, and much of distress and indigence, much of dishonour and iniquity, would be averted from the people of Athens.

ÆSCHINES. But services and friendships——

PHOCION. —are rewarded by friendships and services.

ÆSCHINES. You have never delivered your opinion upon this subject before the people.

PHOCION. While passions and minds are agitated, the fewer opinions we deliver before them the better. We have laws enough ; and we should not accustom men to changes. Though many things might be altered and improved, yet alteration in state-matters, important or unimportant in themselves, is weighty in their complex and their consequences. A little car in motion shakes all the houses of a street : let it stand quiet, and you or I could almost bear it on our foot : it is thus with institutions.

ÆSCHINES. On wills you have excited my inquiry rather than satisfied it : you have given me new thoughts, but you have also made room for more.

PHOCION. Æschines, would you take possession of a vineyard or olive-ground which nobody had given to you ?

ÆSCHINES. Certainly not.

PHOCION. Yet if it were bequeathed by will, you would ?

ÆSCHINES. Who would hesitate ?

PHOCION. In many cases the just man.

ÆSCHINES. In some indeed.

PHOCION. There is a parity in all between a will and my hypothesis of vineyard or olive-ground. Inheriting by means of a will, we take to ourselves what nobody has given.

ÆSCHINES. Quite the contrary : we take what he has given who does not deprive himself of any enjoyment or advantage by his gift.

PHOCION. Again I say, we take it, Æschines, from no giver at all ; for he whom you denominate the giver does not exist : he who does not exist can do nothing, can accept nothing, can exchange nothing, can give nothing.

ÆSCHINES. He gave it while he was living, and while he had these powers and faculties.

PHOCION. If he gave it while he was living, then it was not what lawyers and jurists and legislators call a will or testament, on which alone we spoke.

ÆSCHINES. True ; I yield.

PHOCION. The absurdities we do not see are more numerous and greater than those we discover ; for truly there are few imaginable that have not crept from some corner or other into common use, and these escape our notice by familiarity.

ÆSCHINES. We pass easily over great inequalities, and smaller shock us. He who leaps down resolutely and with impunity from a crag of Lycabettos,* may be lamed perhaps for life by missing a step in the descent from a temple.

Again, if you please, to our first question.

PHOCION. I would change it willingly for another, if you had not dropt something out of which I collect that you think me too indifferent to the administration of public affairs. Indifference to the welfare of our country is a crime ; but when our country is reduced to [1] a condition in which the bad are preferred to the good, the foolish to the wise, hardly any catastrophe is to be deprecated or opposed that may shake them from their places.

ÆSCHINES. In dangerous and trying times they fall naturally and necessarily, as flies drop out of a curtain let down in winter. Should the people demand of me what better I would propose than my adversaries, such are the extremities to which their boisterousness and levity have reduced us, I can return no answer. We are in the condition of a wolf biting off his leg to escape from the trap that has caught it.

* Called afterwards *Ankesmos*.—W. S. L.
[1] 1st ed. reads : " such a condition that."

PHOCION. Calamities have assaulted mankind in so great a variety of attacks, that nothing new can be devised against them. He who would strike out a novelty in architecture, commits a folly in safety; his house and he may stand : he who attempts it in politics, carries a torch, from which at the first narrow passage we may expect a conflagration. Experience is our only teacher both in war and peace As we formerly did against the Lacedæmonians and their allies, we might by our naval superiority seize or blockade the maritime towns of Philip ; we might conciliate Sparta, who has outraged and defied him ; we might wait even for his death, impending from drunkenness, lust, ferocity, and inevitable in a short space of time from the vengeance to which they expose him at home. It is a dangerous thing for a monarch to corrupt a nation yet uncivilised ; to corrupt a civilised one is the wisest thing he can do.

ÆSCHINES. I see no reason why we should not send an executioner to release him from the prison-house of his crimes, with his family to attend him. Kings play at war unfairly with republics : they can only lose some earth and some creatures they value as little, while republics lose in every soldier a part of themselves. Therefore no wise republic ought to be satisfied, unless she bring to punishment the criminal most obnoxious, and those about him who may be supposed to have made him so, his counsellors and his courtiers. Retaliation is not a thing to be feared. You [1] might as reasonably be contented with breaking the tables and chairs of a wretch who hath murdered your children, as with slaying the soldiers of a despot who wages war against you. The least you can do in justice or in safety, is, to demand his blood of the people who are under him, tearing in pieces the nest of his brood. The Locrians have admitted only two new laws in two hundred years ; because he who proposes to establish or to change one, comes with a halter round his throat, and is strangled if his proposition is rejected. Let wars, which ought to be more perilous to the adviser, be but equally so : let those who engage in them perish if they lose, I mean the principals, and new wars will be as rare among others as new laws among the Locrians.

PHOCION. Both laws and wars are much addicted to the process of generation. Philip, I am afraid, has prepared the Athenians for his government ; and yet I wonder how, in a free state, any

[1] From " You " to " brood " added in 3rd ed.

man of common sense can be bribed.[1] The corrupter would only
spend his money on persons of some calculation and reflection :
with how little of either must those be endowed, who do not see that
they are paying a perpetuity for an annuity ! Suppose that they,
amid [2] suspicions, both from him in whose favour, and from those
to whose detriment, they betray, can enjoy everything they receive,
yet what security have their children and dependents ? Property
is usually gained in hope no less of bequeathing than of enjoying
it ; how [3] certain is it that these will lose more than was acquired
for them ! If they lose their country and their laws, what have
they ? The bribes of monarchs will be discovered, by the receiver,
to be like pieces of furniture given to a man who, on returning home,
finds that his house, in which he intended to place them, has another
master. I can conceive no bribery at all seductive to the most
profligate, short of that which establishes the citizen bribed among
the members of a [4] hereditary aristocracy, which in the midst of a
people is a kind of foreign state, where the spoiler and traitor may
take refuge. Now Philip is not so inhuman, as, in case he should
be the conqueror, to inflict on us so humiliating a punishment.
Our differences with him are [5] recent, and he marches from policy,
not from enmity. The Lacedæmonians did indeed attempt it, in
the imposition of the thirty tyrants ; but such a monstrous state
of degradation and of infamy roused us from our torpor, threw under
us and beneath our view all other wretchedness, and we recovered
(I wish we could retain it as easily !) our independence. What
depresses you ?

ÆSCHINES. O ! could I embody the spirit I receive from you,
and present it in all its purity to the Athenians, they would surely
hear me with as much attention, as that invoker and violator of
the Gods, Demosthenes, to whom my blood would be the most
acceptable libation at the feasts of Philip. Pertinacity and clamor-
ousness, he imagines, are tests of sincerity and truth ; although
we know that a weak orator raises his voice higher than a powerful
one, as the lame raise their legs higher than the sound. He [6]

---

[1] Æschines was in the pay of Philip.
[2] 1st ed. reads : " amidst suspicions both from him . . . they betray and
from those . . . they have betrayed," etc.
[3] 1st ed. reads : " but how . . . will lose greatly more," etc.
[4] 1st ed. reads : " an."   [5] 1st ed. reads : " are but recent."
[6] From " He " to " died " added in 3rd ed.

censures me for repeating my accusation ; he talks of tautology and diffuseness ; he who tells us gravely that a man had lived *many years*, and—what then ?—that he was rather old when he died ! * Can anything be so ridiculous as the pretensions of this man, who, because I employ no action, says, *action is the first, the second, the third requisite of oratory*, while he himself is the most ungraceful of our speakers, and, even in appealing to the Gods, begins by scratching his head ?

PHOCION. This is surely no inattention or indifference to the powers above. Great [1] men lose somewhat of their greatness by being near us ; ordinary men gain much. As we are drawing nigh to humble buildings, those at a distance beyond them sink below : but we may draw so nigh to the grand and elevated as to take in only a small part of the whole. I smile at reflecting on the levity with which we contemporaries often judge of those [2] authors whom posterity will read with [3] most admiration : such is Demosthenes. Differ as we may from him in politics, we must acknowledge that no language is clearer,[4] no thoughts more natural, no words more proper, no combinations more unexpected, no cadences more diversified and harmonious. Accustomed to consider as the best what is at once the most simple and emphatic, and knowing that what [5] satisfies the understanding, conciliates the ear, I think him little if at all inferior to Aristoteles in style, though in wisdom he is as a mote to a sunbeam ; and [6] superior to my master Plato, excellent as he is ; gorgeous indeed, but becomingly, like wealthy kings. Defective however and faulty must be the composition in prose, which you and I with [7] our uttermost study and attention can not understand. In poetry it is not exactly so : the greater share [8] of it must be intelligible to the multitude ; but in the best

---

* Ἐβίωσε πολλὰ ἐτῆ καὶ ἦν πρεσβύτερος ὅτε ἐτελευτα.—W. S. L.

[1] From " Great " to " whole " added in 2nd ed.

[2] 1st ed. reads : " those great."   [3] 1st ed. reads : " with incessant."

[4] 1st ed reads : " no language is more forcible, more clear, no combinations of words more novel, no sequency of sentences more diversified, more admirably pitched and concerted ! Accustomed," etc.

[5] 1st ed. reads : " whatever."

[6] 1st ed. reads : " much superior to Plato, excellent as was he, gorgeous indeed, but becomingly so, as wealthy monarchs are, and truly a magnificent piece of the Gods' work in their richest materials."

[7] 1st ed. reads : " with all our study and attention."

[8] 1st ed. reads : " the greater part of it . . . intelligible to all : but in the very best there is . . . none besides," etc.

162

there is often an undersong of sense, which none beside the poetical mind, or one deeply versed in its mysteries, can comprehend. Euripides and Pindar have been blamed by many, who perceived not that the arrow drawn against them fell on Homer. The [1] Gods have denied to Demosthenes many parts of genius ; the urbane, the witty, the pleasurable, the pathetic. But, O Æschines ! the tree of strongest fibre and longest duration is not looked up to for its flower nor for its leaf.

Let us praise [2] whatever we can reasonably : nothing is less laborious or irksome, no office is less importunate or nearer a sinecure. Above others praise those who contend with you for glory, since they have already borne their suffrages to your [3] judgment by entering on the same career. Deem it a peculiar talent, and what [4] no three men in any age have possessed, to give each great citizen or great writer his just proportion of applause. A barbarian king or his eunuch can distribute equally and fairly beans and lentils ; but I perceive that Æschines himself finds a difficulty in awarding just commendations.

A few days ago an old woman, who wrote formerly a poem on Codrus, such as Codrus with all his self-devotion would hardly have read to save his country, met me in the street, and taxed me with injustice towards Demosthenes.

" You do not know him," said she ; " he has heart, and somewhat of genius ; true he is singular and eccentric ; yet I assure you I have seen compositions of his that do him credit. We [5] must not judge of him from his speeches in public : there he is violent ; but a billet of his, I do declare, is quite a treasure."

ÆSCHINES. What answer of yours could be the return for such silliness ?

PHOCION. " Lady ! " replied I, " Demosthenes is fortunate to be protected by the same cuirass as Codrus."

The commendations of these people are not always, what you would think them, left-handed and detractive : for singular [6] must

---

[1] From " The " to " leaf " added in 3rd ed.
[2] 1st ed. reads : " Let . . . my Æschines, whatever," etc.
[3] 1st ed. reads : " our judgment."   [4] 1st ed. reads : " such as no."
[5] From " We " to " PHOCION " added in 2nd ed.
[6] 1st ed. reads : " singular and strange must every man appear who is different from his neighbours : and he is the most . . . who is the most . . . If the clouds . . . upon grass or gravel."

every man appear who is different from the rest ; and he is most different from them who is most above them. If the clouds were inhabited by men, the men must be of other form and features than those on earth, and their gait would not be the same as upon the grass or pavement. Diversity no less is contracted by the habitations, as it were, and haunts, and exercises, of our minds. Singularity, when it is natural, requires no apology ; when it is affected, is detestable. Such is that of our young people in bad handwriting. On my expedition to Byzantion, the city decreed that a cloak should be given me worth forty drachmas [1] : and, when I was about to return, I folded it up carefully, in readiness for any service in which I might be employed hereafter. An officer, studious to imitate my neatness, packed up his in the same manner, not without the hope perhaps that I might remark it, and my servant, or his, on our return, mistook it. I sailed for Athens ; he, with a detachment, for Heraclea ; whence he wrote to me that he had sent my cloak, requesting his own by the first conveyance. The name was quite illegible, and the carrier, whoever he was, had pursued his road homeward : I directed it then, as the only safe way, if indeed there was any safe one, *to the officer who writes worst at Heraclea.*

Come, a few more words upon Demosthenes. Do not, my friend, inveigh against him, lest a part of your opposition be attributed to envy. How many arguments is it worth to him if you appear to act from another motive than principle ! True, his eloquence is imperfect : what among men is not ? In his repartees there is no playfulness, in his voice there is no flexibility, in his action there is neither dignity nor grace : but how often has he stricken you dumb with his irony ! how often has he tossed you from one hand to the other with his interrogatories ! Concentrated [2] are his arguments, select and distinct and orderly his topics, ready and unfastidious his expressions, popular his allusions, plain his illustrations, easy the swell and subsidence of his periods, his dialect purely Attic. Is this no merit ? Is it none in an age of idle rhetoricians, who have forgotten how their fathers and mothers spoke to them ?

ÆSCHINES.[3] But what repetitions !

---

[1] 1st ed. reads : " drachmæ."

[2] 1st ed. reads : " What harmony of periods, what choice of expressions, how popular . . . illustrations, his dialect purely Attic," omitting " easy " to " periods."

[3] From " ÆSCHINES " to " own " added in 2nd ed.

ÆSCHINES AND PHOCION

PHOCION. If a thing is good it may be repeated ; not indeed too frequently nor too closely, nor in words exactly the same. The repetition shows no want of invention : it shows only what is uppermost in the mind, and by what the writer is most agitated and inflamed.

ÆSCHINES. Demosthenes tells us himself, that he has prepared fifty-six commencements for his future speeches : how can he foresee the main subject of them all ? They are indeed all invectives against Philip : but does Demosthenes imagine that Philip is not greatly more fertile in the means of annoyance than any Athenian is in the terms of vituperation ? And which gives most annoyance ? Fire and sword ravage far and wide : the tongue can not break through the shield nor extinguish the conflagration : it brings down many blows, but heals no wounds whatever.

PHOCION. I perceive in the number of these overtures to the choruses of the Furies, a stronger argument of his temerity than your acuteness hath exposed. He must have believed that Philip could not conquer us before he had time enough to compose and deliver his fifty-six speeches. I differ from him widely in my cal culation. But, returning to your former charge, I would rather praise him for what he has omitted, than censure him for what he has repeated.

ÆSCHINES. And I too.

PHOCION. Those words were spoken in the tone of a competitor rather than of a comrade, as you soon may be.

ÆSCHINES. I am jealous then ? Did I demonstrate any jealousy of him when I went into the Peloponnese, to second and propell the courage his representations of the common danger had excited ? where I beheld the youths of Olynthus, sent as slaves and donatives to his partisans, in that country of degenerate and dastard Greeks ! What his orations had failed to bring about, my energy and zeal, my sincerity and singleness of aim, effected. The Athenians there followed me to the temple of Agraulos,[1] and denounced in one voice the most awful imprecations against the Peloponnesians corrupted by the gold of Macedon.

PHOCION. You have many advantages over your rival : let him have some over you. There are merits which appear demerits to vulgar minds and inconsiderate auditors. Many, in the populace

[1] Perhaps " Aglauros."

of hearers and readers, want links and cramps to hold together the thoughts that are given them, and cry out if you hurry them on too fast. You must leap over no gap, or you leave them behind and startle them from following you. With them the pioneer is a cleverer man than the commander. I have observed in Demosthenes and Thucydides, that they lay it down as a rule, never to say what they have reason to suppose would occur to the auditor and reader in consequence of anything said before, knowing everyone to be more pleased and more easily led by us, when we bring forward his thoughts indirectly and imperceptibly, than when we elbow and outstrip them with our own. The [1] sentences of your adversary are stout and compact as the Macedonian phalanx, animated and ardent as the sacred band of Thebes. Praise him, Æschines, if you wish to be victorious ; if you acknowledge you are vanquished, then revile him and complain. In composition I know not a superior to him ; and in an assembly of the people he derives advantages from his defects themselves, from the violence of his action and from the vulgarity of his mien. Permit him to possess these advantages over you ; look on him as a wrestler whose body is robust, but whose feet rest upon something slippery : use your dexterity, and reserve your blows. Consider him, if less excellent as a statesman, citizen, or soldier, rather as a genius or demon, who, whether beneficent or malignant, hath, from an elevation far above us, launched forth many new stars into the firmament of mind.[2]

ÆSCHINES. O that we had been born in other days ! The best men always fall upon the worst.

PHOCION. The Gods have not granted us, Æschines, the choice of being born when we would ; that of dying when we would, they have. Thank them for it, as one among the most excellent of their gifts, and [3] remain or go, as utility or dignity may require. Whatever can happen to a wise and virtuous man from his worst enemy, whatever is most dreaded by the inconsiderate and irresolute, has happened to him frequently from himself, and not only without his inconvenience, but without his observation. We are prisoners

---

[1] 1st ed. reads : " His sentences are . . . Praise him, my Æschines . . . if you acknowledge that you . . . In . . . not any . . . consider him as a wrestler . . . Regard him, if less," etc.

[2] 2nd ed. has note here.

[3] 1st ed. reads : " and wait not for horn or herald : a whistle is here a signal. Whatever," etc.

as often as we bolt our doors, exiles as often as we walk to Munychia, and dead as often as we sleep.   It would be a folly and a shame to argue that these things are voluntary, and that what our enemy imposes are not : they should be the more if they befall us from necessity, unless necessity be a weaker reason [1] than caprice.   In fine, Æschines, I shall then call the times bad when they make me so : at present they are to be borne, as must [2] be the storm that follows them.

[1] 1st ed. reads : " with us than."   [2] 1st ed. reads : " as must also be."

XII. ALEXANDER AND THE PRIEST OF HAMMON

331 B.C.

(Imag. Convers., iv., 1829 ; *Wks.,* i., 1846 ; *Imag. Convers. Gk. and Rom.,* 1853 ; *Wks.,* 1876.)

ALEXANDER. Like [1] my father, as ignorant men called King Philip, I have at all times been the friend and defender of the Gods.

PRIEST. Hitherto it was rather my belief that the Gods may befriend and defend us mortals : but I am now instructed that a king of Macedon has taken them under his shield. Philip, if report be true, was less remarkable for his devotion.

ALEXANDER. He was the most religious prince of the age.

PRIEST. On what, O Alexander, rests the support of such an exalted title ?

ALEXANDER. Not only did he swear more frequently and more awfully than any officer in the army, or any priest in the temples, but his sacrifices were more numerous and more costly.

PRIEST. More costly ? It must be either to those whose ruin is consummated or to those whose ruin is commenced ; in other words, either to the vanquished, or to those whose ill-fortune is of earlier date, the born subjects of the vanquisher.

ALEXANDER. He exhibited the surest and most manifest proof of his piety when he defeated Œnomarchus, general of the Phocians, who had dared to plough a piece of ground belonging to Apollo.

PRIEST. Apollo might have made it as hot work for the Phocians who were ploughing his ground, as he formerly did at Troy to those unruly Greeks who took away his priest's daughter. He shot a good many mules, to show he was in earnest, and would have gone on shooting both cattle and men until he came at last to the offender.

ALEXANDER. He instructed kings by slaying their people before their eyes : surely he would never set so bad an example as striking

[1] From " Like " to " another " not in 1st ed.

168

at the kings themselves. Philip, to demonstrate in the presence of all Greece his regard for Apollo of Delphi, slew six thousand, and threw into the sea three thousand, enemies of religion.

PRIEST. Alexander! Alexander! the enemies of religion are the cruel, and not the sufferers by cruelty. Is it unpardonable in the ignorant to be in error about their Gods when the wise are in doubt about their fathers?

ALEXANDER. I am not : Philip is not mine.

PRIEST. Probable enough.

ALEXANDER. Who then is, or ought to be, but Jupiter himself?

PRIEST. The priests of Pella are abler to return an oracle on that matter than we of the Oasis.

ALEXANDER. We have no oracle at Pella.

PRIEST. If you had, it might be dumb for once.

ALEXANDER. I am losing my patience.

PRIEST. I have given thee part of mine, seeing thee but scantily provided ; yet, if thy gestures are any signification, it sits but awkwardly upon thy shoulders.

ALEXANDER. This to me! the begotten of a God! the benefactor of all mankind.

PRIEST. Such as Philip was to the three thousand, when he devised so magnificent a bath for their recreation. Plenty of pumice! rather a lack of napkins!

ALEXANDER. No trifling! no false wit!

PRIEST. True wit, to every man, is that which falls on another.

ALEXANDER. To come at once to the point ; I am ready to prove that neither Jason nor Bacchus, in their memorable expeditions, did greater service to mankind than I have done, and am about to do.

PRIEST. Jason [1] gave them an example of falsehood and ingratitude : Bacchus made them drunk : thou appearest a proper successor to these worthies.

ALEXANDER. Such insolence to crowned heads! such levity on heroes and Gods!

PRIEST. Hark ye, Alexander! we priests are privileged.

ALEXANDER. I too am privileged to speak of my own great actions ; if not as liberator of Greece and consolidator of her disjointed and jarring interests, at least as the benefactor of Egypt and of Jupiter.

---

[1] 1st ed. reads " Jason fleeced them," and omits " such " to " heads."

PRIEST. Here indeed it would be unseemly to laugh ; for it is evident on thy royal word that Jupiter is much indebted to thee ; and equally evident, from the same authority, that thou wantest nothing from him but his blessing—unless it be a public acknowledgment that he has been guilty of another act of bastardy, more becoming his black curls than his grey decrepitude.

ALEXANDER. Amazement ! to talk thus of Jupiter !

PRIEST. Only to those who are in his confidence : a mistress for instance, or a son, as thou sayest thou art.

ALEXANDER. Yea, by my head and by my sceptre am I.   Nothing is more certain.

PRIEST. We will discourse upon that presently.

ALEXANDER.[1] Discourse upon it this instant.

PRIEST. How is it possible that Jupiter should be thy father, when——

ALEXANDER. When what ?

PRIEST. Couldst not thou hear me on ?

ALEXANDER. Thou askest a foolish question.

PRIEST. I did not ask whether I should be acknowledged the son of Jupiter.

ALEXANDER. Thou indeed !

PRIEST. Yet, by the common consent of mankind, lands and tenements are assigned to us, and we are called " *divine*," as their children ; and there are some who assert that the Gods themselves have less influence and less property on earth than we.

ALEXANDER. All this is well : only use your influence for your benefactors.

PRIEST. Before we proceed any farther, tell me in what manner thou art or wilt ever be the benefactor of Egypt.

ALEXANDER. The same exposition will demonstrate that I shall be likewise the benefactor of Jupiter.   It is my intention to build a city, in a situation very advantageous for commerce : of course the frequenters of such a mart will continually make offerings to Jupiter.

PRIEST. For what ?

ALEXANDER. For prosperity.

PRIEST. Alas ! Alexander, the prosperous make few offerings ; and Hermes has the dexterity to intercept the greater part of them.

---

[1] From " ALEXANDER " to " farther " added in 2nd ed.

ALEXANDER AND THE PRIEST

In Egypt there are cities enow already : I should say too many : for men prey upon one another when they are penned together close.

ALEXANDER. There is then no glory in building a magnificent city ?

PRIEST. Great may be the glory.

ALEXANDER. Here at least thou art disposed to do me justice.

PRIEST. I never heard until this hour that among thy other attainments was architecture.

ALEXANDER. Scornful and insolent man ! dost thou take me for an architect ?

PRIEST. I was about to do so ; and certainly not in scorn, but to assuage the feeling of it.

ALEXANDER. How ?

PRIEST. He who devises the plan of a great city, of its streets, its squares, its palaces, its temples, must exercise much reflection and many kinds of knowledge : and yet those which strike most the vulgar, most even the scientific, require less care, less knowledge, less beneficence, than what are called the viler parts, and are the most obscure and unobserved ; the construction of the sewers ; the method of exempting the aqueducts from the incroachment of their impurities ; the conduct of canals for fresh air in every part of the house, attempering the summer heats ; the exclusion of reptiles ; and even the protection from insects. The conveniences and comforts of life, in these countries, depend on such matters.

ALEXANDER. My architect, I doubt not, has considered them maturely.

PRIEST. Who is he ?

ALEXANDER. I will not tell thee : the whole glory is mine : I gave the orders, and first conceived the idea.

PRIEST. A hound upon a heap of dust may dream of a fine city, if he has ever seen one ; and a madman in chains may dream of building it, and may even give directions about it.

ALEXANDER. I will not bear this.

PRIEST. Were it false, thou couldst bear it ; thou wouldst call the bearing of it magnanimity ; and wiser men would do the same for centuries. As such wisdom and such greatness are not what I bend my back to measure, do favour me with what thou wert about to say when thou begannest " nothing is more certain " ; since I presume it must appertain to geometry, of which I am fond.

171

ALEXANDER. I did not come hither to make figures upon the sand.

PRIEST. Fortunate for thee, if the figure thou wilt leave behind thee could be as easily wiped out.

ALEXANDER. What didst thou say ?

PRIEST. I was musing.

ALEXANDER. Even the building of cities is in thy sight neither glorious nor commendable.

PRIEST. Truly, to build them is not among the undertakings I the most applaud in the powerful ; but to destroy them is the very foremost of the excesses I abhor. All the cities of the earth should rise up against the man who ruins one. Until this sentiment is predominant, the peaceful can have no protection, the virtuous no encouragement, the brave no countenance, the prosperous no security. We priests communicate one with another extensively ; and even in these solitudes thy exploits against Thebes have reached and shocked us. What hearts must lie in the bosoms of those who applaud thee for preserving the mansion of a deceased poet in the general ruin, while the relatives of the greatest patriot that ever drew breath under heaven, of the soldier at whose hospitable hearth thy father learned all that thou knowest and much more, of Epaminondas (dost thou hear me ?) were murdered or enslaved. Now begin the demonstration than which " nothing is more certain."

ALEXANDER. Nothing is more certain, or what a greater number of witnesses are ready to attest, than that my mother Olympias, who hated Philip, was pregnant of me by a serpent.

PRIEST. Of what race ?

ALEXANDER. Dragon.

PRIEST. Thy mother Olympias hated Philip, a well-made man, young, courageous, libidinous, witty, prodigal of splendour, indifferent to wealth, the greatest captain, the most jovial companion, and the most potent monarch in Europe.

ALEXANDER. My father Philip, I would have thee to know— I mean reputed father — was also the greatest politician in the world.

PRIEST. This indeed I am well aware of ; but I did not number it among his excellences in the eyes of a woman : it would have been almost the only reason why she should have preferred the serpent, the head of the family. We live here, O Alexander, in solitude ; yet we are not the less curious, but on the contrary the more, to learn what passes in the world around.[1]

Olympias then did really fall in love with a serpent ? and she was induced——

ALEXANDER. Induced ! do serpents induce people ! They coil and climb and subdue them.

PRIEST. The serpent must have been dexterous——

ALEXANDER. No doubt he was.

PRIEST. But women have such an abhorrence of serpents, that Olympias would surely have rather run away.

ALEXANDER. How could she ?

PRIEST. Or called out.

ALEXANDER. Women never do that, lest somebody should hear them.

PRIEST. All mortals seem to bear an innate antipathy to this reptile.

ALEXANDER. Mind ! mind what thou sayest ! Do not call my father a reptile.

PRIEST. Even thou, with all thy fortitude, wouldst experience a shuddering at the sight of a serpent in thy bed-clothes.

ALEXANDER. Not at all. Beside, I do not hesitate in my belief that on this occasion it was Jupiter himself. The priests in Macedon were unanimous upon it.

PRIEST. When it happened ?

ALEXANDER. When it happened no one mentioned it, for fear of Philip.

PRIEST. What would he have done ?

ALEXANDER. He was choleric.

PRIEST. Would he have made war upon Jupiter ?

ALEXANDER. By my soul ! I know not ; but I would have done it in his place. As a son, I am dutiful and compliant : as a husband and king, there is not a thunderbolt in heaven that should deter me from my rights.

PRIEST. Did any of the priesthood see the dragon, as he was entering or retreating from the chamber ?

---

[1] 1st ed. adds : " and I assure you neither our records nor those of our brothers in Egypt, ancient as they are, go far enough back to show us an instance of any signal politician who was not also a singular cuckold. Thou hast unwittingly thrown in a strong argument in favour of thy divinity. Nevertheless, we must ponder upon it. Olympias," etc.

ALEXANDER. Many saw a great light in it.

PRIEST. He would want one.

ALEXANDER. This seems like irony : sacred things do not admit it. What thousands saw, nobody should doubt. The sky opened, lightnings flew athwart it, and strange voices were heard.

PRIEST. Juno's the loudest, I suspect.

ALEXANDER. Being a king, and the conqueror of kings, let me remind thee, surely I may be treated here with as much deference and solemnity as one priest uses toward another.

PRIEST. Certainly with no less, O king ! Since thou hast insisted that I should devise the best means of persuading the world of this awful verity, thou wilt excuse me, in thy clemency, if my remarks and interrogatories should appear prolix.

ALEXANDER. Remark [1] anything ; but do not interrogate and press me : kings are unaccustomed to it. I will consign to thee every land from the centre to the extremities of Africa ; the Fortunate Isles will I also give to thee, adding the Hyperborean : I wish only the consent of the religious who officiate in this temple, and their testimony to the world in declaration of my parentage.

PRIEST. Many thanks ! we have all we want.

ALEXANDER. I can not think you are true priests then ; and if your oath on the divinity of my descent were not my object, and therefore not to be abandoned, I should regret that I had offered so much in advance, and should be provoked to deduct one half of the Fortunate Isles, and the greater part of the Hyperborean.

PRIEST. Those are exactly the regions, O king, which our moderation would induce us to resign. Africa, we know, is worth little : yet we are as well contented with the almonds, the dates, the melons, the figs, the fresh butter, the stags,[2] the antelopes, the kids, the tortoises, and the quails about us, as we should be if they were brought to us after fifty days' journey through the desert.

ALEXANDER. Really now, is it possible that, in a matter so evident, your oracle can find any obstacle or difficulty in proclaiming me what I am ?

PRIEST. The difficulty (slight it must be acknowledged) is this : our Jupiter is horned.

---

[1] 1st ed. reads : " Ask anything : but do not press me. Kings are not used to it."

[2] 1st ed. omits " the stags," and adds " the young boars " after " kids."

ALEXANDER AND THE PRIEST

ALEXANDER. So was my father.[1]

PRIEST. The children of Jupiter love one another : this we believe here in Libya.

ALEXANDER. And rightly : no affection was ever so strong as that of Castor and Pollux. I myself feel a genuine love for them, and greater still for Hercules.

PRIEST. If thou hadst a brother or sister on earth, Jove-born, thou wouldst embrace the same most ardently.

ALEXANDER. As becomes my birth and heart.

PRIEST. O Alexander ! may thy godlike race never degenerate !

ALEXANDER. Now indeed the Powers above do inspire thee.

PRIEST. Jupiter, I am commanded by him to declare, is verily thy father.

ALEXANDER. He owns me then ! he owns me ! What sacrifice worthy of this indulgence can I offer to him ?

PRIEST. An obedient mind, and a camel-load of nard and amomum for his altar.

ALEXANDER. I smell here the exquisite perfume of benzoin.

PRIEST. It grows in our vicinity. The nostrils of Jupiter love changes : he is consistent in all parts, being Jupiter. He has other sons and daughters in the world, begotten by him under the same serpentine form, although unknown to common mortals.

ALEXANDER. Indeed !

PRIEST. I declare it unto thee.

ALEXANDER. I can not doubt it then.

PRIEST. Not all indeed of thy comeliness in form and features, but awful and majestic. It is the will of Jupiter, that, like the Persian monarchs, whose sceptre he hath transferred to thee, thou marriest thy sister.

ALEXANDER. Willingly. In what land upon earth liveth she whom thou designest for me ?

PRIEST. The Destinies and Jupiter himself have conducted thee, O Alexander, to the place where thy nuptials shall be celebrated.

ALEXANDER. When did they so ?

PRIEST. Now ; at this very hour.

ALEXANDER. Let me see the bride, if it be lawful to lift up her veil.

PRIEST. Follow me.

ALEXANDER. The steps of this cavern are dark and slippery ;

[1] 1st ed. adds : " not indeed while he played the dragon, but before and after."

but it terminates, no doubt, like the Eleusinian, in pure light and refreshing shades.

PRIEST. Wait here an instant : it will grow lighter.

ALEXANDER. What do I see yonder ?

PRIEST. Where ?

ALEXANDER. Close under the wall, rising and lowering, regularly and slowly, like a long weed on a quiet river,[1] when a fragment hath dropt into it from the bank above.

PRIEST. Thou descriest, O Alexander, the daughter of Jupiter, the watchful virgin, the preserver of our treasures. Without her they might be carried away by the wanderers of the desert ; but they fear, as they should do, the daughter of Jupiter.

ALEXANDER. Hell and Furies ! what hast thou been saying ? I heard little of it. Daughter of Jupiter !

PRIEST. Hast thou any fancy for the silent and shy maiden ? I will leave you together——

ALEXANDER. Orcus and Erebus !

PRIEST. Be discreet ! Restrain your raptures until the rites are celebrated.

ALEXANDER. Rites ! Infernal pest ! O horror ! abomination ! A vast panting snake !

PRIEST. Say " *dragon*," O king ! and beware how thou callest horrid and abominable the truly begotten of our lord thy father.

ALEXANDER. What means this ? inhuman traitor ! Open the door again : lead me back. Are my conquests to terminate in the jaws of a reptile ?

PRIEST. Do the kings of Macedon call their sisters such names ?

ALEXANDER. Let me out, I say !

PRIEST. Inconstant man ! I doubt even whether the marriage hath been consummated. Dost thou question her worthiness ? prove her, prove her. We have certain signs and manifestations that Jupiter begat this powerful creature, thy elder sister. Her mother hid her shame and confusion in the desert, where she still wanders, and looks with an evil eye on everything in the form of man. The poorest, vilest, most abject of the sex, holdeth her head no lower than she.

ALEXANDER. Impostor !

PRIEST. Do not the sympathies of thy heart inform thee that this solitary queen is of the same lineage as thine ?

---

[1] 1st ed. ends this speech at " river."

ALEXANDER AND THE PRIEST

ALEXANDER. What temerity! what impudence! what deceit!

PRIEST. Temerity! How so, Alexander! Surely man can not claim too near an affinity to his Creator, if he will but obey him, as I know thou certainly wilt in this tender alliance. Impudence and deceit were thy other accusations: how little merited! I only traced the collateral branches of the genealogical tree thou pointedst out to me.

ALEXANDER. Draw back the bolt: let me pass: stand out of my way. Thy hand upon my shoulder! Were my sword beside me, this monster should lick thy blood.

PRIEST. Patience! O king! The iron portal is in my hand: if the hinges turn, thy godhead is extinct. No, Alexander, no! it must not be.

ALEXANDER. Lead me then forth. I swear to silence.

PRIEST. As thou wilt.

ALEXANDER. I swear to friendship; lead me but out again.

PRIEST. Come; although I am much interested in the happiness of his two children whom I serve——

ALEXANDER. Persecute me no longer; in the name of Jupiter!

PRIEST. I can hardly give it up. To have been the maker of such a match! what felicity! what glory! Think once more upon it. There are many who could measure themselves with thee, head to head; let me see the man who will do it with your child at the end of the year, if thou embracest with good heart and desirable success this daughter of deity.

ALEXANDER. Enough, my friend! I have deserved it; but we must deceive men, or they will either hate us or despise us.

PRIEST. Now thou talkest reasonably. I here pronounce thy divorce. Moreover, thou shalt be the son of Hammon in Libya, of Mithras in Persia, of Philip in Macedon, of Olympian Jove in Greece: but never for the future teach priests new creeds.

ALEXANDER. How my father Philip would have laughed over his cups at such a story as this!

PRIEST. Alexander! let it prove to thee thy folly.

ALEXANDER. If such is my folly, what is that of others? Thou wilt acknowledge and proclaim me the progeny of Jupiter.

PRIEST. Ay, ay.

ALEXANDER. People must believe it.

PRIEST. The only doubt will be among the shrewder, whether,

being so extremely old and having left off his pilgrimages so many years, he could have given our unworthy world so spirited an offspring as thou art.

Come and sacrifice.

ALEXANDER. Priest! I see thou art a man of courage : henceforward we are in confidence. Take mine with my hand : give me thine. Confess to me, as the first proof of it, didst thou never shrink back from so voracious and intractable a monster as that accursed snake ?

PRIEST. We caught her young, and fed her on goat's milk, as our Jupiter himself was fed in the caverns of Crete.

ALEXANDER. *Your* Jupiter ! *that* was another.

PRIEST. Some people say so : but the same cradle serves for the whole family, the same story will do for them all. As for fearing this young personage in the treasury-vault, we fear her no more, son Alexander, than the priests of Egypt do his holiness the crocodile-god. The Gods and their pedagogues are manageable to the hand that feeds them.

ALEXANDER. Canst thou talk thus ?

PRIEST. Of false Gods, not of the true one.

ALEXANDER. One ! are there not many ? Some dozens ? some hundreds ?

PRIEST. Not in our vicinity ; praised be Hammon ! And plainly to speak, there is nowhere another, let who will have begotten him, whether on cloud or meadow, feather-bed or barn-floor, worth a salt locust or a last year's date-fruit.

These are our mysteries, if thou must needs know them ; and those of other priesthoods are the like.

Alexander, my boy, do not stand there, with thy arms folded and thy head aside, pondering. Jupiter the Ram for ever !

ALEXANDER. Glory to Jupiter the Ram ! [1]

PRIEST. Thou stoppest on a sudden thy prayers and praises to father Jupiter. Son Alexander ! art thou not satisfied ? What ails thee, drawing the back of thy hand across thine eyes ?

ALEXANDER. A little dust flew into them as the door opened.

PRIEST. Of that dust are the sands of the desert and the kings of Macedon.

[1] In 1st ed. the Conversation ends here.

XIII. ARISTOTELES AND CALLISTHENES

330 B.C.

(Imag. Convers., ii., 1824 ; *Imag. Convers.*, ii., 1826; *Wks.*, 1846 ;
Imag. Convers. Gk. and Rom., 1853 ; *Wks.*, 1876.)

ARISTOTELES. I rejoice, O Callisthenes, at your return ; and the more as I see you in the dress of your country ; while others, who appear to me of the lowest rank by their language and physiognomy, are arrayed in the Persian robe, and mix the essence of rose with pitch.

CALLISTHENES. I thank the Gods, O Aristoteles, that I embrace you again ; that my dress is a Greek one and an old one ; that the conquests of Alexander have cost me no shame and have encumbered me with no treasures.

ARISTOTELES. Jupiter ! what then are those tapestries, for I will not call them dresses, which the slaves are carrying after you, in attendance (as they say) on your orders.

CALLISTHENES. They are presents from Alexander to Xenocrates ; by which he punishes, as he declared to the Macedonians, both me and you. And I am well convinced that the punishment will not terminate here, but that he, so irascible and vindictive, will soon exercise his new dignity of godship, by breaking our heads, or, in the wisdom of his providence, by removing them an arm's length from our bodies.

ARISTOTELES. On this subject we must talk again. Xenocrates [1] is indeed a wise and virtuous man ; and although I could wish that Alexander had rather sent him a box of books than a bale of woollen, I acknowledge that the gift could hardly have been better bestowed.

CALLISTHENES. You do not appear to value very highly the learning of this philosopher.

ARISTOTELES. To talk and dispute are more the practices of the

---

[1] From " Xenocrates " to " ARISTOTELES. Alexander hath," etc., added in 2nd ed.

Platonic school than to read and meditate. Talkative men seldom read. This is among the few truths which appear the more strange the more we reflect upon them. For what is reading but silent conversation ? People make extremely free use of their other senses ; and I know not what difficulty they could find or apprehend in making use of their eyes, particularly in the gratification of a propensity which they indulge so profusely by the tongue. The fatigue, you would think, is less ; the one organ requiring much motion, the other little. Added to which, they may leave their opponent when they please, and never are subject to captiousness or personality. In open contention with an argumentative adversary, the worst brand a victor imposes is a blush. The talkative man blows the fire himself for the reception of it ; and we can not deny that it may likewise be suffered by a reader, if his conscience lies open to reproach : yet even in this case, the stigma is illegible on his brow ; no one triumphs in his defeat, or even freshens his wound, as may sometimes happen, by the warmth of sympathy. All men, you and I among the rest, are more desirous of conversing with a great philosopher, or other celebrated man, than of reading his works. There are several reasons for this ; some of which it would be well if we could deny or palliate. In justice to ourselves and him, we ought to prefer his writings to his speech ; for even the wisest say many things inconsiderately ; and there never was one of them in the world who ever uttered extemporaneously three sentences in succession, such as, if he thought soundly and maturely upon them afterward, he would not in some sort modify and correct. Effrontery and hardness of heart are the characteristics of every great speaker I can mention, excepting Phocion ; and if he is exempt from them, it is because eloquence, in which no one ever excelled or ever will excell him, is secondary to philosophy in this man, and philosophy to generosity of spirit. On the same principle as impudence is the quality of great speakers and disputants, modesty is that of great readers and composers. Not only are they abstracted by their studies from the facilities of ordinary conversation, but they discover, from time to time, things of which they were ignorant before, and on which they had not even the ability of doubting. We, my Callisthenes, may consider them not only as gales that refresh us while they propell us forward, but as a more compendious engine of the Gods, whereby we are brought securely into harbour, and deeply laden with imperishable wealth. Let us then strive day and night to increase the number of these beneficent beings, and to stand among them in the sight of the living and the future. It is required of us that we give more than we received.

CALLISTHENES. O my guide and teacher ! you are one of the blessed few at whose hands the Gods may demand it : if they had intended to place it in my duties, they would have chosen me a different master. How small a part of what I have acquired from you (and to you I owe all of knowledge and wisdom I possess) shall I be able to transmit to others !

ARISTOTELES. Encourage better hopes. Again I tell you, it is required of us, not merely that we place the grain in a garner, but that we ventilate and sift it, that we separate the full from the empty, the faulty from the sound, and that, if it must form the greater, it do not form the more elegant part of the entertainment our friends expect from us. I am now in the decline of life : to shove me from behind would be a boyish trick : but wherever I fall I shall fall softly : the Gods having placed me in a path out of which no violence can remove me. In youth our senses and the organs of them wander ; in the middle of life they cease to do it ; in old age the body itself, and chiefly the head, bends over and points to the earth which must soon receive it, and partakes in some measure of its torpor.

CALLISTHENES. You appear to me fresh and healthy, and your calmness and indifference to accidents are the effects of philosophy rather than of years.

ARISTOTELES. Plato is older by twenty, and has lost nothing of juvenility but the colour of his hair. The higher delights of the mind are in this, as in everything else, very different in their effects from its seductive passions. These cease to gratify us the sooner the earlier we indulge in them : on the contrary, the earlier we indulge in thought and reflection the longer do they last and the more faithfully do they serve us. So far are they from shortening or debilitating our animal life, that they prolong and strengthen it greatly. The body is as much at repose in the midst of high imaginations as in the midst of profound sleep. In imperfect sleep it wears away much, as also in imperfect thoughts ; in thoughts that can not rise from the earth and sustain themselves above it. The object which is in a direct line behind a thing, seems near : now nothing is in a more direct line than death to life : why should it not also be considered, on the first sight, as near at hand ? Swells and depressions, smooth ground and rough, usually lie between ; the distance may be rather more or rather less ; the proximity is certain. Alexander, a God, descends from his throne to conduct me.

CALLISTHENES. Endurance on the part of the injured is more pathetic than passion. The intimate friends of this conductor will quarrel over his [1] carcass while yet warm, as dogs over a dish after supper. How different are our conquests from his ! how different our friends ! not united for robbery and revelry, but joyous in discovery, calm in meditation, and intrepid in research. How often, and throughout how many ages, shall you be a refuge from such men as he and his accomplices : how often will the studious, the neglected, the deserted, fly toward you for compensation in the wrongs of fortune, and for solace in the rigour of destiny ! His judgment-seat is covered by his sepulchre : after one year hence no appeals are made to him : after ten thousand there will be momentous questions, not of avarice or litigation, not of violence or fraud, but of reason and of science, brought before your judgment-seat and settled by your decree. Dyers and tailors, carvers and gilders, grooms and trumpeters, make greater men than God makes ; but God's last longer, throw them where you will.

ARISTOTELES. Alexander hath really punished me by his [2] gifts to Xenocrates ; for he obliges me to send him the best tunic I have : and you know that in my wardrobe I am, as appears to many, unphilosophically splendid. There are indeed no pearls in this tunic ; but golden threads pursue the most intricate and most elegant design, the texture is the finest of Miletus, the wool is the softest of Tarentum, and the purple is Hermionic. He will sell Alexander's dresses, and wear mine ; the consequence of which will be imprisonment or scourges.

CALLISTHENES. A provident God forsooth in his benefits is our Alexander !

ARISTOTELES. Much to be pitied if ever he returns to his senses ! Justly do we call barbarians the wretched nations that are governed by one man [3] ; and among them the most deeply plunged in barbarism is the ruler. Let us take any favourable specimen : Cyrus for

---

[1] *Works*, 1876, reads : " our carcase."   [2] 1st ed. reads : " splendid gifts."
[3] 1st ed. reads : " Kings."

instance, or Cambyses, or this Alexander : for however much you and I may despise him, seeing him often and nearly, he will perhaps leave behind him as celebrated a name as they. He is very little amid philosophers, though [1] very great amid monarchs. Is he not undoing with all his might what every wise man, and indeed every man in the order of things, is most solicitous to do ? Namely, doth [2] he not abolish kindly and affectionate intercourse ? doth [2] he not draw a line of distinction (which of all follies and absurdities is the wildest and most pernicious) between fidelity and truth ? In the hour of distress and misery the eye of every mortal turns to friendship : in the hour of gladness and conviviality what is our want ? it is [3] friendship. When the heart overflows with gratitude, or with any other sweet and sacred sentiment, what is the word to which it would give utterance ? *my friend.* Having thus displaced the right feeling, he finds it necessary to substitute at least a strong one. The warmth which should have been diffused from generosity and mildness, must come from the spiceman, the vintner, and the milliner ; he must be perfumed, he must be drunk, he must toss about shawl and tiara. You [4] would imagine that his first passion, his ambition, had an object : yet, before he was a God, he prayed that no one afterward [5] might pass the boundaries of his expedition : and he destroyed at Abdera, and in other places, the pillars erected as memorials by the Argonauts and by Sesostris.

CALLISTHENES.[6] I have many doubts upon the Argonauts. We Greeks are fond of attributing to ourselves all the great actions of remote antiquity : we feign that Isis, *Daughter of Inachus,* taught the Egyptians laws and letters. It may be questioned whether the monuments assigned to the Argonauts were not really those of Sesostris or Osiris, or some other eastern conqueror ; and even whether the tale of Troy be not, in part at least, translated. Many principal names, evidently not Grecian, and the mention of a language spoken by the Gods (meaning their representatives and officials) in which the rivers and other things are professed to be called differently from what they were called among men, are the foundations of my query. The Hindoos, the Egyptians, and

---

[1] 1st ed. reads : " but very great."
[2] 1st ed. reads : " does."   [3] 1st ed. reads : " 'tis."
[4] 1st ed. reads : " One would."   [5] 1st ed. reads : " afterwards."
[6] In 1st and 2nd eds. this speech, with slight alterations, appears as a note.

probably the Phrygians (a very priestly nation), had their learned language, quite distinct from the vulgar.*

ARISTOTELES.[1] We will discuss this question another time. Perhaps you were present when Alexander ran around the tomb of Achilles in honour of his memory : if Achilles were now living, or any hero like him, Alexander would swear his perdition. Neither his affection for virtue nor his enmity to vice is pure or rational. Observation has taught me that we do not hate those who are worse than ourselves because they are worse, but because we are liable to injury from them, and because (as almost always is the case) they are preferred to us ; while those who are better we hate purely for being so. After their decease, if we remit our hatred, it is because then they are more like virtue in the abstract than virtuous men, and are fairly out of our way.

CALLISTHENES.[2] Disappointment made him at all times outrageous. What is worse, he hated his own virtues in another ; as dogs growl at their own faces in a mirror. The courage of Tyre, and many other cities, provoked not admiration but cruelty. Even his friends were unspared ; even Clitus and Parmenio.

ARISTOTELES. Cruelty, if we consider it as a crime, is the greatest of all : if we consider it as a madness, we are equally justifiable in applying to it the readiest and the surest means of suppression. Bonds may hold the weak ; the stronger break them, and strangle the administrator. Cruelty quite destroys our sympathies, and, doing so, supersedes and masters our intellects. It removes from us those who can help us, and brings against us those who can injure us. Hence it opposes the great principle of our nature, self-preservation, and endangers not only our well-being, but our being. Reason is then the most perfect when it enables us in the highest degree to benefit our fellow-men ; reason is then the most deranged when there is that over it which disables it. Cruelty is that. As for the wisdom of Alexander, I do not expect from a Macedonian, surrounded [3] by flatterers and drinkers, the prudence of an Epaminondas or a Phocion : but educated by such a father

* The *Galliambic* of Catullus may be a relic (the only one) of Phrygian poetry. He resided in the country, and may have acquired the language ; but his translation came through the Greek.—W. S. L.

[1] From " ARISTOTELES " to " time " added in 3rd ed.

[2] From " CALLISTHENES " to " that " added in 3rd ed.

[3] From " surrounded " to " drinkers " added in 3rd ed.

184

as Philip, and having with him in his army so many veteran captains, it excited no small ridicule in Athens, when it was ascertained that he and Darius, then equally eager for combat, missed each other's army in Cilicia.

CALLISTHENES. He has done great things, but with great means ; the generals you mention overcame more difficulties with less, and never were censured for any failure from deficiency of foresight.

ARISTOTELES. There is as much difference between Epaminondas and Alexander as between the Nile and a winter torrent. In this there is more impetuosity, foam, and fury ; more astonishment from spectators ; but it is followed by devastation and barrenness. In that there is an equable, a steady, and perennial course, swelling from its ordinary state only for the benefit of mankind, and subsiding only when that has been secured.

I have not mentioned Phocion so often as I ought to have done : but now, Callisthenes, I will acknowledge that I consider him as the greatest man upon earth. He foresaw long ago what has befallen our country ; and while others were proving to you that your wife, if a good woman, should be at the disposal of your friend,[1] and that if you love your children you should procure them as many fathers as you can, Phocion was practising all the domestic and all the social duties.

CALLISTHENES. I have often thought that his style resembles yours. Are you angry ?

ARISTOTELES. I will not dissemble to you that mine was formed upon his. Polieuctus, by no means a friend to him, preferred it openly to that of Demosthenes, for its brevity, its comprehensiveness, and its perspicuity. There is somewhat more of pomp and solemnity in Demosthenes, and perhaps of harmony ; but his [2] warmth is on many occasions the warmth of coarseness, and his ridicule the roughest part of him ; while in Phocion there is the acuteness of Pericles, and, wherever it is requisite, the wit of Aristophanes. He conquered with few soldiers, and he convinced with few words. I know not what better description I could give you, either of a great captain or a great orator.

Now imagine for a moment the mischief which the system of

---

[1] 1st ed. reads : " next neighbour " for " friend." This is a criticism of Plato's Republic.

[2] From " his " to " while " added in 3rd ed.

Plato, just alluded to, would produce : that women should be common. We hear that among the Etrurians they were so, and perhaps are yet : but of what illustrious action do we read ever performed by that ancient people ?   A thousand years have elapsed without a single instance on record of courage or generosity.   With us one word, altered only in its termination, signifies both *father* and *country :* can he who is ignorant of the one be solicitous about the other ?   Never was there a true patriot who was not, if a father, a kind one : never was there a good citizen who was not an obedient and reverential son.   Strange, to be ambitious of pleasing the multitude, and indifferent to the delight we may afford to those nearest us, our parents and our children ! Ambition is indeed the most inconsiderate of passions, none of which are considerate ; for the ambitious man, by the weakest inconsistency, proud as he may be of his faculties, and impatient as he may be to display them, prefers the opinion of the ignorant to his own.   He would be what others can make him, and not what he could make himself without them.   Nothing in fact is consistent and unambiguous but virtue.

Plato would make wives common, to abolish selfishness ; the mischief which above others it would directly and immediately bring forth.   There is no selfishness where there is a wife and family : the house is lighted up by the mutual charities : everything achieved for them is a victory, everything endured for them is a triumph.   How many vices are suppressed, that there may be no bad example ! how many exertions made, to recommend and inculcate a good one ! Selfishness then is thrown out of the question.   He would perhaps render men braver by his exercises in the common field of affections. Now bravery is of two kinds ; the courage of instinct and the courage of reason : animals have more of the former, men more of the latter ; for I would not assert, what many do, that animals have no reason, as I would not that men have no instinct.   Whatever creature can be taught, must be taught by the operation of reason upon reason, small as may be the quantity called forth or employed in calling it, and however harsh may be the means.   Instinct has no operation but upon the wants and desires.   Those who entertain a contrary opinion, are unaware how inconsequently they speak when they employ such expressions as these, " We are taught by instinct." Courage, so necessary to the preservation of states, is not weakened by domestic ties, but is braced by them.   Animals protect their young while they know it to be theirs, and neglect it when the traces of that memory are erased. Man can not so soon lose the memory of it, because his recollective faculties are more comprehensive and more tenacious, and because, while in the brute creation the parental love, which in most is only on the female side, lessens after the earlier days, his increases as the organs of the new creature are developed. There is a desire of property in the sanest and best men, which Nature seems to have implanted as conservative of her works, and which is necessary to encourage and keep alive the arts. Phidias and our friend Apelles would never have existed as the Apelles and Phidias they appear, if property (I am ashamed of the solecism which Plato now forces on me) were in common. A part of his scheme indeed may be accomplished in select and small communities, holden together by some religious bond, as we find among the disciples of Pythagoras : but he never taught his followers that prostitution is a virtue, much less that it is the summit of perfection. They revered him, and deservedly, as a father. As what father ? Not such as Plato would fashion ; but as a parent who had gained authority over his children by his assiduous vigilance, his tender and peculiar care, in separating them as far as possible from whatever is noxious in an intercourse with mankind.

To complete the system of selfishness, idleness, and licentiousness, the worshipful [1] triad of Plato, nothing was wanting but to throw all other property where he had thrown the wives and children. Who then should curb the rapacious ? who should moderate the violent ? The weaker could not work, the stronger would not. Food and raiment would fail ; and we should be reduced to something worse than a state of nature, into which we can never be cast back, any more than we can become children again. Civilisation suddenly retrograde, generates at once the crimes and vices, not only of its various stages, but of the state anterior to it, without any of its advantages, if it indeed have any. Plato would make for ever all the citizens, what we punish with death a single one for being once. He is a man of hasty fancy and indistinct [2] reflection ; more different from Socrates than the most violent of his adversaries. If he had said that in certain cases a portion of landed property should be divided among the citizens, he had spoken sagely and equitably. After a long war, when a state is oppressed by debt,

---

[1] 1st ed. reads : " republican triad."   [2] 1st ed. reads : " slow reflection."

and when many who have borne arms for their country have moreover consumed their patrimony in its service, these, if they are fathers of families, should receive allotments from the estates of others who are not, and who either were too young for warfare, or were occupied in less dangerous and more lucrative pursuits. It is also conducive to the public good that no person should possess more than a certain and definite extent of land, to be limited by the population and produce : else the freedom of vote and the honesty of election must be violated, and the least active members of the community will occupy those places which require the most activity. This is peculiarly needful in mercantile states, like ours, that everyone may enjoy the prospect of becoming a landholder, and that the money accruing from the sale of what is curtailed on the larger properties, may again fall into commerce. A state may eventually be reduced to such distresses by war, even after victories, that it shall be expedient to deprive the rich of whatever they possess beyond the portion requisite for the decent and frugal sustenance of a family. This extremity it is difficult to foresee ; nor do I think it is arrived at until the industrious and well-educated, in years of plenty, are unable by all their exertions to nourish and instruct their children. A speculative case, which it can not be dangerous or mischievous to state ; for certainly, when it occurs, the sufferers will appeal to the laws and forces of Nature, and not to the schools of rhetoric or philosophy. No situation can be imagined more painful or more abominable than this : while many, and indeed most, are worse than that whereunto the wealthier would be reduced in amending it; since they would lose no comforts, no conveniences, no graceful and unincumbering ornaments of life, and few luxuries ; which would be abundantly compensated to the generality of them, by smoothening their mutual pretensions, and by extinguishing the restless spirit of their rivalry.

CALLISTHENES. The visions of Plato have led to Reason : I marvel less that he should have been so extravagant, than that he should have scattered on that volume so little of what we admire in his shorter Dialogues.

ARISTOTELES. I respect his genius, which however has not accompanied all his steps in this discussion : nor indeed do I censure in him what has been condemned by Xenophon, who wonders that he should attribute to Socrates long dissertations on the soul and other abstruse doctrines, when that singularly acute reasoner discoursed with his followers on topics only of plain utility. For it is requisite that important things should be attributed to important men ; and a sentiment would derive but small importance from the authority of Crito or Phædo. A much greater fault is attributable to Xenophon himself, who has not even preserved the coarse features of nations and of ages in his *Cyropædia*. A small circle of wise men should mark the rise of mind, as the Egyptian priests marked the rise of their river, and should leave it chronicled in their temples. Cyrus should not discourse like Solon.

CALLISTHENES. You must likewise then blame Herodotus.

ARISTOTELES. If I blame Herodotus, whom can I commend ? He reminds me of Homer by his facility and his variety, and by the suavity and fulness of his language. His view of history was, nevertheless, like that of the Asiatics, who write to instruct and please. Now truly there is little that could instruct, and less that could please us, in the actions and speeches of barbarians, from among whom the kings alone come forth distinctly. Delightful tales and apposite speeches are the best things you could devise ; and many of these undoubtedly were current in the East, and were collected by Herodotus ; some, it is probable, were invented by him. It is of no importance to the world whether the greater part of historical facts, in such countries, be true or false ; but they may be rendered of the highest, by the manner in which a writer of genius shall represent them. If history were altogether true, it would be not only undignified but unsightly : great orators would often be merely the mouth-pieces of prostitutes, and great captains would be hardly more than gladiators or buffoons. The prime movers of those actions which appall and shake the world, are generally the vilest things in it ; and the historian, if he discovers them, must conceal them or hold them back.

CALLISTHENES. Pray tell me whether, since I left Athens, your literary men are busy.

ARISTOTELES. More than ever ; as the tettix chirps loudest in time of drought. Among them we have some excellent writers, and such as (under Pallas) will keep out the Persian tongue from the Piræus. Others are employed in lucrative offices, are made ambassadors and salt-surveyors, and whatever else is most desirable to common minds, for proving the necessity of more effectual (this is always the preamble) and less changeful laws, such as those of the Medes and Indians. Several of our orators, whose grandfathers were in a condition little better than servile, have had our fortunes and lives at their disposal, and are now declaiming on the advantages of what they call " regular government." You would suppose they meant that perfect order which exists when citizens rule themselves, and when every family is to the republic what every individual is to the family ; a system of mutual zeal and mutual forbearance. No such thing : they mean a government with themselves at the head, and such as may ensure to them impunity for their treasons and peculations. One of them a short time ago was deputed to consult with Metanyctius, a leading man among the Thracians, in what manner and by what instalments a sum of money, lent to them by our republic, should be repaid. Metanyctius burst into laughter on reading the first words of the decree. " Dine with me," said he, " and we will conclude the business when we are alone." The dinner was magnificent ; which in such business is the best economy : few contractors or financiers are generous enough to give a plain one. " Your republic," said Metanyctius, " is no longer able to enforce its claim ; and we are as little likely to want your assistance in future, as you would be inclined to afford it. A seventh of the amount is at my disposal : you shall possess it. I shall enjoy about the same emolument for my fidelity to my worthy masters. The return of peace is so desirable, and regular government so divine a blessing, added to which, your countrymen are become of late so indifferent to inquiry into what the factious call abuses, that, I pledge my experience, you will return amid their acclamations and embraces."

Our negotiator became one of the wealthiest men in the city, although wealth is now accumulated in some families to such an amount, as our ancestors, even in the age of Crœsus or of Midas, would have deemed incredible. For wars drive up riches in heaps, as winds drive up snows, making and concealing many abysses. Metanyctius was the more provident and the more prosperous of the two. I know not in what king's interest he was, but probably the Persian's ; be this as it may, it was resolved for the sake of good *understanding* (another new expression) to abolish the name of republic throughout the world. This appeared an easy matter. Our negotiator rejoiced in the promise exacted from him, to employ his address in bringing about a thing so desirable : for *republic* sounded in his ears like *retribution*. It was then demanded that laws should be abolished, and that kings should govern at their sole discretion. This was better, but more difficult to accomplish. He promised it however ; and a large body of barbarian troops was raised in readiness to invade our territory, when the decree of Alexander reached the city, ordering that the states both of Greece and Asia should retain their pristine laws. The conqueror had found letters and accounts which his loquacity would not allow him to keep secret ; and the negotiator, whose opinion (a very common one) was, that exposure alone is ignominy, at last severed his weason with an ivory-handled knife.[1]

CALLISTHENES. On this ivory the Goddess of our city will look down with more complacency than on that whereof her own image is composed ; and the blade should be preserved with those which, on the holiest of our festivals, are displayed to us in the handful of myrtle, as they were carried by Harmodius and Aristogiton. And now tell me, Aristoteles, for the question much interests me, are you happy in the midst of Macedonians, Illyrians, and other strange creatures, at which we wonder when we see their bodies and habiliments like ours ?

ARISTOTELES. Dark reflections do occasionally come, as it were by stealth, upon my mind ; but philosophy has power to dispell them. I care not whether the dog that defends my house and family be of the Laconian breed or the Molossan : if he steals my bread or bites the hand that offers it, I strangle him or cut his throat, or engage a more dexterous man to do it, the moment I catch him sleeping.

CALLISTHENES. The times are unfavourable to knowledge.

ARISTOTELES. Knowledge and wisdom are different. We may know many things without an increase of wisdom ; but it would be a contradiction to say that we can know anything new without an increase of knowledge. The knowledge that is to be acquired by communication, is intercepted or impeded by tyranny. I have lost an ibis, or perhaps a hippopotamus, by losing the favour of Alexander ; he has lost an Aristoteles. He may deprive me of life ; but in doing it, he must deprive himself of all he has ever been

[1] Metanyctius is Metternich ; the ambassador, Castlereagh. In 1st ed. the passage from " severed " to " Aristogiton " is represented only by asterisks.

contending for, of glory ; and even a more reasonable man than he, will acknowledge that there is as much difference between life and glory, as there is between an ash-flake from the brow of Etna, and the untameable and eternal fire within its centre. I may lose disciples : he may put me out of fashion : a tailor's lad can do as much. He may forbid the reading of my works ; less than a tailor's lad can do that. Idleness can do it, night can do it, sleep can do it, a sunbeam rather too hot, a few hailstones, a few drops of rain, a call to dinner. By his wealth and power he might have afforded me opportunities of improving some branches of science, which I alone have cultivated with assiduity and success. Fools may make wise men wiser more easily than wise men can make them so. At all events, Callisthenes, I have prepared for myself a monument, from which perhaps some atoms may be detached by time, but which will retain the testimonials of its magnificence and the traces of its symmetry, when the substance and site of Alexander's shall be forgotten. Who knows but that the very ant-hill whereon I stand, may preserve its figure and contexture, when the sepulchre of this Macedonian shall be the solitary shed of a robber, or the manger of mules and camels ! * If I live I will leave behind me the history of our times, from the accession of Philip to the decease of Alexander. For our comet must disappear soon ; the moral order of the world requires it. How happy and glorious was Greece at the commencement of the period ! how pestilential was the folly of those rulers, who rendered, by a series of idle irritations and untimely attacks, a patient for Anticyra the arbiter of the universe !

I will now return with you to Plato, whose plan of government, by the indulgence of the Gods, has lain hitherto on their knees.†

CALLISTHENES. I was unwilling to interrupt you ; otherwise I should have remarked the bad consequences of excluding the poets from his commonwealth ; not because they are in general the most useful members of it, but because we should punish a song more severely than a larceny. There are verses in Euripides such as every man utters who has the tooth-ache : and all expressions of

---

* Chrysostom, in his 25th homily, says, that neither the tomb of Alexander nor the day of his death was known. Ποῦ, εἰπέ μοι, τὸ σῆμα ᾿Αλεξάνδρου ; δεῖξόν μοι, καὶ εἰπὲ τὴν ἡμέραν καθ᾿ ἣν ἐτελεύτησε.—W. S. L.

† The Homeric expression for " remaining to be decreed by them." Θεῶν ἐπὶ γούνασι κεῖται.—W. S. L.

ardent love have the modulation and emphasis of poetry. What a spheristerion is opened here to the exercise of informers ! We should create more of these than we should drive out of poets. Judges would often be puzzled in deciding a criminal suit ; for, before they could lay down the nature of the crime, they must ascertain what are the qualities and quantities of a dithyrambic. Now, Aristoteles, I suspect that even you can not do this : for I observe in Pindar a vast variety of commutable feet, sonorous, it is true, in their cadences, but irregular and unrestricted. You avoid, as all good writers do carefully, whatever is dactylic ; for the dactyl is the bindweed of prose ; but I know not what other author has trimmed it with such frugal and attentive husbandry.*

* Callisthenes means the instance where another dactyl, or a spondee, follows it ; in which case only is the period to be called dactylic. Cicero on one occasion took it in preference to a weak elision, or to the concurrence of two *esses*.

> "Quinctus Mutius augur
> Scævola multa ; ac . . ."

He judged rightly ; but he could easily have done better. Longinus says that dactyls are the noblest of feet and the most adapted to the sublime. He adduces no proof, although he quotes a sentence of Demosthenes as *resembling* the dactylic.

> Τουτο το ψηφισμα τον τοτε τῇ πολει περισταντα
> κινδυνον παρελθειν εποιησεν ὡσπερ νεφος.

Here is plenty of alliteration, but only *one* dactyl, for τουτο το is not one, being followed by ψ. The letter τ recurs nine times in fifteen syllables. A dactyl succeeded by a dichoree, or by a trochee with a spondee at the close, is among the sweetest of pauses ; the gravest and most majestic is composed of a dactyl, a dichoree, and a dispondee. He however will soon grow tiresome who permits his partiality to any one close to be obtrusive or apparent.

The remark attributed to Callisthenes, on the freedom of Aristoteles from pieces of verse in his sentences, is applicable to Plato, and surprisingly, if we consider how florid and decorated is his language. Among the Romans T. Livius is the most abundant in them ; and among the Greeks there is a curious instance in the prefatory words of Dionysius of Halicarnassus. Φύσεως δὴ νόμος ἅπασι κοινὸς, ὃν οὐδεὶς καταλύσει χρόνος, ἄρχειν ἀεὶ τῶν ἡττόνων τοὺς κρείττονας.

These words appear to have been taken from some tragedy : the last constitute a perfect iambic ; and the preceding, with scarcely a touch, assume the same appearance : the diction too is quite poetical : ἅπασι κοινὸς . . . καταλύσει, &c.

> Ἅπασι κοινός ἐστι πῆς φύσεως νόμος,
> Ὃν . . . οὐδεὶς . . . καταλύσει χρόνος,
> Ἄρχειν ἀεὶ τῶν ἡττόνων τοὺς κρείττονας.

In the Gorgias of Plato is the same idea in nearly the same words. Δηλοῖ δὲ ταῦτα πολλαχοῦ ὅτι οὕτως ἔχει, καὶ ἐν τοῖς ἄλλοις ζωοῖς, καὶ τῶν ἀνθρώπων ἐν ὅλαις ταῖς πόλεσι καὶ γένεσιν, ὅτι οὕτω τὸ δίκαιον κέκριται, τὸν κρείττω τοῦ ἥττονος ἄρχειν καὶ πλέον ἔχειν.—W. S. L.

One [1] alone, in writing or conversation, would subject a man to violent suspicion of bad citizenship ; and he who should employ it twice in a page or an oration, would be deemed so dangerous and desperate a malefactor, that it might be requisite to dig a pitfall or to lay an iron trap for him, or to noose him in his bed.

ARISTOTELES.[2] Demosthenes has committed it in his first *Philippic*, where two dactyls and a spondee come after a tumultuous concourse of syllables, many sounding alike. Οὐδε γαρ οὑτος παρα την αυτου ρωμην τοσουτον επηυξηται ὁσον παρα την ἡμετεραν αμελειαν. Here are seven dactyls : the same number is nowhere else to be found within the same number of words.

CALLISTHENES. Throughout your works there is certainly no period that has not an iambic in it : now our grammarians tell us that one is enough to make a verse, as one theft is enough to make a thief : an informer then has only to place it last in his bill of indictment, and not Minos himself could absolve you.

ARISTOTELES. They will not easily take me for a poet.

CALLISTHENES. Nor Plato for anything else : he would be like a bee caught in his own honey.

ARISTOTELES. I must remark to you, Callisthenes, that among the writers of luxuriant and florid prose, however rich and fanciful, there never was one who wrote good poetry. Imagination seems to start back when they would lead her into a narrower walk, and to forsake them at the first prelude of the lyre. Plato has written much poetry, of which a few epigrams alone are remembered. He burned his iambics, but not until he found that they were thoroughly dry and withered. If ever a good poet should excell in prose, we, who know how distinct are the qualities, and how great must be the comprehension and the vigour that unites them, shall contemplate him as an object of wonder, and almost of worship. It is remarkable in Plato that he is the only florid writer who is animated. He will always be admired by those who have attained much learning and little precision, from the persuasion that they understand him, and that others do not ; for men universally are ungrateful toward him who instructs them, unless in the hours or in the intervals of instruction he present a sweet cake to their self-love.

CALLISTHENES. I never saw two men so different as you and he.

---

[1] From " One alone " to " bed " added in 2nd ed.
[2] From " ARISTOTELES " to " words " added in 3rd ed.

ARISTOTELES AND CALLISTHENES

ARISTOTELES. Yet many of those sentiments in which we appear most at variance, can be drawn together until they meet. I had represented excessive wealth as the contingency most dangerous to a republic ; he took the opposite side, and asserted that excessive poverty is more.* Now wherever there is excessive wealth, there is also in the train of it excessive poverty ; as where the sun is brightest the shade is deepest. Many republics have stood for ages, while no citizen of them was in very great affluence, and while on the contrary most were very poor : but none hath stood long after many, or indeed a few, have grown inordinately wealthy. Riches cause poverty, then irritate, then corrupt it ; so throughout their whole progress and action they are dangerous to the state. Plato defends his thesis with his usual ingenuity ; for if there is nowhere a worse philosopher, there is hardly anywhere a better writer. He says, and truly, that the poor become wild and terrible animals, when they no longer can gain their bread by their trades and occupations : and that, laden to excess with taxes, they learn a lesson from Necessity, which they never would have taken up without her. Upon this all philosophers, all men of common sense indeed, think alike. Usually, if not always, the poor are quiet while there is among them no apprehension of becoming poorer, that is, while the government is not oppressive and unjust : but the rich are often the most satisfied while the government is the most unjust and oppressive. In civil dissensions, we find the wealthy lead forth the idle and dissolute poor against the honest and industrious ; and generally with success : because the numbers are greater in calamitous times ; because this party has ready at hand the means of equipment ; because the young and active, never prone to reflection, are influenced more by the hope of a speedy fortune than by the calculation of a slower ; and because there are few so firm and independent as not to rest willingly on patronage, or [1] so blind and indifferent as not to prefer that of the most potent.

In writing on government, we ought not only to search for what is best, but for what is practicable. Plato has done neither, nor

---

* It is evident that Aristoteles wrote his *Polity* after Plato, for he animadverts on a false opinion of Plato's in the proœmium : but many of the opinions must have been promulgated by both, before the publication of their works.—W.S.L.

[1] From " or " to " indifferent " added in 3rd ed.

indeed has he searched at all ; instead of it he has thought it sufficient to stud a plain argument with an endless variety of bright and prominent topics. Now diversity of topics has not even the merit of invention in every case : he is the most inventive who finds most to say upon one subject, and renders the whole of it applicable and useful. Splendid things are the most easy to find and the most difficult to manage. If I order a bridle for my horse, and he of whom I order it brings me rich trappings in place of it, do I not justly deem it an importunate and silly answer to my remonstrances, when he tells me that the trappings are more costly than the bridle ?

Be assured, my Callisthenes, I speak not from any disrespect to a writer so highly and so justly celebrated. Reflecting with admiration upon his manifold and extraordinary endowments, I wish the more earnestly he always had been exempt from contemptuousness and malignity. We have conversed heretofore on his conduct toward Xenophon, and indeed toward other disciples of Socrates, whom [1] the same age and the same studies, and whom the counsels and memory of the same master, should have endeared to him. Toward me indeed he is less blameable. I had collected the documents on which I formed an exact account of the most flourishing states, and of the manners, laws, and customs, by which they were so, being of opinion that no knowledge is of such utility to a commonwealth. I had also, as you remember, drawn up certain rules for poetry, taking my examples from Homer principally, and from our great dramatists. Plato immediately forms a republic in the clouds, to overshadow all mine at once, and descends only to kick the poets through the streets. Homer, the chief object of my contemplation, is the chief object of his attack. I acknowledge that poets of the lower and middle order are in general bad members of society : but the energies which exalt one to the higher, enable him not only to adorn but to protect his country. Plato says, the Gods are degraded by Homer : yet Homer has omitted those light and ludicrous tales of them, which rather suit the manners of Plato than his. He thought about the Gods, I suspect, just as you and I do, and cared as little how Homer treated them : yet, with the prison of Socrates before his eyes, and his own *Dialogues* under them, he had the cruelty to cast forth this effusion against the mild Euripides. His souls and their occupancy of bodies are not to be spoken of with

[1] From " whom " to " blameable " added in 3rd ed.

196

gravity, and, as I am inclined for the present to keep mine where it is, I will be silent on the subject.

CALLISTHENES. I must warn you, my friend and teacher, that your Macedonian pupil is likely to interrupt your arrangements in that business. I am informed, and by those who are always credible in such assertions, that, without apologies, excuses, and protestations, Aristoteles will follow the shades of Clitus and Parmenio. There is nothing of which Alexander is not jealous; no, not even eating and drinking. If any great work is to be destroyed, he must do it with his own hands. After he had burned down the palace of Cyrus, the glory of which he envied a strumpet, one Polemarchus thought of winning his favour by demolishing the tomb : he wept for spite and hanged him. Latterly he has been so vain, mendacious, and irrational, as to order not only suits of armour of enormous size, but even mangers commensurate, to be buried in certain parts where his battles were fought, that when in after-ages they happen to be dug up, it may appear that his men and horses were prodigious. If he had sent the report before him he would have been somewhat less inconsiderate, for it might among weak barbarians have caused terror and submission. But by doing as he did, he would leave a very different impression from what he designed, if indeed men regarded it at all ; for no glory could arise from conquering with such advantages of superior force. They who are jealous of power, are so from a consciousness of strength : they who are jealous of wisdom, are so from a consciousness of wanting it. Weakness has its fever—— But you appear grave and thoughtful.

ARISTOTELES. The barbarians no more interest me than a shoal of fishes would do.

CALLISTHENES. I entertain the same opinion.

ARISTOTELES. Of their rulers equally ?

CALLISTHENES. Yes, certainly ; for among them there can be no other distinction than in titles and in dress. A Persian and a Macedonian, an Alexander and a Darius, if they oppress the liberties of Greece, are one.

ARISTOTELES. Now, Callisthenes ! if Socrates and Anytos were in the same chamber, if the wicked had mixed poison for the virtuous, the active in evil for the active in good, and some divinity had placed it in your power to present the cup to either, and, touching your head, should say, " This head also is devoted to the Eumenides if the choice be wrong," what would you resolve ?

CALLISTHENES. To do that by command of the God which I would likewise have done without it.

ARISTOTELES. Bearing in mind that a myriad of conquerors is not worth the myriadth part of a wise and virtuous man, return, Callisthenes, to Babylon, and see that your duty be performed.

XIV. EPICURUS,* LEONTION, AND TERNISSA

306 B.C.

(*Imag. Convers.*, v., 1829 ; *Wks.*, i., 1846 ; *Imag. Convers.*
Gk. and Rom., 1853 ; *Wks.*, ii., 1876.)

LEONTION. Your situation for a garden,[1] Epicurus, is, I think, very badly chosen.

EPICURUS. Why do you think so, my Leontion ?

LEONTION. First, because it is more than twenty stadia † from the city.

EPICURUS. Certainly the distance is inconvenient, my charming friend ! it is rather too far off for us [2] to be seen, and rather too near for us [2] to be regretted. Here however I shall build no villa, nor anything else, and the longest time we can be detained, is from the rising to the setting sun. Now, pray, your other reason why the spot is so ineligible.

LEONTION. Because it commands no view of the town or of the

---

* Cicero was an opponent of Epicurus, yet in his treatise *On Friendship* he says, " De quâ Epicurus quidem ita dicit ; omnium rerum quas ad *beate vivendum* sapientia comparaverit, nihil esse majus amicitiâ ; nihil uberius, nihil **jucundius**." This is oratorical and sententious : he goes on, praising the founder and the foundation. " Neque verò hoc oratione solùm sed *multo magis vitâ et moribus* comprobavit. Quod quàm magnum sit, fictæ veterum fabulæ declarant, in quibus tam multis tamque variis ab ultimâ antiquitate repetitis, tria vix amicorum paria reperiuntur, ut ad Orestem pervenias profectus a Theseo. At verò Epicurus unâ in domo, et eâ quidem angustâ, quàm magnos quantâque amoris conspiratione consentientes tenuit amicorum greges. *Quod fit etiam nunc ab Epicureis.*" Certain it is, that moderation, forbearance, and what St. Paul calls *charity*, never flourished in any sect of philosophy or religion, so perfectly and so long as among the disciples of Epicurus.

Cicero adds in another work, " De sanctitate, de pietate adversus Deos libros scripsit Epicurus : at quomodo in his loquitur ? ut Coruncanium aut Scævolam Pontifices Maximos te audire dicas."

Seneca, whose sect was more adverse, thus expresses his opinion : " Mea quidem ista sententia (et hoc nostris invitis popularibus dicam) sancta Epicurum et recta præcipere, et, si propius accesseris, tristia."—W. S. L.

[1] 1st ed. reads : " my dear Epicurus."   † Two miles and a half.—W. S. L.
[2] 1st ed. reads : " one to be seen . . . one to be regretted."

harbour, unless we mount upon that knoll, where we could scarcely stand together, for the greater part is occupied by those three pinasters, old and horrible as the three Furies. Surely you will cut them down.

EPICURUS. Whatever Leontion commands. To me there is this advantage in a place at some distance from the city. Having by no means the full possession of my faculties, where I hear unwelcome and intrusive voices, or unexpected and irregular sounds that excite me involuntarily to listen, I assemble and arrange my thoughts with freedom and with pleasure in the fresh air,[1] under the open sky : and they are more lively and vigorous and exuberant when I catch them as I walk about, and commune with them in silence and seclusion.

LEONTION. It always has appeared to me that conversation brings them forth more readily and plenteously : and that the ideas of one person no sooner come out than another's follow them, whether from the same side or from the opposite.

EPICURUS. They do : but these are not the thoughts we keep for seed : they come up weak by coming up close together. In the country the mind is soothed and satisfied : here is no restraint of motion or of posture. These things, little and indifferent as they may seem, are not so : for the best tempers have need of ease and liberty, to keep them in right order long enough for the purposes of composition : and many a froward axiom, many an inhumane thought, hath arisen from sitting inconveniently, from hearing a few unpleasant sounds, from the confinement of a gloomy chamber, or from the want of symmetry in [2] it. We are not aware of this, until we find an exemption from it in groves, on promontories, or along the sea-shore, or wherever else we meet Nature face to face, undisturbed and solitary.

TERNISSA.[3] You would wish us then away ?

EPICURUS. I speak of solitude : you of desolation.

TERNISSA. O flatterer ! is this philosophy ?

EPICURUS. Yes ; if you are a thought the richer or a moment the happier for it.

TERNISSA. Write it down then in the next volume you intend to publish.

---

[1] 1st ed. reads : " and the open sky."   [2] 1st ed. reads : " a part of it."
[3] From " TERNISSA " to " nearly " added in 2nd ed.

EPICURUS, LEONTION, AND TERNISSA

LEONTION. I interpose and controvert it. That is not philosophy which serves only for one.

EPICURUS. Just criterion! I will write down your sentence instead, and leave mine at the discretion of Ternissa. And now, my beautiful Ternissa, let me hear *your* opinion of the situation I have chosen. I perceive that you too have fixed your eyes on the pinasters.

TERNISSA. I will tell you in verses; for I do think these are verses, or nearly:

> I hate those trees that never lose their foliage:
> They seem to have no sympathy with Nature:
> Winter and Summer are alike to them.

The broad and billowy summits of yon monstrous trees, one would imagine, were made for the storms to rest upon when they are tired of raving. And what bark! It occurs to me, Epicurus, that I have rarely seen climbing plants attach themselves to these trees, as they do to the oak, the maple, the beech, and others.

LEONTION. If your remark be true, perhaps the resinous are not embraced by them so frequently because they dislike the odour of the resin, or some other property of the juices; for they too have their affections and antipathies, no less than countries and their climes.

TERNISSA. For shame! what would you with me?

EPICURUS. I would not interrupt you while you were speaking, nor while Leontion was replying; this is against my rules and practice; having now ended, kiss me, Ternissa!

TERNISSA. Impudent man! in the name of Pallas, why should I kiss you?

EPICURUS. Because you expressed hatred.

TERNISSA. Do we kiss when we hate?

EPICURUS. There is no better end of hating. The sentiment should not exist one moment; and if the hater gives a kiss on being ordered to do it, even to a tree or a stone, that tree or stone becomes the monument of a fault extinct.

TERNISSA. I promise you I never will hate a tree again.

EPICURUS. I told you so.

LEONTION. Nevertheless I suspect, my Ternissa, you will often be surprised into it.   I was very near saying, " I hate these rude square stones ! "   Why did you leave them here, Epicurus ?

EPICURUS. It is true, they are the greater part square, and seem to have been cut out in ancient times for plinths and columns : they are also rude.   Removing the smaller, that I might plant violets and cyclamens [1] and convolvuluses and strawberries, and such other herbs as grow willingly in dry places, I left a few of these for seats, a few for tables and for couches.

LEONTION. Delectable couches !

EPICURUS. Laugh as you may, they will become so when they are covered with moss and ivy, and those other two sweet plants, whose names I do not remember to have found in any ancient treatise, but which I fancy I have heard Theophrastus call " Leontion " and " Ternissa."

TERNISSA. The bold insidious false creature !

EPICURUS. What is that volume ? may I venture to ask, Leontion? Why do you blush ?

LEONTION. I do not blush about it.

EPICURUS. You are offended then, my dear girl.

LEONTION. No, not offended.   I will tell you presently what it contains.   Account to me first for your choice of so strange a place to walk in : a broad ridge, the summit and one side barren, the other a wood of rose-laurels impossible to penetrate.   The worst of all is, we can see nothing of the city or the Parthenon, unless from the very top.

EPICURUS. The place commands, in my opinion, a most perfect view.

LEONTION. Of what, pray ?

EPICURUS. Of itself ; seeming to indicate that we, Leontion, who philosophise, should do the same.

LEONTION. Go on, go on !   say what you please : I will not hate anything yet.   Why have you torn up by the root all these little mountain-ash trees ? [2]   This is the season of their beauty : come, Ternissa, let us make ourselves necklaces and armlets, such as may captivate old Sylvanus and Pan : you shall have your choice.   But why have you torn them up ?

EPICURUS. On the contrary, they were brought hither this morn-

---

[1] Not in 1st ed. : " cyclamens . . . convolvuluses."
[2] Not in 1st ed. : " little . . . trees."

ing. Sosimenes is spending large sums of money on an olive-ground, and has uprooted some hundreds of them, of all ages and sizes. I shall cover the rougher part of the hill with them, setting the clematis and vine and honey-suckle against them, to unite them.

TERNISSA. O what a pleasant thing it is to walk in the green light of the vine-leaves, and to breathe the sweet odour of their invisible flowers !

EPICURUS. The scent of them is so delicate that it requires a sigh to inhale it ; and this, being accompanied and followed by enjoyment, renders the fragrance so exquisite. Ternissa, it is this, my sweet friend, that made you remember the green light of the foliage, and think of the invisible flowers as you would of some blessing from heaven.

TERNISSA. I see feathers flying at certain distances just above the middle of the promontory : what can they mean ?

EPICURUS. Can not you imagine them to be feathers from the wings of Zethes and Caläis, who came hither out of Thrace to behold the favourite haunts of their mother Oreithyia ? From the precipice that hangs over the sea a few paces from the pinasters, she is reported to have been carried off by Boreas ; and these remains of the primeval forest have always been held sacred on that belief.

LEONTION. The story is an idle one.

TERNISSA. O no, Leontion ! the story is very true.

LEONTION. Indeed ?

TERNISSA. I have heard not only odes, but sacred and most ancient hymns upon it ; and the voice of Boreas is often audible here, and the screams of Oreithyia.

LEONTION. The feathers then really may belong to Caläis and Zethes.

TERNISSA. I don't believe it : the winds would have carried them away.

LEONTION. The Gods, to manifest their power, as they often do by miracles, could as easily fix a feather eternally on the most tempestuous promontory, as the mark of their feet upon the flint.

TERNISSA. They could indeed : but we know the one to a certainty, and have no such authority for the other. I have seen these pinasters from the extremity of the Piræus, and have heard mention of the altar raised to Boreas : where is it ?

EPICURUS. As it stands in the centre of the platform, we can not see it from hence : there is the only piece of level ground in the place.

LEONTION. Ternissa intends the altar to prove the truth of the story.

EPICURUS. Ternissa is slow to admit that even the young can deceive, much less the old : the gay, much less the serious.

LEONTION. It is as wise to moderate our belief as our desires.

EPICURUS. Some minds require much belief, some thrive on little. Rather an exuberance of it is feminine and beautiful. It acts differently on different hearts : it troubles some, it consoles others : in the generous it is the nurse of tenderness and kindness, of heroism and self-devotion : in the ungenerous it fosters pride, impatience of contradiction and appeal, and, like some waters, what it finds a dry stick or hollow straw, it leaves a stone.

TERNISSA. We want it chiefly to make the way of death an easy one.

EPICURUS. There is no easy path leading out of life, and few are the easy ones that lie within it. I would adorn and smoothen the declivity, and make my residence as commodious as its situation and dimensions may allow : but principally I would cast underfoot the empty fear of death.

TERNISSA. O ! how can you ?

EPICURUS. By many arguments already laid down : then by thinking that some perhaps, in almost every age, have been timid and delicate as Ternissa ; and yet have slept soundly, have felt no parent's or friend's tear upon their faces, no throb against their breasts : in short, have been in the calmest of all possible conditions, while those around were in the most deplorable and desperate.

TERNISSA. It would pain me to die, if it were only at the idea that anyone I love would grieve too much for me.

EPICURUS. Let the loss of our friends be our only grief, and the apprehension of displeasing them our only fear.

LEONTION. No apostrophes ! no interjections ! Your argument was unsound ; your means futile.

EPICURUS. Tell me then, whether the horse of a rider on the road should not be spurred forward if he started at a shadow.

LEONTION. Yes.

EPICURUS. I thought so : it would however be better to guide

EPICURUS, LEONTION, AND TERNISSA

him quietly up to it, and to show him that it was one. Death is less than a shadow : it represents nothing, even imperfectly.

LEONTION. Then at the best what is it ? why care about it, think about it, or remind us that it must befall us ? Would you take the same trouble, when you see my hair entwined with ivy, to make me remember that, although the leaves are green and pliable, the stem is fragile and rough, and that before I go to bed I shall have many knots and intanglements to extricate ? Let me have them ; but let me not hear of them until the time is come.

EPICURUS. I would never think of death as an embarrassment, but as a blessing.

TERNISSA. How ! a blessing ?

EPICURUS. What, if it makes our enemies cease to hate us ? what, if it makes our friends love us the more ?

LEONTION. Us ? According to your doctrine, we shall not exist at all.

EPICURUS. I spoke of that which is consolatory while we are here, and of that which in plain reason ought to render us contented to stay no longer. You, Leontion, would make others better : and better they certainly will be, when their hostilities languish in an empty field, and their rancour is tired with treading upon dust. The generous affections stir about us at the dreary hour of death, as the blossoms of the Median apple swell and diffuse their fragrance in the cold.

TERNISSA. I can not bear to think of passing the Styx, lest Charon should touch me : he is so old and wilful, so cross and ugly.

EPICURUS. Ternissa ! Ternissa ! I would accompany you thither, and stand between. Would not you too, Leontion ?

LEONTION. I don't know.

TERNISSA. O ! that we could go together !

LEONTION. Indeed !

TERNISSA. All three, I mean—I said—or was going to say it. How ill-natured you are, Leontion ! to misinterpret me ; I could almost cry.

LEONTION. Do not, do not, Ternissa ! Should that tear drop from your eyelash you would look less beautiful.

EPICURUS. Whenever [1] I see a tear on a beautiful young face,

[1] From " Whenever " to " EPICURUS " added in 2nd ed.

twenty of mine run to meet it. If it is well to conquer a world, it is better to conquer two.

TERNISSA. That is what Alexander of Macedon wept because he could not accomplish.

EPICURUS. Ternissa! we three can accomplish it; or any one of us.

TERNISSA. How? pray!

EPICURUS. We can conquer this world and the next: for you will have another, and nothing should be refused you.

TERNISSA. The next by piety : but this, in what manner?

EPICURUS. By indifference to all who are indifferent to us; by taking joyfully the benefit that comes spontaneously; by wishing no more intensely for what is a hair's breadth beyond our reach than for a draught of water from the Ganges; and by fearing nothing in another life.

TERNISSA. This, O Epicurus! is the grand impossibility.

EPICURUS. Do you believe the Gods to be as benevolent and good as you are? or do you not?

TERNISSA. Much kinder, much better in every way.

EPICURUS. Would you kill or hurt the sparrow that you keep in your little dressing-room with a string around the leg, because he hath flown where you did not wish him to fly?

TERNISSA. No : it would be cruel : the string about the leg of so little and weak a creature is enough.

EPICURUS. You think so; I think so; God thinks so. This I may say confidently : for whenever there is a sentiment in which strict justice and pure benevolence unite, it must be his.

TERNISSA. O Epicurus! when you speak thus——

LEONTION. Well, Ternissa! what then?

TERNISSA. When Epicurus teaches us such sentiments as this, I am grieved that he has not so great an authority with the Athenians as some others have.

LEONTION. You will grieve more, I suspect, my Ternissa, when he possesses that authority.

TERNISSA. What will he do?

LEONTION. Why turn pale? I am not about to answer that he will forget or leave you. No; but the voice comes deepest from the sepulchre, and a great name hath its root in the dead body. If you invited a company to a feast, you might as well place round the table live sheep and oxen, and vases of fish and cages of quails, as you would invite a company of friendly hearers to the philosopher who is yet living.* One would imagine that the iris of our intellectual eye were lessened by the glory of his presence, and that, like eastern kings, he could be looked at near only when his limbs are stiff, by waxlight, in closed curtains.

EPICURUS. One of whom we know little leaves us a ring or other token of remembrance, and we express a sense of pleasure and of gratitude ; one of whom we know nothing writes a book, the contents of which might (if we would let them) have done us more good and might have given us more pleasure, and we revile him for it. The book may do what the legacy can not ; it may be pleasurable and serviceable to others as well as ourselves : we would hinder this too. In fact, all other love is extinguished by self-love : beneficence, humanity, justice, philosophy, sink under it. While we insist that we are looking for Truth, we [1] commit a falsehood. It never was the first object with anyone, and with few the second.

Feed unto replenishment your quieter fancies, my sweetest little Ternissa ! and let the Gods, both youthful and aged, both gentle and boisterous, administer to them hourly on these sunny downs : what can they do better ?

LEONTION. But those feathers, Ternissa, what God's may they be ? since you will not pick them up, nor restore them to Caläis nor to Zethes.

TERNISSA. I do not think they belong to any God whatever ; and shall never be persuaded of it unless Epicurus says it is so.

LEONTION. O unbelieving creature ! do you reason against the immortals.

TERNISSA. It was yourself who doubted, or appeared to doubt, the flight of Oreithyia. By admitting too much we endanger our religion. Beside, I think I discern some upright stakes at equal distances, and am pretty sure the feathers are tied to them by long strings.

EPICURUS. You have guessed the truth.

TERNISSA. Of what use are they there ?

* Seneca quotes a letter of Epicurus, in which his friendship with Metrodorus is mentioned, with a remark that the obscurity in which they had lived, so great indeed as to let them rest almost unheard of, in the midst of Greece, was by no means to be considered as an abatement of their good fortune.—W. S. L.

[1] 1st ed. reads : " we lie most deeply. It," etc.

EPICURUS. If you have ever seen the foot of a statue broken off just below the ankle, you have then, Leontion and Ternissa, seen the form of the ground about us. The lower extremities of it are divided into small ridges, as you will perceive if you look round ; and these are covered with corn, olives, and vines. At the upper part, where cultivation ceases, and where those sheep and goats are grazing, begins my purchase. The ground rises gradually unto near the summit, where it grows somewhat steep, and terminates in a precipice. Across the middle I have traced a line, denoted by those feathers, from one dingle to the other ; the two terminations of my intended garden. The distance is nearly a thousand paces, and the path, perfectly on a level, will be two paces broad, so that I may walk between you ; but another could not join us conveniently. From this there will be several circuitous and spiral, leading by the easiest ascent to the summit ; and several more, to the road along the cultivation underneath : here will however be but one entrance.[1] Among the projecting fragments and the massive stones yet standing of the boundary-wall, which old pomegranates imperfectly defend, and which my neighbour has guarded more effectively against invasion, there are hillocks of crumbling mould, covered in some places with a variety of moss ; in others are elevated tufts, or dim labyrinths, of eglantine.

TERNISSA. Where will you place the statues ? for undoubtedly you must have some.

EPICURUS. I will have some models for statues. Pygmalion prayed the Gods to give life to the image he adored : I will not pray them to give marble to mine. Never may I lay my wet cheek upon the foot under which is incribed the name of Leontion or Ternissa !

LEONTION. Do not make us melancholy [2] : never let us think that the time can come when we shall lose our friends. Glory, literature, philosophy, have this advantage over friendship : remove one object from them, and others fill the void ; remove one from friendship, one only, and not the earth, nor the universality of worlds, no, nor the intellect that soars above and comprehends them, can replace it.

EPICURUS. Dear Leontion ! always amiable, always graceful !

---

[1] 1st ed. reads : " entrance. Wild pomegranates and irregular tufts of gorse unite their forces against invasion. TERNISSA," etc.

[2] 1st ed. reads : " melancholic."

how lovely do you now appear to me ! what beauteous action accompanied your words !

LEONTION. I used none whatever.

EPICURUS. That white arm was then, as it is now, over the shoulder of Ternissa ; and her breath imparted a fresh bloom to your cheek, a new music to your voice. No friendship is so cordial or so delicious as that of girl for girl ; no hatred so intense and immovable as that of woman for woman. In youth you love one above the others of your sex : in riper age you hate all, more or less, in proportion to similarity of accomplishments and pursuits ; which sometimes (I wish it were oftener) are bonds of union to men. In us you more easily pardon faults than excellences in each other. *Your* tempers are such, my beloved scholars, that even this truth does not ruffle them ; and such is your affection, that I look with confidence to its unabated ardour at twenty.

LEONTION. O then I am to love Ternissa almost fifteen months !

TERNISSA. And I am destined to survive the loss of it three months above four years !

EPICURUS. Incomparable creatures ! may it be eternal ! In loving ye shall follow no example : ye shall step securely over the iron rule laid down for others by the destinies, and *you* for ever be Leontion, and *you* Ternissa.

LEONTION. Then indeed we should not want statues.

TERNISSA. But men, who are vainer creatures, would be good for nothing without them : they must be flattered, even by the stones.

EPICURUS. Very true. Neither the higher arts nor the civic virtues can flourish extensively without the statues of illustrious men. But gardens are not the places for them. Sparrows wooing on the general's truncheon (unless he be such a general as one of ours in the last war), and snails besliming the emblems of the poet, do not remind us worthily of their characters. Porticoes are their proper situations, and those the most frequented. Even there they may lose all honour and distinction, whether from the thoughtlessness of magistrates or from the malignity of rivals. Our own city, the least exposed of any to the effects of either, presents us a disheartening example. When the Thebans in their jealousy condemned Pindar to the payment of a fine, for having praised the Athenians too highly, our citizens erected a statue of bronze to him.

LEONTION. Jealousy of Athens made the Thebans fine him ; and jealousy of Thebes made the Athenians thus record it.

EPICURUS. And jealousy of Pindar, I suspect, made some poet persuade the arcons to render the distinction a vile and worthless one, by placing his effigy near a king's, one Evagoras of Cyprus.

TERNISSA. Evagoras, I think I remember to have read in the inscription, was rewarded in this manner for his reception of Conon, defeated by the Lacedemonians.

EPICURUS. Gratitude was due to him, and some such memorial to record it. External reverence should be paid unsparingly to the higher magistrates of every country who perform their offices [1] exemplarily : yet they are not on this account to be placed in the same degree with men of primary genius. They never exalt the human race, and rarely benefit it ; and their benefits are local and transitory, while those of a great writer are universal and eternal.

If the Gods did indeed bestow on us a portion of their fire, they seem to have lighted it in sport and left it : the harder task and the nobler is performed by that genius who raises it clear and glowing from its embers, and makes it applicable to the purposes that dignify or delight our nature. I have ever said, " Reverence the rulers." Let then his image stand ; but stand apart from Pindar's. Pallas and Jove ! defend me from being carried down the stream of time among a shoal of royalets, and the rootless weeds they are hatched on.

TERNISSA. So much pity would deserve the exemption, even though your writings did not hold out the decree.

LEONTION. Child, the compliment is ill turned : if you are ironical, as you must be on the piety of Epicurus, Atticism requires that you should continue to be so, at least to the end of the sentence.

TERNISSA. Irony is my abhorrence. Epicurus may appear less pious than some others ; but I am certain he is more ; otherwise the Gods would never have given him——

LEONTION. What ? what ? let us hear !

TERNISSA. Leontion !

LEONTION. Silly girl ! Were there any hibiscus or broom growing near at hand, I would send him away and whip you.

EPICURUS. There is fern, which is better.

LEONTION. I was not speaking to you : but now you shall have

---

[1] 1st ed. reads : " as becomes them."

something to answer for yourself. Although you admit no statues in the country, you might at least methinks have discovered a retirement with a fountain in it : here I see not even a spring.

EPICURUS. Fountain I can hardly say there is ; but on the left there is a long crevice or chasm, which we have never yet visited, and which we can not discern until we reach it. This is full of soft mould, very moist ; and many high reeds and canes are growing there ; and the rock itself too drips with humidity along it, and is covered with more tufted moss and more variegated lichens. This crevice, with its windings and sinuosities, is about four hundred paces long, and in many parts eleven, twelve, thirteen feet wide, but generally six or seven. I shall plant it wholly with lilies of the valley : leaving the irises which occupy the sides as well as the clefts, and also those other flowers of paler purple, from the autumnal cups of which we collect the saffron ; and forming a narrow path of such turf as I can find there, or rather following it as it creeps among the bays and hazels and sweet-briar, which have fallen at different times from the summit, and are now grown old, with an infinity of prim roses at the roots. There are nowhere twenty steps without a projection and a turn, nor in any ten together is the chasm of the same width or figure. Hence the ascent in its windings is easy and imperceptible quite to the termination, where the rocks are somewhat high and precipitous : at the entrance they lose themselves in privet and elder, and you must make your way between them through the canes. Do not you remember where I carried you both across the muddy hollow in the foot-path ?

TERNISSA. Leontion does.

EPICURUS. That place is always wet ; not only in this month of Puanepsion,* which we are beginning to-day, but in midsummer. The water that causes it, comes out a little way above it, but originates from the crevice, which I will cover at top with rose-laurel and mountain-ash, with clematis and vine ; and I will intercept the little rill in its wandering, draw it from its concealment, and place it like Bacchus under the protection of the nymphs, who will smile upon it in its marble cradle, which¹ at present I keep at home.

---

* The Attic month of Puanepsion had its commencement in the latter days of October : its name is derived from πύανα, the legumes which were offered in sacrifice to Apollo at that season.—W. S. L.

¹ From " which " to " home " added in 2nd ed.

TERNISSA. Leontion! why do you turn away your face? have the nymphs smiled upon you in it?

LEONTION. I bathed in it once, if you must know, Ternissa! Why now, Ternissa, why do you turn away yours? have the nymphs frowned upon you for invading their secrets?

TERNISSA. Epicurus, you are in the right to bring it away from Athens; from under the eye of Pallas: she might be angry.

EPICURUS. You approve of its removal then, my lovely friend?

TERNISSA. Mightily.

(*Aside.*) I wish it may break in pieces on the road.

EPICURUS. What did you say?

TERNISSA. I wish it were now on the road—that I might try whether it would hold me—I mean with my clothes on.

EPICURUS. It would hold you, and one a span longer. I have another in the house; but it is not decorated with fauns and satyrs and foliage, like this.

LEONTION. I remember putting my hand upon the frightful satyr's head, to leap in: it seems made for the purpose. But the sculptor needed not to place the naiad quite so near: he must have been a very impudent man: it is impossible to look for a moment at such a piece of workmanship.

TERNISSA. For shame! Leontion!—why, what was it? I do not desire to know.

EPICURUS. I don't remember it.

LEONTION. Nor I neither; only the head.

EPICURUS. I shall place the satyr toward the rock, that you may never see him, Ternissa.

TERNISSA. Very right; he can not turn round.

LEONTION. The poor naiad had done it, in vain.

TERNISSA. All these labourers will soon finish the plantation, if you superintend them, and are not appointed to some magistrature.

EPICURUS. Those who govern us are pleased at seeing a philosopher out of the city, and more still at finding, in a season of scarcity, forty poor citizens, who might become seditious, made happy and quiet by such employment.

Two evils, of almost equal weight, may befall the man of erudition: never to be listened to, and to be listened to always. Aware of these, I devote a large portion of my time and labours to the cultivation of such minds as flourish best in cities, where my garden at the gate, although smaller than this, we find sufficiently capacious. There I secure my listeners : here my thoughts and imaginations have their free natural current, and tarry or wander as the will invites : may it ever be among those dearest to me ! those whose hearts possess the rarest and divinest faculty, of retaining or forgetting at option what ought to be forgotten or retained.

LEONTION. The whole ground then will be covered with trees and shrubs ?

EPICURUS. There are some protuberances in various parts of the eminence, which you do not perceive till you are upon them or above them. They are almost level at the top, and overgrown with fine grass ; for they catch the better soil, brought down in small quantities by the rains. These are to be left unplanted ; so is the platform under the pinasters, whence there is a prospect of the city, the harbour, the isle of Salamis, and the territory of Megara. " What then," cried Sosimenes, " you would hide from your view my young olives, and the whole length of the new wall I have been building at my own expense between us ! and, when you might see at once the whole of Attica, you will hardly see more of it than I could buy."

LEONTION. I do not perceive the new wall, for which Sosimenes, no doubt, thinks himself another Pericles.

EPICURUS. Those old junipers quite conceal it.

TERNISSA. They look warm and sheltering : but I like the rose-laurels much better ; and what a thicket of them there is !

EPICURUS. Leaving all the larger, I shall remove many thousands of them ; enough to border the greater part of the walk, intermixed with roses.

TERNISSA.[1] Do, pray, leave that taller plant yonder, of which I see there are several springing in several places out of the rock : it appears to have produced on a single stem a long succession of yellow flowers ; some darkening and fading, others running up and leaving them behind, others showing their little faces imperfectly through their light green veils.

LEONTION. Childish girl ! she means the mullen ; and she talks about it as she would have talked about a doll, attributing to it feelings and aims and designs. I saw her stay behind to kiss it ; no doubt, for being so nearly of her own highth.

[1] From " TERNISSA " to " return " added in 2nd ed.

TERNISSA. No indeed, not for that ; but because I had broken off one of its blossoms unheedingly, perhaps the last it may bear, and because its leaves are so downy and pliant ; and because nearer the earth some droop and are decaying, and remind me of a parent who must die before the tenderest of her children can do without her.

EPICURUS. I will preserve the whole species ; but you must point out to me the particular one as we return. There is an infinity of other plants and flowers, or weeds as Sosimenes calls them, of which he has cleared his olive-yard, and which I shall adopt. Twenty of his slaves came in yesterday, laden with hyacinths and narcissuses, anemones and jonquils. " The curses of our vineyards," cried he, " and good neither for man nor beast. I have another estate infested with lilies of the valley : I should not wonder if you accepted these too."

" And with thanks," answered I.

The whole of his remark I could not collect : he turned aside, and (I believe) prayed. I only heard " Pallas "—" father " —" sound mind "—" inoffensive man "—" good neighbour." As we walked together I perceived him looking grave, and I could not resist my inclination to smile as I turned my eyes toward him. He observed it, at first with unconcern, but by degrees some doubts arose within him, and he said, " Epicurus, you have been throwing away no less than half a talent [1] on this sorry piece of mountain, and I fear you are about to waste as much in labour : for nothing was ever so terrible as the price we are obliged to pay the workman, since the conquest of Persia, and the increase of luxury in our city. Under three obols [2] none will do his day's work. But what, in the name of all the deities, could induce you to plant those roots, which other people dig up and throw away ? "

" I have been doing," said I, " the same thing my whole life through, Sosimenes ! "

" How ! " cried he : " I never knew that."

" Those very doctrines," added I, " which others hate and extirpate, I inculcate and cherish. They bring no riches, and therefore are thought to bring no advantage : to me they appear the more advantageous for that reason. They give us immediately what we solicit through the means of wealth. We toil for the wealth first ; and then it remains to be proved whether we can purchase

[1] Note, 1st ed. : " 108 pounds sterling."   [2] Note, 1st ed. : " about 4d."

with it what we look for. Now, to carry our money to the market, and not to find in the market our money's worth, is great vexation : yet much greater has already preceded, in running up and down for it among so many competitors, and through so many thieves."

After a while he rejoined, " You really then have not over-reached me ? "

" In what ? my friend ! " said I.

" These roots," he answered, " may perhaps be good and saleable for some purpose. Shall you send them into Persia ? or whither ? "

" Sosimenes ! I shall make love-potions of the flowers."

LEONTION. O Epicurus ! should it ever be known in Athens that they are good for this, you will not have, with all your fences of prunes and pomegranates, and precipices with briar upon them, a single root left under ground after the month of Elaphebolion.*

EPICURUS. It is not everyone that knows the preparation.

LEONTION. Everybody will try it.

EPICURUS. And you too, Ternissa ?

TERNISSA. Will you teach me ?

EPICURUS. This, and anything else I know. We must walk together when they are in flower.

TERNISSA. And can you teach me then ?

EPICURUS. I teach by degrees.

LEONTION. By very slow ones, Epicurus ! I have no patience with you : tell us directly.

EPICURUS. It is very material what kind of recipient you bring with you. Enchantresses use a brazen one : silver and gold are employed in other arts.

LEONTION. I will bring any.

TERNISSA. My mother has a fine golden one : she will lend it me : she allows me everything.

EPICURUS. Leontion and Ternissa ! those eyes of yours brighten at inquiry, as if they carried a light within them for a guidance.

LEONTION. No flattery !

TERNISSA. No flattery ! come, teach us.

EPICURUS. Will you hear me through in silence ?

LEONTION. We promise.

EPICURUS. Sweet girls ! the calm pleasures, such as I hope you will ever find in your walks among these gardens, will improve your

* The thirtieth of Elaphebolion was the tenth of April.—W. S. L.

beauty, animate your discourse, and correct the little that may hereafter rise up for correction in your dispositions. The smiling ideas left in our bosoms from our infancy, that many plants are the favourites of the Gods, and that others were even the objects of their love, having once been invested with the human form, beautiful and lively and happy as yourselves, give them an interest beyond the vision ; yes, and a station, let me say it, on the vestibule of our affections. Resign your ingenuous hearts to simple pleasures ; and there is none in man where men are Attic that will not follow and outstrip their movements.

TERNISSA. O Epicurus !

EPICURUS. What said Ternissa ?

LEONTION. Some of those anemones, I do think, must be still in blossom. Ternissa's golden cup is at home ; but she has brought with her a little vase for the filter—and has filled it to the brim.— Do not hide your head behind my shoulder, Ternissa ! no, nor in my lap.

EPICURUS. Yes, there let it lie, the lovelier for that tendril of sunny brown hair upon it. How it falls and rises ! Which is the hair ? which the shadow ?

LEONTION. Let the hair rest.

EPICURUS. I must not perhaps clasp the shadow !

LEONTION. You philosophers are fond of such unsubstantial things. O ! you have taken my volume. This is deceit.

You live so little in public, and entertain such a contempt for opinion, as to be both indifferent and ignorant what it is that people blame you for.

EPICURUS. I know what it is I should blame myself for, if I attended to them. Prove them to be wiser and more disinterested in their wisdom than I am, and I will then go down to them and listen to them. When I have well considered a thing, I deliver it, regardless of what those think who neither take the time nor possess the faculty of considering anything well, and who have always lived far remote from the scope of our speculations.

LEONTION. In the volume you snatched away from me so slily, I have defended a position of yours which many philosophers turn into ridicule ; namely, that politeness is among the virtues. I wish you yourself had spoken more at large upon the subject.

EPICURUS. It is one upon which a lady is likely to display more ingenuity and discernment. If philosophers have ridiculed my sentiment, the reason is, it is among those virtues which in general they find most difficult to assume or counterfeit.

LEONTION. Surely life runs on the smoother for this equability and polish ; and the gratification it affords is more extensive than is afforded even by the highest virtue. Courage, on nearly all occasions, inflicts as much of evil as it imparts of good. It may be exerted in defence of our country, in defence of those who love us, in defence of the harmless and the helpless : but those against whom it is thus exerted may possess an equal share of it. If they succeed, then manifestly the ill it produces is greater than the benefit : if they succumb, it is nearly as great. For, many of their adversaries are first killed and maimed, and many of their own kindred are left to lament the consequences of the aggression.

EPICURUS. You have spoken first of courage, as that virtue which attracts your sex principally.

TERNISSA. Not me ; I am always afraid of it. I love those best who can tell me the most things I never knew before, and who have patience with me, and look kindly while they teach me, and almost as if they were waiting for fresh questions. Now let me hear directly what you were about to say to Leontion.

EPICURUS. I was proceeding to remark that temperance comes next ; and temperance has then its highest merit when it is the support of civility and politeness. So that I think I am right and equitable in attributing to politeness a distinguished rank, not among the ornaments of life, but among the virtues. And you, Leontion and Ternissa, will have leaned the more propensely toward this opinion, if you considered, as I am sure you did, that the peace and concord of families, friends, and cities, are preserved by it : in other terms, the harmony of the world.

TERNISSA. Leontion spoke of courage, you of temperance : the next great virtue, in the division made by the philosophers, is justice.

EPICURUS. Temperance includes it : for temperance is imperfect if it is only an abstinence from too much food, too much wine, too much conviviality, or other luxury. It indicates every kind of forbearance. Justice is forbearance from what belongs to another. Giving to this one rightly what that one would hold wrongfully, is justice in magistrature, not in the abstract, and is only a part of its office. The perfectly temperate man is also the perfectly just man :

but the perfectly just man (as philosophers now define him) may not be the perfectly temperate one : I include the less in the greater.

LEONTION. We [1] hear of judges, and upright ones too, being immoderate eaters and drinkers.

EPICURUS. The Lacedemonians are temperate in food and courageous in battle : but men like these, if they existed in sufficient numbers, would devastate the universe. We alone, we Athenians, with less military skill perhaps, and certainly less rigid abstinence from voluptuousness and luxury, have set before it the only grand example of social government and of polished life. From us the seed is scattered : from us flow the streams that irrigate it : and ours are the hands, O Leontion, that collect it, cleanse it, deposit it, and convey and distribute it sound and weighty through every race and age.[2] Exhausted as we are by war, we can do nothing better than lie down and doze while the weather is fine overhead, and dream (if we can) that we are affluent and free.

O sweet sea-air ! how bland art thou and refreshing ! Breathe upon Leontion ! breathe upon Ternissa ! bring them health and

---

[1] 1st ed. reads : " We have seen judges, and upright ones too, inordinate eaters and immoderate drinkers."

[2] 1st ed. here inserts : " Therefor, and not from any other cause, altho' we have been leagued of late years with barbarians, whose wills and pleasures we have looked to and consulted, and altho' the upstarts who manage our affairs are at the beck of their satraps, and shield-bearers and cup-bearers, we have not been deprived altogether of our liberties, whatever may have been deducted (for our advantage, no doubt) from the unwieldiness of our estates. Gravity, too, and religion are still potent and prevalent. Those who harangue to us at the great market place, while one hand is filching our purses, lift up the other to the immortal Gods, imploring from their beneficence, that the poorest man in Athens may sit down at dinner with a drachma in his strong box under him.

" LEONTION. The very man does this, I hear, who has taken especial care that no strong box among us shall be without a chink at the bottom ; the very man who asked and received a gratuity from the colleague he had betrayed, belied, and thrown a stone at, for having proved him in the great market place a betrayer and a liar.

" EPICURUS. You have now answered indirectly but forcibly those who blame me for abstaining from public business. What can be imagined more disgraceful and ignominious, than to sit below such a fellow in the council—unless it be to sit beside him ? or what more idle and unavailing than, in the present state of our politics, to oppose him ! Exhausted as we are by war, we can do nothing better than lie down and doze, while the weather is fine overhead, and dream (if we can) that we are rich and free. Our managers are so very modest, they never attempt to reward or to praise any excellent citizen in his life-time ; so very prudent, they reserve such encouragement for him alone who always wanted it ; so very munificent, they give it him all at once, at the hour he is most prest and spirits and serenity, many springs and many summers, and when the vine-leaves have reddened and rustle under their feet.

These, my beloved girls, are the children of Eternity : they played around Theseus and the beauteous Amazon, they gave to Pallas the bloom of Venus, and to Venus the animation of Pallas. Is it not better to enjoy by the hour their soft salubrious influence, than to catch by fits the rancid breath of demagogues ; than to swell and move under it without or against our will ; than to acquire the semblance of eloquence by the bitterness of passion, the tone of philosophy by disappointment, or the credit of prudence by distrust ?   Can fortune, can industry, can desert itself, bestow on us anything we have not here ?

LEONTION. And when shall those three meet ?   The Gods have never united them, knowing that men would put them asunder at their first appearance.

EPICURUS. I am glad to leave the city as often as possible, full as it is of high and glorious reminiscences,[1] and am inclined much

calls loudest for it.   Such is the fervour and purity of their patriotism, they abandon their promises, they violate their oaths, they betray their friends and colleagues, for the improvement of our constitution.   Such and so operative is the force of public good, beyond what it ever was formerly, that even a fugitive slave, a writer of epigrams on walls and of songs on the grease of platters, for attempting to cut the throat of a fellow in the same household, who soon afterward was more successful in doing it himself, is not only called our citizen but elected by a large proportion of the tribes as the most worthy to administer our affairs.   He has nothing now to acquire but a little purity of language, and somewhat of order and ratiocination.   Unhappily, one of the last things he uttered before the judges, showed his want in all its nakedness : it was a eulogy on a drunken old woman, the companion of soldiers and sailors, and lower and viler men; one whose eyes, as much as can be seen of them, are streaky fat floating in semi-liquid rheum : he called her *the pride, the life, and ornament* of polished society.

" LEONTION. Strange collocation of terms, and stranger application !

" TERNISSA. I should have said, if indeed it could be said of such a person, *the ornament, pride, and life.*

" LEONTION. Hardly a Bœtian bullock driver would wedge in *life* between *pride* and *ornament.*

" EPICURUS. There are minds in which everything like is disorderly, coarse, proportionless, and false.   This blunderer would not have discovered his error even if you had pointed it out, but he would have hired from the public treasury and for the public good some dozen of idle vagabonds to persecute you and insult you."

[1] 1st ed. here inserts : " for beside the sufferance of displeasure and disgust, I might do great injury, and bring much contumely on my country ; since, if ever I complained of a rudeness offered to any of my family, male or female, the person who committed it would be appointed next day to some lucrative situation. This I have experienced on a late occasion at the hands of Kenos.   To peculate,

rather to indulge in quieter scenes, whither the Graces and Friendship lead me. I would not contend even with men able to contend with me. You, Leontion, I see, think differently, and have composed at last your long-meditated work against the philosophy of Theophrastus.

LEONTION. Why not ? he has been praised above his merits.

EPICURUS. My Leontion ! you have inadvertently given me the reason and origin of all controversial writings. They flow not from a love of truth or a regard for science, but from envy and ill-will. Setting aside the evil of malignity, always hurtful to ourselves, not always to others, there is weakness in the argument you have adduced. When a writer is praised above his merits in his own times, he is certain of being estimated below them in the times succeeding. Paradox is dear to most people : it bears the appearance of originality, but is usually the talent of the superficial, the perverse, and the obstinate.

Nothing is more gratifying than the attention you are bestowing on me, which you always apportion to the seriousness of my observations. But,[1] Leontion ! Leontion ! you defend me too earnestly. The roses on your cheeks should derive their bloom from a cooler and sweeter and more salubrious fountain. In what mythology (can you tell me, Ternissa ?) is Friendship the mother of Anger ?

TERNISSA. I can only tell you that Love lights Anger's torch very often.

LEONTION. I dislike Theophrastus for his affected contempt of your doctrines.

EPICURUS. Unreasonably, for the contempt of them ; reasonably, if affected. Good men may differ widely from me, and wise ones misunderstand me ; for, their wisdom having raised up to them schools of their own, they have not found leisure to converse with me ; and from others they have received a partial and inexact

to prevaricate, to abandon friends, to betray colleagues, to forswear associates, any one of these formerly was enough to sink a steersman of state in the depth of infamy. Appeals to the glory, the equity, the fair name of such a character, are now too much, too daring, they arouse his choler with his conscience, and, while he is venting in public the whole vocabulary of virtue, fill him up to the throat again with animosity and indignation. Altho' there are many who may be amused at the vagaries and flights and circuitions of profligacy, and at the baseness of those who watch it from their soft benches, with mutual encouragement to louder and louder expressions of admiration, I am inclined," etc.

[1] From " But " to " often " added in 2nd ed.

report. My opinion is, that certain things are indifferent, and
unworthy of pursuit or attention, as lying beyond our research and
almost our conjecture ; which things the generality of philosophers
(for the generality are speculative) deem of the first .importance.
Questions relating to them I answer evasively, or altogether decline.
Again, there are modes of living which are suitable to some and
unsuitable to others. What I myself follow and embrace, what I
recommend to the studious, to the irritable, to the weak in health,
would ill agree with the commonality of citizens. Yet my adversaries cry out, " Such is the opinion and practice of Epicurus."
For instance, I have never taken a wife, and never will take one :
but he from among the mass who should avow his imitation of my
example, would act as wisely and more religiously in saying that
he chose celibacy because Pallas had done the same.

LEONTION. If Pallas had many such votaries she would soon have
few citizens to supply them.

EPICURUS. And extremely bad ones if all followed me in retiring
from the offices of magistracy and of war. Having seen that the
most sensible men are the most unhappy, I could not but examine
the causes of it : and finding that the same sensibility to which
they are indebted for the activity of their intellect, is also the restless
mover of their jealousy and ambition, I would lead them aside from
whatever operates upon these, and throw under their feet the
terrors their imagination has created. My philosophy is not for
the populace nor for the proud : the ferocious will never attain it :
the gentle will embrace it, but will not call it mine. I do not desire
that they should : let them rest their heads upon that part of the
pillow which they find the softest, and enjoy their own dreams
unbroken.

LEONTION. The old are all against you[1]: for the name of pleasure
is an affront to them : they know no other kind of it than that
which has flowered and seeded, and of which the withered stems
have indeed a rueful look. What we call dry they call sound :
nothing must retain any juice in it : their pleasure is in chewing
what is hard, not in tasting what is savoury.

EPICURUS. Unhappily the aged are retentive of long-acquired
maxims, and insensible to new impressions, whether from fancy or

---

[1] 1st ed. reads : " you. EPICURUS. The name . . . rueful look. LEONTION.
They would controvert your positions. EPICURUS. Unhappily," etc.

from truth : in fact, their eyes blend the two together. Well might the poet tell us,

> Fewer the gifts that gnarled Age presents
> To elegantly-handed Infancy,
> Than elegantly-handed Infancy
> Presents to gnarled Age. From both they drop ;
> The middle course of life receives them all,
> Save the light few that laughing Youth runs off with,
> Unvalued as a mistress or a flower.

LEONTION. It [1] is reported by the experienced that our last loves and our first are of equal interest to us.

TERNISSA. Surely they are. What is the difference ? Can you really mean to say, O Leontion, that there are any intermediate ? Why do you look aside ? And you too refuse to answer me so easy and plain a question ?

LEONTION (*to Epicurus*). Although you teach us the necessity of laying a strong hand on the strong affections, you never pull one feather from the wing of Love.

EPICURUS. I am not so irreligious.

TERNISSA. I think he could only twitch it just enough to make the gentle God turn round, and smile on him.

LEONTION. You know little about the matter, but may live to know all. Whatever we may talk of torments, as some do, there must surely be more pleasure in desiring and not possessing, than in possessing and not desiring.

EPICURUS. Perhaps so : but consult the intelligent. Certainly there is a middle state between love and friendship, more delightful than either, but more difficult to remain in.

LEONTION. To be preferred to all others is the supremacy of bliss. Do not you think so, Ternissa ?

TERNISSA. It is indeed what the wise and the powerful and the beautiful chiefly aim at : Leontion has attained it.

EPICURUS. Delightful, no doubt, is such supremacy : but far more delightful is the certainty that there never was any one quite near enough to be given up for us. To be preferred is hardly a compensation for having been long compared. The breath of another's sigh bedims and hangs pertinaciously about the image we adore.

[1] From " It " to " me " added in 2nd ed. (444 words).

EPICURUS, LEONTION, AND TERNISSA

LEONTION. When Friendship has taken the place of Love, she ought to make his absence as little a cause of regret as possible, and it is gracious in her to imitate his demeanour and his words.

EPICURUS. I can repeat them more easily than imitate them.

TERNISSA. Both of you, until this moment, were looking grave ; but Leontion has resumed her smiles again on hearing what Epicurus can do. I wish you would repeat to me, O Epicurus, any words so benign a God hath vouchsafed to teach you ; for it would be a convincing proof of your piety, and I could silence the noisiest tongue in Athens with it.

LEONTION. Simpleton ! we were speaking allegorically.

TERNISSA. Never say that : I do believe the God himself hath conversed with Epicurus. Tell me now, Epicurus, tell me yourself, has not he ?

EPICURUS. Yes.

TERNISSA. In his own form ?

EPICURUS. Very nearly : it was in Ternissa's.

TERNISSA. Impious man ! I am ashamed of you.

LEONTION. Never did shame burn brighter.

TERNISSA. Mind Theophrastus, not me.

LEONTION. Since, in obedience to your institutions, O Epicurus, I must not say I am angry, I am offended at least with Theophrastus, for having so misrepresented your opinions, on the necessity of keeping the mind composed and tranquil, and remote from every object and every sentiment by which a painful sympathy may be excited. In order to display his elegance of language,[1] he runs wherever he can lay a censure on you, whether he believes in its equity or not.

EPICURUS. This is the case with all eloquent men and all disputants. Truth neither warms nor elevates them, neither obtains for them profit nor applause.

TERNISSA. I have heard wise remarks very often and very warmly praised.

EPICURUS. Not for the truth in them, but for the grace, or because they touched the spring of some preconception or some passion. Man is a hater of truth, a lover of fiction.

LEONTION. How [2] then happens it that children, when you have

---

[1] 1st ed. reads : " language and comprehension of thought he."
[2] From " How " to " ribaldry " added in 2nd ed. (460 words).

related to them any story which has greatly interested them, ask immediately and impatiently, *is it true ?*

EPICURUS. Children are not men nor women : they are almost as different creatures, in many respects, as if they never were to be the one or the other : they are as unlike as buds are unlike flowers, and almost as blossoms are unlike fruits. Greatly are they better than they are about to be, unless Philosophy raises her hand above them when the noon is coming on, and shelters them at one season from the heats that would scorch and wither, and at another from the storms that would shatter and subvert them. There are nations, it is reported, which aim their arrows and javelins at the sun and moon, on occasions of eclipse, or any other offence : but I never have heard that the sun and moon abated their course through the heavens for it, or looked more angrily when they issued forth again to shed light on their antagonists. They went onward all the while in their own serenity and clearness, through unobstructed paths, without diminution and without delay : it was only the little world below that was in darkness. Philosophy lets her light descend and enter wherever there is a passage for it : she takes advantage of the smallest crevice, but the rays are rebutted by the smallest obstruction. Polemics can never be philosophers or philotheists : they serve men ill, and their Gods no better : they mar what is solid in earthly bliss by animosities and dissensions, and intercept the span of azure at which the weary and the sorrowful would look up.

Theophrastus is a writer of many acquirements and some shrewdness, usually judicious, often somewhat witty, always elegant : his thoughts are never confused, his sentences are never incomprehensible. If Aristoteles thought more highly of him than his due, surely you ought not to censure Theophrastus with severity on the supposition of his rating me below mine ; unless you argue that a slight error in a short sum is less pardonable than in a longer. Had Aristoteles been living, and had he given the same opinion of me, your friendship and perhaps my self-love might have been wounded ; for, if on one occasion he spoke too favourably, he never spoke unfavourably but with justice. This is among the indications of orderly and elevated minds ; and here stands the barrier that separates them from the common and the waste. Is a man to be angry because an infant is fretful ? Is a philosopher to unpack and throw away his philosophy, because an idiot has

224

tried to overturn it on the road, and has pursued it with jibes and ribaldry ?

LEONTION. Theophrastus would persuade us that, according to your system, we not only should decline the succour of the wretched, but avoid the sympathies that poets and historians would awaken in us. Probably for the sake of introducing some idle verses, written by a friend of his, he says that, following the guidance of Epicurus, we should altogether shun the theatre, and not only when *Prometheus* and *Œdipus* and *Philoctetes* are introduced, but even where generous and kindly sentiments are predominant, if they partake of that tenderness which belongs to pity. I know not what Thracian lord [1] recovers his daughter from her ravisher : such are among the words they exchange.

> *Father.* Insects, that dwell in rotten reeds, inert
> Upon the surface of a stream or pool,
> Then rush into the air on meshy vans,
> Are not so different in their varying lives
> As we are. . . . O ! what father on this earth,
> Holding his child's cool cheek within his palms
> And kissing his fair front, would wish him man ?
> Inheritor of wants and jealousies,
> Of labour, of ambition, of distress,
> And, cruellest of all the passions, lust.
> Who that beholds me, persecuted, scorned,
> A wanderer, e'er could think what friends were mine,
> How numerous, how devoted ? with what glee
> Smiled my old house, with what acclaim my courts
> Rang from without whene'er my war-horse neighed.

> *Daughter.* Thy fortieth birthday is not shouted yet
> By the young peasantry, with rural gifts
> And nightly fires along the pointed hills,
> Yet do thy temples glitter with grey hair
> Scattered not thinly : ah, what sudden change !
> Only thy voice and heart remain the same :
> No, that voice trembles, and that heart (I feel)
> While it would comfort and console me, breaks.

EPICURUS. I would never close my bosom against the feelings of humanity : but I would calmly and well consider by what conduct

---

[1] 1st ed. reads : " lord or hero, after the loss of his dignity and fortune, recovers," etc.

of life they may enter it with the least importunity and violence.
A consciousness that we have promoted the happiness of others,
to the uttermost of our power, is certain not only to meet them at
the threshold, but to bring them along with us, and to render them
accurate and faithful prompters, when we bend perplexedly over
the problem of evil figured by the tragedians. If indeed there
were more of pain than of pleasure in the exhibitions of the
dramatist, no man in his senses would attend them twice. All
the imitative arts have delight for the principal object : the first of
these is poetry : the highest of poetry is tragic.

LEONTION. The epic has been called so.

EPICURUS. Improperly ; for the epic has much more in it of what
is prosaic. Its magnitude is no argument. An Egyptian pyramid
contains more materials than an Ionic temple, but requires less
contrivance, and exhibits less beauty of design. My simile is yet a
defective one ; for, a tragedy must be carried on with an unbroken
interest ; and, undecorated by loose foliage or fantastic branches,
it must rise, like the palm-tree, with a lofty unity. On these matters
I am unable to argue at large, or perhaps correctly : on those
however which I have studied and treated, my terms are so explicit
and clear, that Theophrastus can never have misunderstood them.
Let me recall to your attention but two axioms.

Abstinence from low pleasures is the only means of meriting or
of obtaining the higher.

Kindness in ourselves is the honey that blunts the sting of
unkindness in another.

LEONTION. Explain to me then, O Epicurus, why we suffer so
much from ingratitude.

EPICURUS. We fancy we suffer from ingratitude, while in reality
we suffer from self-love. Passion weeps while she says, " I did not
deserve this from him " : Reason, while she says it, smoothens
her brow at the clear fountain of the heart. Permit me also, like
Theophrastus, to borrow a few words from a poet.

TERNISSA. Borrow as many such as anyone will entrust to you :
and may Hermes prosper your commerce ! Leontion may go to the
theatre then ; for she loves it.

EPICURUS. Girls ! be the bosom friends of *Antigone* and *Ismene ;*
and you shall enter the wood of the Eumenides without shuddering,
and leave it without the trace of a tear. Never did you appear so

graceful to me, O Ternissa ; no, not even after this walk do you ; as when I saw you blow a fly from the forehead of *Philoctetes* in the propylëa. The wing, with which Sophocles and the statuary represent him, to drive away the summer insects in his agony, had wearied his flaccid arm, hanging down beside him.

TERNISSA. Do you imagine then I thought him a living man ?

EPICURUS. The sentiment was both more delicate and more august from being indistinct. You would have done it, even if he *had* been a living man : even if he could have clasped you in his arms, imploring the deities to resemble you in gentleness, you would have done it.

TERNISSA. He looked so abandoned by all, and so heroic, yet so feeble and so helpless ; I did not think of turning round to see if any one was near me ; or else perhaps——

EPICURUS. If you could have thought of looking round, you would no longer have been Ternissa. The Gods would have transformed you for it into some tree.

LEONTION. And Epicurus had been walking under it this day perhaps.

EPICURUS. With Leontion, the partner of his sentiments. But the walk would have been earlier or later than the present hour : since the middle of the day, like the middle of certain fruits, is good for nothing.

LEONTION. For dinner surely.

EPICURUS. Dinner is a less gratification to me than to many : I dine alone.

TERNISSA. Why ?

EPICURUS. To avoid the noise, the heat, and the intermixture both of odours and of occupations. I can not bear the indecency of speaking with a mouth in which there is food. I careen my body (since it is always in want of repair) in as unobstructed a space as I can, and I lie down and sleep awhile when the work is over.

LEONTION. Epicurus ! although it would be very interesting, no doubt, to hear more of what you do after dinner—(*aside to him*) now don't smile : I shall never forgive you if you say a single word —yet I would rather hear a little about the theatre, and whether you think at last that women should frequent it ; for you have often said the contrary.

EPICURUS. I think they should visit it rarely ; not because it excites their affections, but because it deadens them. To me nothing is so odious as to be at once among the rabble and among the heroes, and, while I am receiving into my heart the most exquisite of human sensations, to feel upon my shoulder the hand of some inattentive and insensible young officer.

LEONTION. O very bad indeed ! horrible !

TERNISSA. You quite fire at the idea.

LEONTION. Not I : I don't care about it.

TERNISSA. Not about what is very bad indeed ? quite horrible ?

LEONTION. I seldom go thither.

EPICURUS. The theatre is delightful when we erect it in our own house or arbour, and when there is but one spectator.

LEONTION. You must lose the illusion in great part, if you only read the tragedy, which I fancy to be your meaning.

EPICURUS. I lose the less of it. Do not imagine that the illusion is, or can be, or ought to be, complete. If it were possible, no Phalaris or Perillus could devise a crueller torture. Here are two imitations : first, the poet's of the sufferer ; secondly, the actor's of both : poetry is superinduced. No man in pain ever uttered the better part of the language used by Sophocles. We admit it, and willingly, and are at least as much illuded by it as by anything else we hear or see upon the stage. Poets and statuaries and painters give us an adorned imitation of the object, so skilfully treated that we receive it for a correct one. This is the only illusion they aim at : this is the perfection of their arts.

LEONTION. Do you derive no pleasure from the representation of a consummate actor ?

EPICURUS. High pleasure ; but liable to be overturned in an instant ; pleasure at the mercy of any one who sits beside me. Rarely does it happen that an Athenian utters a syllable in the midst of it : but our city is open to the inhabitants of all the world, and all the world that is yet humanised a woman might walk across in sixty hours. There are even in Greece a few remaining still so barbarous, that I have heard them whisper in the midst of the finest scenes of our greatest poets.

LEONTION. Acorn-fed Chaonians ! [1]

EPICURUS. I esteem all the wise ; but I entertain no wish to

---

[1] 1st ed. reads : " Chaonians ! they must have suffered great pain in the intestines."

imitate all of them in everything. What was convenient and befitting in one or other of them, might be inconvenient and unbefitting
in me. Great names ought to bear us up and carry us through,
but never to run away with us. Peculiarity and solitariness give
an idea to weak minds of something grand, authoritative, and
God-like. To be wise indeed and happy and self-possessed, we must
often be alone : we must mix as little as we can with what is called
society, and abstain rather more than seems desirable even from
the better few.

TERNISSA. You have commanded us at all times to ask you anything we do not understand : why then use the phrase " what is
called society " ? as if there could be a doubt whether we are in
society when we converse with many.

EPICURUS. We may meet and converse with thousands : you and
Leontion and myself could associate with few. *Society*, in the
philosophical sense of the word, is almost the contrary of what it
is in the common acceptation.

LEONTION. Now go on with your discourse.

EPICURUS. When we have once acquired that intelligence of
which we have been in pursuit, we may relax our minds, and lay the
produce of our chase at the feet of those we love.

LEONTION. Philosophers seem to imagine that they can be visible
and invisible at will ; that they can be admired for the display of
their tenets, and unobserved in the workings of their spleen. None
of those whom I remember, or whose writings I have perused, was
quite exempt from it. Among the least malicious is Theophrastus :
could he find no other for so little malice but you ?

EPICURUS. The origin of his dislike to me, was my opinion that
perspicuity is the prime excellence of composition. He and Aristoteles and Plato talk diffusely of attending to harmony, and clap
rhetorical rules before our mouths in order to produce it. Natural
sequences and right subordination of thoughts, and that just proportion of numbers in the sentences which follows a strong concep-
tion, are the constituents of true harmony. You are satisfied with
it and dwell upon it ; which you would vainly hope to do when
you are forced to turn back again to seize an idea or to comprehend
a period. Let us believe that opposition, and even hard words,
are (at least in the beginning) no certain proofs of hatred; although,
by requiring defence, they soon produce heat and animosity in him

who hath engaged in so unwise a warfare. On the other hand, praises are not always the unfailing signs of liberality or of justice. Many are extolled out of enmity to others, and perhaps would have been decried had those others not existed. Among the causes of my happiness, this is one: I never have been stimulated to hostility by any in the crowd that has assailed me. If in my youth I had been hurried into this weakness, I should have regretted it as lost time, lost pleasure, lost humanity.

LEONTION. We may expose what is violent or false in anyone; and chiefly in anyone who injures us or our friends.

EPICURUS. We may.

LEONTION. How then?

EPICURUS. By exhibiting in ourselves the contrary.[1] Such vengeance is legitimate and complete. I found in my early days, among the celebrated philosophers of Greece, a love of domination, a propensity to imposture, a jealousy of renown, and a cold indifference to simple truth. None of these qualities lead to happiness; none of them stand within the precincts of Virtue. I asked myself, " What is the most natural and the most universal of our desires " : I found it was, *to be happy*. Wonderful I thought it, that the gratification of a desire which is at once the most universal and the most natural, should be the seldomest attained. I then conjectured the means; and I found that they vary, as vary the minds and capacities of men; that, however, the principal one lay in the avoidance of those very things which had hitherto been taken up as the instruments of enjoyment and content; such as military commands, political offices, clients, hazardous ventures in commerce, and extensive property in land.

LEONTION. And yet offices, both political and military, must be undertaken; and clients will throng about those who exercise them. Commerce too will dilate with Prosperity, and Frugality will square her farm by lopping off the angles of the next.

EPICURUS. True, Leontion! nor is there a probability that my opinions will pervade the heart of Avarice or Ambition: they will influence only the unoccupied. Philosophy hath led scarcely a single man away from commands or magistracies, until he hath first tried them. Weariness is the repose of the politician, and apathy

[1] 1st ed. reads: " contrary. TERNISSA. Such vengeance is legitimate and complete. EPICURUS. I," etc.

his wisdom. He fancies that nations are contemplating the great man in his retirement, while what began in ignorance of himself is ending in forgetfulness on the part of others. This truth at last appears to him : he detests the ingratitude of mankind : he declares his resolution to carry the earth no longer on his shoulders : he is taken at his word : and the shock of it breaks his heart.

TERNISSA. Epicurus, I have been listening to you with even more pleasure than usual, for you often talk of love, and such other things as you can know nothing about : but now you have gone out of your way to defend an enemy, and to lead aside Leontion from her severity toward Theophrastus.

EPICURUS. Believe me, my lovely friends, he is no ordinary man who hath said one wise thing gracefully in the whole of his existence : now several such are recorded of him whom Leontion hath singled out from my assailants. His style is excellent.

LEONTION. The excellence of it hath been exaggerated by Aristoteles, to lower our opinion of Plato's.

EPICURUS. It may be : I can not prove it, and never heard it.

LEONTION. So blinded indeed is this great master of rhetoric——

EPICURUS. Pardon the rudeness of my interruption, dear Leontion. Do not designate so great a man by a title so contemptible. You are nearly as humiliating to his genius as those who call him the Stagyrite : and those are ignorant of the wrong they do him : many of them are his disciples and admirers, and call him by that name in quoting his authority. Philosophy, until he came among us, was like the habitations of the Troglodytes ; vast indeed and wonderful, but without construction, without arrangement : he first gave it order and system. I do not rank him with Democritus, who has been to philosophers what Homer has been to poets, and who is equally great in imagination and in reflection : but no other has left behind him so many just remarks on such a variety of subjects.

Within one olympiad three men have departed from the world, who carried farther than any other three that ever dwelt upon it, reason,[1] eloquence, and martial glory ; Aristoteles, Demosthenes, and Alexander. Now[2] tell me which of these qualities do you admire the most ?

[1] 1st ed. reads : " reason, patriotism, and ferocity : Aristoteles," etc.
[2] From " Now " to " humour " added in 2nd ed.

LEONTION. Reason.

EPICURUS. And rightly. Among the three characters, the vulgar and ignorant will prefer Alexander ; the less vulgar and ignorant will prefer Demosthenes ; and they who are removed to the greatest distance from ignorance and vulgarity, Aristoteles. Yet, although he has written on some occasions with as much purity and precision as we find in the *Orations* of Pericles, many things are expressed obscurely ; which is by much the greatest fault in composition.

LEONTION. Surely you do not say that an obscurity is worse than a defect in grammar.

EPICURUS. I do say it : for we may discover a truth through such a defect, which we can not through an obscurity. It is better to find the object of our researches in ill condition than not to find it at all. We may purify the idea in our own bath, and adorn it with our own habiliments, if we can but find it, though among the slaves or clowns : whereas, if it is locked up from us in a dark chamber at the top of the house, we have only to walk down-stairs again, disappointed, tired, and out of humour.

But you were saying that something had blinded the philosopher.

LEONTION. His zeal and partiality. Not only did he prefer Theophrastus to everyone who taught at Athens ; not only did he change his original name, for one of so high an import as to signify that he would elevate his language to the language of the Gods ; but he fancied and insisted that the very sound of *Theophrastus* is sweet,* of *Tyrtamus* harsh and inelegant.

EPICURUS. Your ear, Leontion, is the better arbitress of musical sounds, in which (I speak of words) hardly any two agree. But a box on the ear does not improve the organ ; and I would advise you to leave inviolate and untouched all those peculiarities which rest on friendship. The jealous, if we suffered them in the least to move us, would deserve our commiseration rather than our resentment : but the best thing we can do with them is to make them the comedians of our privacy. Some have recently started up among us, who, when they have published to the world their systems of philosophy, or their axioms, or their paradoxes, and find nevertheless that others are preferred to them, persuade their friends and scholars that

---

* Τύρταμος δ' ἐκαλεῖτο πρότερον ὁ Θεόφραστος, μετωνόμασε δ' αὐτὸν ὁ Ἀρισ-τοτέλης Θεόφραστον ἅμα μὲν φεύγων τὴν τοῦ προτέρου ὀνόματος κακοφωνίαν, ἅμα δὲ τὸν τῆς φράσεως αὐτοῦ ζῆλον ἐπισημαινόμενος. Strabo, xiii.—W. S. L.

232

enormous and horrible injustice hath been done toward them. By degrees they cool, however, and become more reasonable : they resign the honour of invention, which always may be contested or ascertained, and invest themselves with what they style much greater, that of learning. What constitutes this glory, on which they plume themselves so joyously and gaudily ? Nothing else than the reading of those volumes which we have taken the trouble to write. A multitude of authors, the greater part of them inferior in abilities to you who hear me, are the slow constructors of reputations which they would persuade us are the solidest and the highest. We teach them all they know : and they are as proud as if they had taught us. There are not indeed many of these parasitical plants at present, sucking us, and resting their leafy slenderness upon us : but whenever books become more numerous, a new species will arise from them, to which philosophers and historians and poets must give way, for, intercepting all above, it will approximate much nearer to the manners and intellects of the people. At last what is most Attic in Athens will be canvassed and discussed in their booth ; and he who now exerciseth a sound and strong judgment of his own, will indifferently borrow theirs, and become so corrupted with it, as ever afterward to be gratified to his heart's content by the impudent laconism of their oracular decisions. These people are the natural enemies of greater : they can not sell their platters of offal while a richer feast is open to the public, and while lamps of profuser light announce the invitation. I would not augur the decay of philosophy and literature: it was retarded by the good example of our ancestors. The seven wise men, as they are called, lived amicably, and, where it was possible, in intercourse. Our seventy wiser (for we may reckon at least that number of those who proclaim themselves so) stand at the distance of a porcupine's shot, and, like that animal, scatter their shafts in every direction, with more profusion than force, and with more anger than aim.

Hither, to these banks of serpolet ; to these strawberries, whose dying leaves breathe a most refreshing fragrance ; to this ivy, from which Bacchus may have crowned himself; let us retire at the voice of Discord. Whom should we contend with ? the less ? it were inglorious : the greater ? it were vain. Do we look for Truth ? she is not the inhabitant of cities nor delights in clamour : she steals upon the calm and meditative as Diana upon Endymion, indulgent in her chastity, encouraging a modest, and requiting a faithful love.

LEONTION. How Ternissa sighs after Truth !

EPICURUS. If Truth appeared in daylight among mortals, she would surely resemble Ternissa. Those white and lucid cheeks, that youth which appears more youthful (for unless we are near her we think her yet a child), and that calm open forehead——

LEONTION. Malicious girl ! she conceals it !

EPICURUS. Ingenious girl ! the resemblance was, until now, imperfect. We must remove the veil ourselves ; for Truth, whatever the poets may tell us, never comes without one, diaphanous or opaque.

If those who differ on speculative points, would walk together now and then in the country, they might find many objects that must unite them. The same bodily feeling is productive in some degree of the same mental one. Enjoyment from sun and air, from exercise and odours, brings hearts together that schools and council-chambers and popular assemblies have stood between for years.

I hope Theophrastus may live, to walk with us among these bushes when they are shadier, and to perceive that all questions, but those about the way to happiness, are illiberal or mechanical or infantine or idle.

TERNISSA. Are geometry and astronomy idle ?

EPICURUS. Such idleness as theirs a wise man may indulge in, when he has found what he was seeking : and, as they abstract the mind from what would prey upon it, there are many to whom I would recommend them earlier, as their principal and most serious studies.

We will return to Theophrastus. He has one great merit in style ; he is select and sparing in the use of metaphors : that man sees badly who sees everything double. He wants novelty and vigour in his remarks both on men and things : neither his subject nor his mind is elevated : here however let me observe, my fair disciples, that he and some others, of whom we speak in common conversation with little deference or reserve, may perhaps attract the notice and attention of the remotest nations in the remotest times. Suppose him to have his defects (all that you or anyone has ever supposed in him), yet how much greater is his intellect than the intellect of any among those who govern the world ! If these appeared in the streets of Athens, you would run to look at them, and ask your friends whether they had seen them pass. If you can not show as much reverence to Theophrastus, the defect is yours. He may not be what his friends have fancied him : but how great must he be to have obtained the partiality of such friends ! how few are greater ! how many millions less !

LEONTION.[1] A slender tree, with scarcely any heart or pith in it, ought at least to have some play of boughs and branches : he, poor man, is inert. The leaves just twinkle, and nothing more.

EPICURUS. He writes correctly and observantly. Even bad writers are blamed unjustly when they are blamed much. In comparison with many good and sensible men, they have evinced no slight degree of intelligence : yet we go frequently to those good and sensible men, and engage them to join us in our contempt and ridicule, of one who not only is wiser than they are, but who has made an effort to entertain or to instruct us, which they never did.

TERNISSA. This is inconsiderate and ungrateful.

EPICURUS. Truly and humanely have you spoken. Is [2] it not remarkable that we are the fondest of acknowledging the least favourable and the least pleasurable of our partialities ? Whether in hatred or love, men are disposed to bring their conversation very near the object, yet shrink at touching the fairer. In hatred their sensibility is less delicate, and the inference comes closer : in love they readily give an arm to a confidant, almost to the upper step of their treasury.

LEONTION. How unworthy of trust do you represent your fellow men ! But you began by censuring *me*. In my Treatise I have only defended your tenets against Theophrastus.

EPICURUS. I am certain you have done it with spirit and eloquence, dear Leontion ; and there are but two words in it I would wish you to erase.

LEONTION. Which are they ?

EPICURUS. Theophrastus and Epicurus. If you love me, you will do nothing that may make you uneasy when you grow older ; nothing that may allow my adversary to say, " Leontion soon forgot her Epicurus." My maxim is, never to defend my systems or paradoxes : if you undertake it, the Athenians will insist that I impelled you

[1] From " LEONTION " to " observantly " added in 2nd ed.
[2] From " Is " to " me " added in 2nd ed.

secretly, or that my philosophy and my friendship were ineffectual on you.

LEONTION. They shall never say that.

EPICURUS.[1] I would entreat you to dismiss altogether things quite unworthy of your notice, if your observations could fall on any subject without embellishing it. You do not want these thorns to light your fire with.

LEONTION. Pardon the weak arm that would have defended what none can reach.

EPICURUS. I am not unmoved by the kindness of your intentions. Most people, and philosophers too, among the rest, when their own conduct or opinions are questioned, are admirably prompt and dexterous in the science of defence ; but when another's are assailed, they parry with as ill a grace and faltering a hand as if they never had taken a lesson in it at home. Seldom will they see what they profess to look for ; and, finding it, they pick up with it a thorn under the nail. They canter over the solid turf, and complain that there is no corn upon it : they canter over the corn, and curse the ridges and furrows. All schools of philosophy, and almost all authors, are rather to be frequented for exercise than for freight : but this exercise ought to acquire us health and strength, spirits and good-humour. There is none of them that does not supply some truth useful to every man, and some untruth equally so to the few that are able to wrestle with it. If there were no falsehood in the world, there would be no doubt ; if there were no doubt, there would be no inquiry ; if no inquiry, no wisdom, no knowledge, no genius ; and Fancy herself would lie muffled up in her robe, inactive, pale, and bloated. I wish we could demonstrate the existence of utility in some other evils as easily as in this.

LEONTION. My remarks on the conduct and on the style of Theophrastus are not confined to him solely. I have taken at last a general view of our literature, and traced as far as I am able its deviation and decline. In ancient works we sometimes see the mark of the chisel ; in modern we might almost suppose that no chisel was employed at all, and that everything was done by grinding and rubbing. There is an ordinariness, an indistinctness, a generalisation, not even to be found in a flock of sheep. As most reduce what is sand into dust, the few that avoid it run to a contrary

---

[1] From " EPICURUS " to " reach " added in 2nd ed.

extreme, and would force us to believe that what is original must be unpolished and uncouth.

EPICURUS. There have been in all ages, and in all there will be, sharp and slender heads, made purposely and peculiarly for creeping into the crevices of our nature. While we contemplate the magnificence of the universe, and mensurate the fitness and adaptation of one part to another, the small philosopher hangs upon a hair or creeps within a wrinkle, and cries out shrilly from his elevation that we are blind and superficial. He discovers a wart, he prys into a pore, and he calls it knowledge of man. Poetry and criticism, and all the fine arts, have generated such living things, which not only will be co-existent with them, but will (I fear) survive them. Hence history takes alternately the form of reproval and of panegyric ; and science in its pulverised state, in its shapeless and colourless atoms, assumes the name of metaphysics. We find no longer the rich succulence of Herodotus, no longer the strong filament of Thucydides, but thoughts fit only for the slave, and language for the rustic and the robber. These writings can never reach posterity, nor serve better authors near us : for who would receive as documents the perversions of venality and party ? Alexander we know was intemperate, and Philip both intemperate and perfidious : we require not a volume of dissertation on the thread of history, to demonstrate that one or other left a tailor's bill unpaid, and the immorality of doing so ; nor a supplement to ascertain on the best authorities which of the two it was. History should explain to us how nations rose and fell, what nurtured them in their growth, what sustained them in their maturity ; not which orator ran swiftest through the crowd from the right hand to the left, which assassin was too strong for manacles, or which felon too opulent for crucifixion.

LEONTION. It is better, I own it, that such writers should amuse our idleness than excite our spleen.

TERNISSA. What is spleen ?

EPICURUS. Do not ask her ; she can not tell you. The spleen, Ternissa, is to the heart what Arimanes is to Oromazes.

TERNISSA. I am little the wiser yet. Does he ever use such hard words with you ?

LEONTION. He means the evil Genius and the good Genius, in the theogony of the Persians ; and would perhaps tell you, as he hath told me, that the heart in itself is free from evil, but very capable of receiving and too tenacious of holding it.

EPICURUS. In our moral system, the spleen hangs about the heart and renders it sad and sorrowful, unless we continually keep it in exercise by kind offices, or in its proper place by serious investigation and solitary questionings. Otherwise it is apt to adhere and to accumulate, until it deadens the principles of sound action, and obscures the sight.

TERNISSA. It must make us very ugly when we grow old.

LEONTION. In youth it makes us uglier, as not appertaining to it : a little more or less ugliness in decrepitude is hardly worth considering, there being quite enough of it from other quarters : I would stop it here, however.

TERNISSA. O what a thing is age !

LEONTION. Death without death's quiet.[1] But we will converse upon it when we know it better.

EPICURUS. My beloved ! we will converse upon it at the present hour, while the harshness of its features is indiscernible, not only to you, but even to me, who am much nearer to it. Disagreeable things, like disagreeable men, are never to be spoken of when they are present. Do we think, as we may do in such a morning as this, that the air awakens the leaves around us only to fade and perish ? Do we, what is certain, think that every note of music we ever heard, every voice that ever breathed into our bosoms, and played upon its instrument the heart, only wafted us on a little nearer to the tomb ? Let the idea not sadden but compose us. Let us yield to it, just as season yields to season, hour to hour, and with a bright serenity, such as Evening is invested with by the departing Sun.

What ! are the dews falling, Ternissa ? Let them not yet, my lovely one !

TERNISSA. You soothe me, but to afflict me after ; you teach me, but to grieve.

EPICURUS. And what just now ?

TERNISSA. You are many years in advance of us, and may leave us both behind.

EPICURUS. Let not the fault be yours.

LEONTION. How can it ?

[1] 1st ed. reads: "quiet. EPICURUS. We will converse upon it when we know it better." Then from " EPICURUS " to " tenderness " added in 2nd ed.

EPICURUS, LEONTION, AND TERNISSA

EPICURUS. The heart, O Leontion, reflects a fuller and a fairer image of us than the eye can.

TERNISSA. True, true, true !

LEONTION. Yes ; the heart recomposes the dust within the sepulchre, and evokes it ; the eye too, even when it has lost its brightness, loses not the power of reproducing the object it delighted in. It sees amid the shades of night, like the Gods.

EPICURUS. Sobs, too ! Ah, these can only be suppressed by force.

LEONTION. By such ! She will sob all day before she is corrected.

TERNISSA. Loose me. Leontion makes me blush.

LEONTION. I ?

TERNISSA. It was you then, false Epicurus ! Why are you not discreeter ? I wonder at you. If I could find my way home alone, I would go directly.

LEONTION. Take breath first.

TERNISSA. O how spiteful ! Go away, tormenting girl, you shall not kiss me.

LEONTION. Why ? did *he ?*

TERNISSA. No indeed ; as you saw. What a question ! Kiss me ? for shame ; he only held me in his arms a little. Do not make him worse than he is.

LEONTION. I wonder he ventured. These little barks are very dangerous. Did you find it an easy matter to keep on your feet, Epicurus ?

EPICURUS. We may venture, in such parties of pleasure, on waves which the sun shines on ; we may venture on affections which, if not quite tranquil, are genial to the soul. Age alone interposes its chain of icy mountains, and the star above their summit soon droops behind. Heroes and demigods have acknowledged it. Recite to me, O Ternissa, in proof of this, the scene of *Peleus and Thetis.*[1]

TERNISSA. You do not believe in Goddesses ; and I do not believe in age.

LEONTION. Whosoever fears neither, can repeat it.

EPICURUS. Draw, each of you, one of these blades of grass I am holding, and the drawer of the shortest shall repeat it.

TERNISSA. O Epicurus ! have you been quite fair ?

EPICURUS. Why doubt me ?

---

[1] This scene is printed as a separate dialogue in *Imag. Convers.*, v., 1829. There is a verse rendering of it in *Hellenics*, 2nd ed., 1859.

TERNISSA. Mine, I see, is the shortest. I drew out from your closed hand the blade which stood above the other.

EPICURUS. Such grasses, like such men, may deceive us.

TERNISSA. Must I begin ? You both nod. Leontion, you are poetical : I can only feel poetry. I can not read it tolerably ; and I am sure to forget it if I trust to memory. Beside, there is something in the melody of this in particular which I sadly fear will render me inarticulate.

EPICURUS. I will relieve you from half your labour, by representing the character of *Peleus*.

TERNISSA. Let me down.

EPICURUS. The part will never permit it.

TERNISSA. I continue mute then. Be quiet. I can not speak a syllable unless I am on my feet again.

LEONTION. She will be mute a long while, like the Pythoness, and speak at last.

TERNISSA. Mischievous creature ! as if you could possibly tell what is passing in my mind. But will not you, Epicurus, let me fall, since it must (I see) be repeated so ? Shall I begin ? for I am anxious to have it over.

LEONTION. Why don't you ? we are as anxious as you are.

TERNISSA (*as Thetis*). " O Peleus ! O thou whom the Gods conferred on me for all my portion of happiness—and it was (I thought) too great——

EPICURUS (*as Peleus*). " Goddess ! to me, to thy Peleus, O how far more than Goddess ! why [1] then this sudden silence ? why these tears ? The last we shed were when the Fates divided us, saying the Earth was not thine, and the brother of Zeus, he [1] the ruler of the waters, had called thee. Those that fall between the beloved at parting, are bitter, and ought to be : woe to him who wishes they were not ! but those that flow again at the returning light of the blessed feet, should be refreshing and divine as morn.

TERNISSA (*as Thetis*). " Support me, support me in thy arms, once more, once only. Lower not thy shoulder from my cheek, to gaze at those features that (in times past) so pleased thee. The sky is serene ; the heavens frown not on us : do they then prepare for us fresh sorrow ? Prepare for us ! ah me ! the word of Zeus is spoken : our Achilles is discovered : he is borne away in the black

[1] From " why " to " silence " and " he " to " waters " added in 2nd ed.

240

hollow ships of Aulis, and would have flown faster than they sail, to Troy.

" Surely there are those among the Gods, or among the Goddesses, who might have forewarned me : and they did not ! Were there no omens, no auguries, no dreams, to shake thee from thy security ? no priest to prophesy ? And what pastures are more beautiful than Larissa's ? what victims more stately ? Could [1] the soothsayers turn aside their eyes from these ?

EPICURUS (*as Peleus*). " Approach with me and touch the altar, O my beloved ! Doth not thy finger now impress the soft embers of incense ? how often hath it burned, for him, for thee ! And the lowings of the herds are audible for their leaders, from the sources of Apidanus and Enipeus to the sea-beach. They [2] may yet prevail.

TERNISSA (*as Thetis*). " Alas ! alas ! Priests [3] can foretell but not avert the future ; and all they can give us are vain promises and abiding fears.

EPICURUS (*as Peleus*). " Despond not, my long-lost Thetis ! Hath not a God led thee back to me ? why not hope then he will restore our son ? Which of them all hath such a boy offended ?

TERNISSA (*as Thetis*). " Uncertainties . . . worse than uncertainties . . . overthrow and overwhelm me.

EPICURUS (*as Peleus*). " There is a comfort in the midst of every uncertainty, saving those which perplex the Gods and confound the godlike, Love's. Be comforted ! not by my kisses, but by my words. Achilles may live till our old age. *Ours !* Had I forgotten thy divinity ? forgotten it in thy beauty ? Other mortals think their beloved partake of it then mostly when they are gazing on their charms ; but thy tenderness is more than godlike ; and never have I known, never have I wished to know, whether aught in our inferior nature may resemble it.

TERNISSA [4] (*as Thetis*). " A mortal so immutable ! the Powers above are less.

EPICURUS (*as Peleus*). " Time without grief would not have greatly changed me.

---

[1] From " Could " to " these " added in 2nd ed.
[2] From " They " to " alas ! " added in 2nd ed.
[3] From " Priests " to " fears " in 1st ed. is spoken by *Peleus*.
[4] From " TERNISSA " to " sorrows " added in 2nd ed.

TERNISSA (*as Thetis*). " There is a loveliness which youth may be without, and which the Gods want. To the voice of compassion not a shell in all the ocean is attuned ; and no tear ever dropped upon Olympus. Thou lookest as fondly as ever, and more pensively. Have time and grief done this ? and they alone ? my Peleus ! Tell me again, have no freshly fond anxieties—— ?

EPICURUS (*as Peleus*). " Smile thus ! O smile anew and forget thy sorrows. Ages shall fly over my tomb, while thou art flourishing in imperishable youth, the desire of Gods, the [1] light of the depths of Ocean, the inspirer and sustainer of ever-flowing song.

TERNISSA (*as Thetis*). " I receive thy words, I deposit them in my bosom, and bless them. Gods *may* desire me : I have loved Peleus. Our union had many obstacles ; the envy of mortals, the jealousy of immortals, hostility and persecution from around, from below, and from above.[2] When we were happy they parted us : and again they unite us in eternal grief.

EPICURUS (*as Peleus*). " The wish of a divinity is powerfuller than the elements, and swifter than the light. Hence thou (what to me is impossible) mayst see the sweet Achilles every day, every hour.

TERNISSA (*as Thetis*). " How few ! alas how few ! I see him in the dust, in agony, in death : I see his blood on the flints, his yellow hair flapping in its current, his hand unable to remove it from his eyes. I hear his voice ; and it calls not upon me ! Mothers are soon forgotten ! It is weakness to love the weak ! I could not save him ! He would have left the caverns of Ocean,[3] and the groves and meadows of Elysium, though resounding with the songs of love and heroism, for a field of battle.

EPICURUS (*as Peleus*). " He [3] may yet live many years. Troy hath been taken once already.

TERNISSA (*as Thetis*). " He must perish ; and at Troy ; and now.

EPICURUS (*as Peleus*). " The *now* of the Gods is more than life's

---

[1] From " the " to " song " added in 2nd ed.

[2] 1st ed. reads : " above. Remember these : and they will make thee silent ; they will repress thy idle consolations. How cruel we once thought them ! O that they could have been more afflicting ! Then might our loss—no, never, never could it—have been less severe. I see him in the dust," etc.

[3] 1st ed. reads : " the caverns of Ocean, the halls of Pluto, the groves . . . "; and *Peleus* replies, " He . . . years. Why should I repeat it ? Troy . . . already, and may still resist more than one war."

242

duration : other Gods and other worlds are formed within it. If indeed he must perish at Troy, his ashes will lie softly on hers. Thus fall our beauteous son ! thus rest Achilles !

TERNISSA (*as Thetis*). " Twice nine years have scarcely yet passed over his head, since ' O the youth of Æmathia ! O the swift, the golden-haired Peleus ! ' were the only words sounded in the halls of Tethys. How many shells were broken for their hoarseness ! how many reproofs were heard by the Tritons for interrupting the slumbers—of those who never slept ! But they feigned sound sleep : and joy and kindness left the hearts of sisters. We [1] loved too well for others to love *us*.

" Why do I remember the day ? why do I remind thee of it ?— my Achilles dies ! it was the day that gave me my Achilles ! Dearer he was to me than the light of heaven, before he ever saw it : and how much dearer now ! when, bursting forth on earth like its first dayspring, all the loveliness of Nature stands back, and grows pale and faint before his.[2] He is what thou wert when I first beheld thee. How can I bear again so great a deprivation ?

EPICURUS (*as Peleus*). " O, thou art fallen ! thou art fallen through my embrace, when I thought on him more than on thee. Look up again ; look, and forgive me. No : thy forgiveness I deserve not—but did I deserve thy love ? Thy solitude, thy abasement, thy [3] parental tears, and thy fall to the earth, are from me ! Why [4] doth aught of youth linger with me ? why not come age and death ? The monster of Calydon made (as thou knowest) his first and most violent rush against this arm ; no longer fit for war, no longer a defence to the people. And is the day too come when it no longer can sustain my Thetis ?

TERNISSA (*as Thetis*). " Protend it not to the skies ! invoke not, name not, any deity ! I fear them all. Nay, lift me not thus above thy head, O Peleus ! reproaching the Gods with such an awful look ; with a look of beauty which they will not pity, with a look of defiance which they may not brook.

EPICURUS (*as Peleus*). " Doth not my hand enclasp that slender foot, at which the waves of Ocean cease to be tumultuous, and the

---

[1] From " We " to " us " added in 2nd ed.
[2] In 1st ed. the speech of *Thetis* ends at " before his."
[3] From " thy " to " tears " added in 2nd ed.
[4] From " Why " to " death " added in 2nd ed.

243

children of Æolus to disturb their peace ? O, if in the celestial coolness of thy cheek, now resting on my head, there be not the breath and gift of immortality ; O, if Zeus hath any thunder-bolt in reserve for me ; let this, my beloved Thetis, be the hour ! "

LEONTION. You have repeated it admirably ; and you well deserve to be seated as you are, on the only bank of violets in this solitary place. Indeed you must want repose. Why do you continue to look sad ? It is all over. Ah my silly comfort ! That may be the reason.

TERNISSA. I shall be very angry with him for the way (if you saw it) in which he made me slip down : and I should have been so at the time, if it would not have hurt the representation.

Yes, indeed, you may expect it, sir !

EPICURUS. I shall always say, " at any hour but this."

TERNISSA. Talk reasonably ; and return to your discourse on age. I wish you had a little more of its prudence and propriety.

EPICURUS. And what else ?

TERNISSA. O ! those are quite enough.

EPICURUS. There we agree. And now for obedience to your wishes. Peleus, you observe, makes no complaint that age is advancing on him : death itself is not unwelcome : for he had been happier than he could ever hope to be again. They who have long been wretched wish for death : they who have long been fortunate, may with equal reason : but it is wiser in each condition to await it than to desire it.

TERNISSA. I love to hear stories of heroic men, in whose bosoms there is left a place for tenderness.

Leontion said that even bad writers may amuse our idle hours : alas ! even good ones do not much amuse mine, unless [1] they record an action of love or generosity. As for the graver, why can not they come among us and teach us, just as you do ?

EPICURUS. Would you wish it ?

TERNISSA. No, no ; I do not want them : only I was imagining how pleasant it is to converse as we are doing, and how sorry I should be to pore over a book instead of it. Books always make me sigh, and think about other things. Why do you laugh, Leontion ?

EPICURUS. She was mistaken in saying bad authors may amuse

[1] From " unless " to " graver " added in 2nd ed.

our idleness. Leontion knows not then how sweet and sacred idleness is.

LEONTION. To render it sweet and sacred, the heart must have a little garden of its own, with its umbrage and fountains and perennial flowers ; a careless company ! Sleep is called sacred as well as sweet by Homer : and idleness is but a step from it. The idleness of the wise and virtuous should be both, it being the repose and refreshment necessary for past exertions and for future : it punishes the bad man, it rewards the good : the deities enjoy it, and Epicurus praises it. I was indeed wrong in my remark : for we should never seek amusement in the foibles of another, never in coarse language, never in low thoughts. When the mind loses its feeling for elegance, it grows corrupt and grovelling, and seeks in the crowd what ought to be found at home.

EPICURUS. Aspasia believed so, and bequeathed to Leontion, with every other gift that Nature had bestowed upon her, the power [1] of delivering her oracles from diviner lips.

LEONTION. Fie ! Epicurus ! It is well you hide my face for me with your hand. Now take it away : we can not walk in this manner.

EPICURUS. No word could ever fall from you without its weight ; no breath from you ought to lose itself in the common air.

LEONTION. For shame ! What would you have ?

TERNISSA. He knows not what he would have nor what he would say. I must sit down again. I declare I scarcely understand a single syllable. Well, he is very good, to tease you no longer. Epicurus has an excellent heart ; he would give pain to no one ; least of all to you.

LEONTION. I have pained him by this foolish book, and he would only assure me that he does not for a moment bear me malice. Take the volume : take it, Epicurus ! tear it in pieces.

EPICURUS. No, Leontion ! I shall often look with pleasure on this trophy of brave humanity : let me kiss the hand that raises it !

TERNISSA. I am tired of sitting : I am quite stiff : when shall we walk homeward ?

EPICURUS. Take my arm, Ternissa !

TERNISSA. O ! I had forgotten that I proposed to myself a trip

[1] 1st ed. reads : " power and authority of stamping her thoughts with this more beautiful effigy."

as far up as the pinasters, to look at the precipice of Oreithyia. Come along! come along! how alert does the sea-air make us! I seem to feel growing at my feet and shoulders the wings of Zethes or Calaïs.

EPICURUS. Leontion walks the nimblest to-day.

TERNISSA. To display her activity and strength, she runs before us. Sweet Leontion, how good she is! but she should have stayed for us: it would be in vain to try to overtake her.

No, Epicurus! Mind! take care! you are crushing these little oleanders—and now the strawberry plants—the whole heap—Not I, indeed. What would my mother say, if she knew it? And Leontion? she will certainly look back.

EPICURUS. The fairest of the Eudaimones never look back : such are the Hours and Love, Opportunity and Leontion.

TERNISSA. How could you dare to treat me in this manner? I did not say again I hated anything.

EPICURUS. Forgive me!

TERNISSA. Violent creature!

EPICURUS. If tenderness is violence. Forgive me; and say you love me.

TERNISSA.[1] All at once? could you endure such boldness?

EPICURUS. Pronounce it! whisper it!

TERNISSA. Go, go. Would it be proper?

EPICURUS. Is that sweet voice asking its heart or me? let the worthier give the answer.

TERNISSA. O Epicurus! you are very, very dear to me—and are the last in the world that would ever tell you were called so.

---

[1] 1st ed. reads: "TERNISSA. All at once? EPICURUS. Pronounce it! whisper! TERNISSA. Can I? Ought I? EPICURUS," etc.

XV. EPICURUS AND METRODORUS

(*Wks.*, ii., 1876.)

EPICURUS. Welcome, old friend, welcome! Sit down by me. Menander came to visit me this morning. *He* battled with the Sun for the encounter; the earliest of the stars appears to have guided *you*.

METRODORUS. If I now could wish anything, I might wish that I had met him here.

EPICURUS. He brought with him his usual affability and good-humour, with as much of wit and wisdom as friendship stands in need of; and now comes the only other I desired to see, the quieter Metrodorus.

METRODORUS. Menander is true and faithful. He is not composed of such light materials as to be shaken off his pedestal by popular applause. Acknowledging the claims of friendship, he discharges them readily and completely.

EPICURUS. He visits me seldom, but never unwillingly or in haste to go away.

METRODORUS. This is scarcely to be numbered among his various merits, although he is courted no less by the powerful than by the people, and loves conviviality.

EPICURUS. Some are well fitted for conviviality, others for public life, others for discussion, others (much the fewer) for retirement. They are no philosophers who lay down strictly one rule and regulation for all. Exercise, which is needful for health, is not conducive to it at every hour or for every man. Weak plants perish in the sunshine, stronger spring up to meet it. Menander is one of these. You and I shall never say as many wise things as he hath said, nor pour them into so many or so willing ears. Compare the apothegms of Euripides with his, and then you may compare the heavy old iron coinage of Sparta with the golden of our city—sharp, well-rounded, and fresh and lustrous from the mint.

247

METRODORUS. Beside, the one comes often from those who have no reason or right to utter it, the other never. Menander knows and observes the character of the times : Euripides jumbles in his loose leather bag a coinage which thereby loses much of its weight, together with the distinctness of the figures which it should represent.

EPICURUS. Observing his allusions from past ages to the present, it must not be forgotten that there are remarks which are applicable to almost all times, and moral and political features transmitted from generation to generation. Similar characters will re-appear in similar circumstances, and re-produce similar events. Manners vary much oftener and much more widely than vices and virtues.

METRODORUS. Homer hath represented the civilisation of Europe far lower than of Asia. Priam, Hector, Glaucus, Sarpedon, excell the heroes and demigods, and even the Gods, of our continent.

EPICURUS. I wish you had been here with Menander and me— not indeed this morning, but a few months ago, that you might have listened to his discourse when he compared the wisdom of past ages with ours. Few men are less enthusiastic, none more liberal, none more discerning in the distribution of praise.

METRODORUS. Yet every man has preferences, if not prejudices ; I never heard from Menander to what authors he was most inclined.

EPICURUS. Homer and Herodotus.

METRODORUS. I should have fancied that Thucydides would have taken the second place with him, for the style of Thucydides much resembles his in terseness. Added to which, he cherishes the love of those institutions under which he, like ourselves, was born and educated.

EPICURUS. On the side of Herodotus there was also a similarity. Herodotus, like Menander, was too wise, too even-tempered, to run headlong into the poisonous thorns of party, or the perplexing entanglements of State-machinery.

METRODORUS. But he mingles truth with fable.

EPICURUS. They who do it not in their writings do it in their lives. All history is fabulous.

METRODORUS. Surely we know many facts, and may reasonably believe many others.

EPICURUS. We know few perfectly, and must sift the rest. Point out to me the historian who can explain all the motives to all the actions performed by Pericles, the wisest ruler that ever ruled any portion of mankind ; yet there are citizens now living whose fathers held offices in his administration, and who must often have heard his merits brought into discussion and debate. Epaminondas, who comes nearest to him, is less ambiguous. That he is unequalled in strategy is now denied, since Alexander of Macedon made wider conquests. When men are thrown on the ground and trampled on, they lose their senses, and, if able to calculate at all, miscalculate the stature of those who stand over them. The architect who constructed the city of Alexandria is held in lower estimation than the destroyer who burnt Persepolis. Teachers will teach the young this pernicious falsehood, confounding high and low, right and wrong, in many lands, for many generations. Converse with any ten citizens on the merits of Demosthenes, and you will find yourself in the minority. Yet, in elevation of soul, and ability to raise others up to it, inasmuch as they had breath within them to bear the elevation, no mortal, not even Solon, ever approached him.

METRODORUS. Wonderful then that the wicked should have prevailed ! Here is indeed a strong argument that the Gods take no interest in the affairs of men.

EPICURUS. It is asserted, and become approved, that " truth is powerful and will prevail." I would rather believe in the idlest tale about the Gods than in this. When is truth to prevail ? Did it ever ? In tangible matters, in experimental, we have found much truth, and shall find more ; but while the passions and desires of men exist, proportionately so long will truth hide her face from them, or show it partially, as one ashamed.

METRODORUS. The passions are more powerful and more immortal than the Gods. If the Gods speak, which they rarely do, the passions drown their voices. Religious men acknowledge this, hypocrites and profligates alone deny it.

EPICURUS. Religion is in danger of exhaustion and demise by over-working on credulity. Our Athenians are the most devout of men ; yet they are reluctant to admit among their Jupiters the Lybian ram, or his foundling kid, pastured on the mountains of Macedonia. The soldiers of that country walk daily up to the Parthenon, yet continue they so obtuse that they laugh in our faces when we open to them the most holy of our mysteries. Although they hold Pallas in veneration, it appears to diminish rather than to increase, when their arch-priest informs them that our virgin

Goddess sprang, armed from head to foot, in full stature, from her father's forehead, and without aperture made in it; furthermore, if she was married to as many as Venus was, none of them could extract from her a particle of her virginity. Nay, she might bear child after child, and still retain it, just as safe and sound as when she herself was one. Moreover, there are certain priests in countries far distant from Athens, who never heard about the forehead, and who substitute another miracle, affirming that our protectress was endowed with virginity by hereditary descent; that it was the mother's long after the daughter's birth, and that between them, with sacerdotal co-operation, they select a number of favourites on whom the same privilege is conferred. Several of the Gods have changed or modified their nature; others in their senility have been wheedled into adoptions. Silenus stood his ground (if riding an ass may be called so) age after age; at last comes forward a more drunken rival, and swings him off the saddle. Surely the son of Jupiter Hammon has a better right to the favour of the nymphs. This latest God had a short life and a merry one, although having lived like a lion, he died like a rat. His predecessors sailed upon clouds, which dissolved under them, exhibiting here and there the imaginary form of plants and animals, driven forth to fresh pasturage. The goat of Ida will suckle new Jupiters when the elder is starved to death upon Olympus.

METRODORUS. People hate us mortally when we drive their fears away from them; they have been so long accustomed to handle the mask, and to clap it before their faces, that, if we snatch it off, they are comfortless, inconsolable, and ferocious. Pomps and ceremonies will always draw after them the masses of mankind. There is an outcry against us for atheism; do the outcryers know the full meaning of the word? Let them be informed that atheists are to be classed under three heads: disbelievers in any Gods; believers in a dozen or a score of them, but apart from human cares and concerns; and believers that they mix in them somewhat too freely and indiscriminately, believers who find them guilty of cruelty, jealousy, vengeance, and injustice. These we shall rather call dystheists than atheists. Men in all nations and in all times have displayed more zeal and ability in pulling down the Gods to their own level, than in raising themselves ever so little toward the Gods.

EPICURUS. It is better that a thing or agent do not exist at all,

250

than exist for evil. A God cannot be corporeal. Surely he needs no part of our configuration, and can be reduced to none of our necessities and infirmities.

METRODORUS. Priests bring the substance and mould the form ; and the Gods in return give them the corn-field out of which they were digged. They can show you the charter and the seal. Sterile as is the soil of Attica, there are priests upon it (as I hear from those who uphold their dignity) drawing from the sweat of the labourer many hundred talents annually ; it has even been reported that some of them have an income equivalent to what supports all the veteran soldiers whom the calamities of our last war have spared, alive though mutilated.

EPICURUS. Be no such visionary, Metrodorus, as to imagine that hierax, a bird of prey, has any relationship to hïerateia. Do not believe that any free State ever bore this domination, or that the policy of any conqueror would permit it. Religion must be clothed in superhuman splendour, that the eyes may be taken off from the heart. If the heart could be looked into and consulted, the temples would not be destroyed, but every house would become one. Domestic duties would supersede street processions, and prayer would be no longer a commodity for sale. God wanted no archetype for man, and man wanted none for God. Concerning these matters we have conversed and written, but not for the multitude. To the multitude we can only say, be patient, temperate, forbearing, helpful. Practise these duties, and you will be the happier ; neglect them, and you will suffer. Your wrath is effectually the wrath of the Gods ; they can inflict no heavier curse than you thereby are inflicting on yourselves.

METRODORUS. Many, O Epicurus, have received from you, and have profited by, this doctrine ; but grosser minds require grosser nourishment. The very most we can reasonably hope is, that the authority of priests shall never supersede the authority of magistrates, or be employed in aiding the oppressor, instead of comforting and strengthening the oppressed.

EPICURUS. Republics have at no time endured this ignominy, nor in ours has a perfidious and ferocious conqueror imposed it.

METRODORUS. Well I know that, even with me, you are averse to the discussion of politics, as the matter most likely to disturb the equipoise of the mind ; but we are living at a time when our very existence as a nation is involved in them. The aristocracy placed at the side of Philip the most able, and indeed the only able one, of our generals. His probity and his prejudices clung together.

EPICURUS. Unhappy Phœcian; unhappy Athens! When Thebes fell the earth recoiled; nothing stood upright but Demosthenes. Thousands at his voice rose up again from the dust only to fall for ever on the plain of Chœroneia.

METRODORUS. Institutions are now established for the benefit of a few families. Instead of a Theseus, a Cecrops, a Codrus, and a Solon, what bestial men are now become our governors!

EPICURUS. Philip left a successor who inherited all his vices, little of his sagacity, which in a prince is sometimes equivalent to a virtue. But Philip might have been the benefactor, not only of his own people, but also of many others. Perhaps, as a politician, it was reasonable in him to attempt a conquest of Bœotia, and the whole coast as far as Byzantium, and beyond. Yet even that is doubtful; for although the city is the best adapted to commerce of any in Europe, it might on that very account become his capital, and thereby have changed the character and counteracted the interests of the Macedonians. It would, however, have preserved to him a barrier against the Scythians, who, whenever they become as unwise as we are, will attempt to extend their prodigiously vast territory, and go hunting in pursuit of riches and luxuries. I do not wonder, nor am I displeased, at finding you inattentive to my discourse.

METRODORUS. Pardon me, pardon me; my thoughts were wandering far from public affairs, and (may I confess it) even from this quiet scene. I came late to you that your other friends might have been gone away, and that I might confer with you privately.

EPICURUS. On what subject?

METRODORUS. I hardly dare lay it before you.

EPICURUS. Speak confidently. There are many things of which I am utterly ignorant, much as I may have thought about them. You will presently find it out.

METRODORUS. Never was I less bold in asking a question. Would you advise me to marry?

EPICURUS. Certainly not. You are richer in wisdom than in the ordinary means of living; do not throw away that, and the credit it gives you. Perhaps there may be a trifle of dower; but, O

EPICURUS AND METRODORUS

Metrodorus, there is much, very much, which a father has no power of giving with his daughter.

METRODORUS. I expect no dower, or very little, for Phædimus has two sons, and another daughter, who is lame and helpless. It is this, besides my knowledge of his poverty and probity, which makes me desirous of acceding to his wishes.

EPICURUS. To marry his daughter?

METRODORUS. Even so. Believe me (indeed I know you do) I never once thought of what might lie within his competence of bestowing on his child. You smile.

EPICURUS. With your sagacity, great as it is, you have not comprehended me. What the father is unable to give, the daughter may be equally unable. You are my elder by several years, O Metrodorus,* and can hardly hope to live long enough to superintend the education of a family. If you are happy now, continue so; if unhappy, avoid the chance of being so more and more. The head beginning to bend under the weight of years droops irrecoverably at a small addition falling on it suddenly and unexpectedly. When a man utters the commonest, the most ancient, the most eternal of exclamations, *How could I ever have been such a fool!* we may be sure that others have already said the same thing of him, and not with the same dejection. Pleasures are soon absorbed; they soon evaporate in the heat of youth, and leave no traces behind them; but sorrows lay waste what they overflow, and we have neither time nor art to remove the obstruction and counteract the sterility.

METRODORUS. O Epicurus! Are we not all of us desirous to communicate with a friend our anxiety and our content? Should we not participate and exchange them?

EPICURUS. Communicate your happiness freely; confine your discontent within your own bosom. There chastise it; be sure it deserves its chastisement.

METRODORUS. In my proposed change of life I see nothing to reprehend, and little to fear.

EPICURUS. On the sea before you the venture is a costly one, the wrecks frequent. Let those hoist the sails who know how to reef them. At our time of life, Metrodorus, the comeliness of form and feature has left us. Nature ordains that these should attract the

---

* He married late and left young children, recommended by the kindest of philosophers to the care of their mutual friends.—W. S. L.

other sex towards us. It may be that in earlier days they made an impression which years have not effaced. Is it so, my friend, with you?

METRODORUS. No, indeed; but she loves me because her father loves me, and, let me add, because you do.

EPICURUS. Such a contract of marriage is not sealed with a wax which soon loses its impression.

METRODORUS. Blessings on the man who made her heart docile and virtuous; 'twas you.

EPICURUS. I do not remember to have seen her. Is she young and personable?

METRODORUS. Alas! she is young; her twenty-fifth year is commencing. I never heard that she is handsome; she may be. But O, Epicurus, if you could see her spin! if you could taste (as I hope you will soon do at our wedding-feast) the delicious rye-bread she makes! I do assure you that, with the barley and millet in it, it is as white as my hand.

EPICURUS. Here, my old friend, we are within the range of probabilities.

METRODORUS. O Epicurus! I am transported at the prospect of my happiness. When she loses her father, she will find me.

EPICURUS. Now say I to you, Metrodorus, what I never said to another: I deliver to your keeping the most abstruse and the most dubious of my doctrines. Never divulge it.

METRODORUS. Impart it first.

EPICURUS. Marry. Good, generous Metrodorus, in thy heart lies thy wisdom; nor there only: the vase is capacious, but the luxuriant plant overruns the marge on every side.

METRODORUS. You ponder, even after the delivery of your sentence.

EPICURUS. There are two things which, beyond all others, both experienced and inexperienced should alike be slow to recommend.

METRODORUS. Have you stated them in any of your writings?

EPICURUS. I often have reflected, but never have written upon them. The two things are medicine and matrimony. What is good for this patient is inapplicable to that. How many have murdered both stranger and friend by advising a medicament which to others may perhaps have been salutary! How many have found under the saffron strewn thinly in the path of Hymen, the pungent and crooked and entangling thorn ! Inconsiderate, and worse than inconsiderate, is inducing the unwary to deviate from a path which lies open and smooth before him, and where he is walking on contentedly. The married soon discover each other's faults and imperfections ; soon lose sight of what attracted them, and the eyes sometimes droop, sometimes wander. The bride too frequently sheds her petals in the porch ; the wife treads upon them, and they are swept away. Instead of lute and lyre, sounds are presently heard within the house louder than the cymbal, but unlike it, unless in clashing. It will not be thus with you, my Metrodorus ; therefore to you say I—*marry ! marry !*

XVI. MENANDER AND EPICURUS[1]

(*Fraser's Magazine*, 1856 ; *Wks.*, ii., 1876.)

EPICURUS. Menander ! can it be Menander I see before me ?
Ah ! indeed it is ; for no other man alive would press so heartily
the hand of an old friend.

MENANDER. Do not lose your philosophy in your emotion, my
Epicurus.

EPICURUS. I would lose it any day on such a bargain.   There is
no danger of any man carrying his best affections to excess, provided
they be not adulterated with worse.

MENANDER. Do you know what day it is ?

EPICURUS. I know it, and was thinking of it when you entered
the garden.

MENANDER. Alas ! my Epicurus, on this very day we behold the
middle of our centenary.

EPICURUS. True ; but why *alas ?*   We may do wiser things, and
utter wiser, than we ever have yet done or uttered.   Even you may ;
altho' I always have thought you, beyond all comparison, the wisest
man Greece ever gave birth to.

MENANDER. Is such an opinion as consistent with philosophy as
with friendship ?

EPICURUS. I do not always weigh my words before I utter them,
but I always weigh my thoughts before I turn them out into words.
Among the most celebrated of our philosophers, as they were pleased
to call themselves, I have found little else than clever quibbles and
defence of pernicious falsehoods.   I should have called Demosthenes
the wisest of mankind, he being at once the most acute, the most
eloquent, the most virtuous, the most patriotic.   But this last virtue,
which was perhaps the most prominent of them, induces me to think

---

[1] Forster gave this as the Second Conversation of Menander and Epicurus,
but Landor obviously intended it to precede what Forster took to be the First
Conversation.

him defective in solidity of wisdom. He defended the Commonwealth when he stood alone ; was this rational ?

MENANDER. He defended my father : and then also he stood
alone.

EPICURUS. But there he knew his power of persuasion and his
probability of gaining the cause. Against the Macedonian no chance
remained. And now, Menander, let me ask you a question. Did
you ever, in the course of your life, hear me converse with you or any
man so long on politics ?

MENANDER. Never ; and I may with equal confidence ask of you
the same question in regard to me. There is only one government
worth defending, and even that government is neither worth anxiety
nor productive of it. Here it lies : with me under a loose and flowing
robe, with you under one shorter and more succinct. Leontion, and
that pretty little Themisto, whom Leontion used to call *Terenissa*,
and she herself and you *Ternissa*, never agitated to more than a
sunny ripple your gentle and fond bosom. Glycera with me was
more mischievously playful, and dipt her wand more deeply.

EPICURUS. Are you never discomposed, O Menander, at seeing
those coarser images and grosser follies which you describe with such
accuracy and in such diversity ?

MENANDER. Not at all : nor indeed do I see the hundredth part
of them. Imagination is quite as fond of comedy as of the tragic
or epic.

EPICURUS. But you must sometimes have walked in unseemly
and uncleanly places.

MENANDER. Rarely and unwillingly. Others have lived and
laboured for me. Precious stones are embedded in sterile rocks, and
pearls in foul putridity. I do not gather them, altho' I polish, wear,
and display them.

Leontion more than once has puzzled and perplext me by the
intricacies of her discourse, and by attempting to lead me into
abstruse investigations ; Glycera, on the contrary, is so simple,
I would not say *silly*, that I pick up from her incessantly fresh ideas,
or the nutriment of them, without her ever perceiving or suspecting
it, which would render her intolerably vain. The sweetness of her
temper would not let her be arrogant if she found me out, but she
would become less girlish. If we would caress we must stoop.

EPICURUS. Leontion is age-ing a little. Death had pity on

Ternissa, and crowned her in her spring of youth. There is only one cypress in this garden : under it, surrounded by strawberries, lies Ternissa. O Menander! how these plants, planted by her, cooled my cheek, how nearly they comforted my heart, the first moment I threw myself upon them!

MENANDER. And there are those who eulogize, and also those who rebuke, the apathy of Epicurus!

EPICURUS. Both are right. The passion of love may be indulged by good citizens, the sentiment by the wise recluse. Ternissa died on my bosom and died happy ; less happy would she have been had I died on hers. She bequeathed me this thought for the assuagement of my grief ; it were ungrateful to renounce or to forget it.

MENANDER. Leontion, with her usual affability and politeness, congratulates me always on the success of my comedies.

EPICURUS. Then you must meet often ; for altho' you sometimes are less popular than your competitor, you excell him invariably.

MENANDER. I asked Polemon [1] whether he never blushed at the preference given to him over me.

" *What is a blush,*" said Polemon, " *when it is to be divided among so many ?* "

EPICURUS. I never heard of this reply.

MENANDER. I doubt whether he repeated it to anyone : I have not until now.

EPICURUS. You retain your equanimity on your defeat, as indeed I might have expected you would do.

MENANDER. Surely it is the least you might have expected from me, when our defeats and failures affect with no small pleasure so many of our friends. They receive a great satisfaction in meeting us with their condolences, and in lifting up their eyes at the injustice of the world.

As you never go to the theatre, and are contented to hear from me the philosophy I throw occasionally on the stage, I will repeat to you a couple of verses from my successful opponent ; not that in this matter we are opponents at all, neither of us being in the sad category here described.

> There are two miseries in human life ;
> To live without a friend, and with a wife.

---

[1] " Polemon " : Philemon, competitor against Menander.

MENANDER AND EPICURUS

Such are the expressions of *Misogamos*. When they were reported to Diogenes on his death-bed at Corinth, he raised himself up on his elbow, and said, " I am no conjectural critic, but I suspect the young poet wrote *dog*, not *friend*, unless he intended a·synonym."

Polemon writes admirably, and possesses the advantage of studying his own personages. Neither you nor I are much disposed to mingle with the people, or to face them on any occasion.

EPICURUS. It is what beyond all things I have the most avoided, unless it be to sit down at dinner with several others. Loud language, discharges of it across the table, the smell of meat intermixed with it, and often both of them together in the same mouth at the same time, would be to me such a penalty as your graver brethren of the buskin never have inflicted on the most criminal in the infernal regions.

MENANDER. Many thanks to you, Epicurus, for giving me the frame-work of a new comedy. What think you of some such title as *The Deipnosophists ?*

EPICURUS. Our Macedonians would delight in it ; but it requires the exertion of your whole genius to make it palatable to our *Demos*. Something of the Attic is yet left in Attica.

MENANDER. The Demos could swallow fare even less delicate, set before them by Aristophanes. Observe, whatever may be my self-complacency, I lay no claim to equality with the most harmonious and facetious of poets. Ages will pass away, and crops of follies will spring up season after season, and be mowed down again, but never will comedian arise to the level of this Hymettian lark, building the nest upon the ground, and soaring in full song among the *clouds*.

EPICURUS. I have conversed with few poets familiarly ; you are the only one I ever encountered free from invidiousness and self-conceit. Aristophanes, in his *Birds*, has turned into well-merited ridicule the framers of imaginary commonwealths. If any such could be introduced into our country, they who sigh at all would sigh for the return of the Macedonians. To me the fresh air of this elevated garden is a perennial fountain of delight ; *you* must breathe the breath of the people.

MENANDER. I confess to you, I enjoy it.

EPICURUS. May you never lose your enjoyment, or experience a diminution of it. Every man should enjoy what he can enjoy innocently, and without trespassing upon others. You have written more than any man, and better than any. Even in Homer there are tedious passages, and long ones, but I question whether the most fastidious critic would expunge twenty verses from your hundred thousand.

MENANDER. Gently ! gently ! Hundred thousand !

EPICURUS. You have composed nearly a hundred comedies : each contains at least a thousand verses ; some contain many more.

MENANDER. Is it possible ?

EPICURUS. Possible is it that any poet in existence has never counted the lines he wrote ?

MENANDER. Jocularity made me insensible to labour, and I never counted the seeds I scattered from my sack over so extensive a field.

I wonder whether the greatest of our poets, since Homer, could have felt the same degree of pleasure. Æschylus, I am inclined to believe, is almost as inventive as even Homer himself. We have no other poet who either has displayed much invention or much discrimination and truth of character. Poor Æschylus ! what must he have suffered while he and his Prometheus were under the vulture, and creatures more ferocious than vultures stood taunting round about. He had his task to do, and he did it ; how grandly !

I do not believe you care very much about poetry.

EPICURUS. Perhaps it is because I am so ignorant of it. I confess to you that, when I used to read tragedies, they affected me more than I thought desirable. I collect from your comedies what are the manners of the Athenians, and I read of them more complacently than I could live among them. We are pleased in pictures with what would displease us in real life.

MENANDER. May I walk up to the cypress ?

EPICURUS. Yes, if you promise me that you will not break off a particle.

MENANDER. I promise ; let us go.

EPICURUS. Menander ! go alone. You are among the few I would ever walk a hundred paces with, and thither not even with you. Gather as many strawberries as you can find, for the day is hot, and they are refreshing. The few violets have ceased to blossom, but there is another flower, which Ternissa transplanted from among the rocks into this little mound : it was her favourite, and I can not but fancy that it returns me the odour of her cool sweet face; it is the white cyclamen : you may gather one flower, but not give it away when you go home.

MENANDER. Parsimonious man ! I will obey, however.

EPICURUS. So soon returned ?

MENANDER. There is no inscription.

EPICURUS. Ah,[1] yes there is.

MENANDER. I did not see it.

EPICURUS. It is not well you should. The cypress, the cyclamen, the violet, will outlast it. Pure, tender love wrote it where none shall find it.

I often bring her image before me ; gentle, serene, impassive. Menander ! my Menander ! Life has much to give us, and Death has little to take away ! therefore the one is to be cherished, the other neither to be deplored nor feared. While we retain our memory, we also retain, if we are wise and virtuous, the best of our affections ; when we lose it, we lose together with it the worst of our calamities. Sleep, every night, deprives men of that faculty which it is (inconsiderately !) thought an evil to lose in the last days of life.

MENANDER. Frankly do I confess to you, Epicurus, that I would rather lose my memory than my teeth. One of these losses carries its own remedy with it : we know not, or know but imperfectly, that it is gone : of the other loss we are reminded at least twice a day, and we curse the impotence of cookery. At present I am spared my maledictions : I carry my arms stoutly in high polish, especially when I celebrate the intermarriage of young kid with old chian. There are among us some who, on their return from Persia and Babylonia, have introduced loud music into dinner-parties. Can you imagine anything more barbarous ? A festival ought to be a solemnity, and a dinner-party is a festival. During the meal there ought to be silence ; after it music as much as you please : it dilutes the grossness of conversation, and corrects its insipidity. Added to which, there is somewhat in music which breathes an aroma over the wine.

EPICURUS. Of this you can judge better than I can, who drink water only ; and I would rather see kid upon the mountain than upon the table. Yet I also have my delicacies : I am much addicted

---

[1] The punctuation here is not Forster's, but the exclamation mark **after** " take away," below, is retained as more Landorian than that supplied by Crump's text.

to sweet and light cakes flavoured with rose-water, and to whatever is composed of fruit and cream, not excluding from my hospitable board any quail or partridge that may alight upon it. I do not perceive, my Menander, that the advance of age has produced any material difference in our tempers and dispositions.

MENANDER. O my friend, you have always been readier to scrutinize your own heart than your neighbour's. Perhaps I never exhibited in your presence the imperfections of mine; indeed in your company I never was inclined to be impetuous or impatient. Bad men grow worse by keeping, as bad wines do. The unwise are rendered more morose by years, the wise more temperate and gentle. You, who are the essence of tranquillity, are unchanged for the worse or the better, while other philosophers indulge their pride, their arrogance, their resentments, toward those nearest them, reserving all their good qualities for the Gods. Tranquillity is enjoyment, and it is folly to look for it elsewhere. The passions drive it from the house; it is hazarded in society; it is lost in crowds. Philosophy will always bring it to us, if she knows where to find us and we will wait for her : but we must not behave like children who fight for the ball. She avoids contention, and never scolds or wrangles, never puzzles with a maze of thorny interrogations, in which Truth is farther out of sight at every turn, and the artificer of the clipped hedge shows us no way out of the labyrinth.

You are among the few, or I should rather have said you stand the foremost and most distinct, of those who walk quietly with her and converse unostentatiously. It is not pride which withholds you from turning round upon the captious and casting them at your feet.

EPICURUS. I never answer an adversary.

MENANDER. You confer enough of honour by hearing him.

EPICURUS. Even this honour I have no right to claim.

MENANDER. But there are extravagancies which you might correct without exciting your bile (if you have any in you) by the least of intercourse.

EPICURUS. I suspect, my good Menander, that you enjoy the follies of men in our rotten state as flies enjoy fruit in its decay.

MENANDER. What can we do with such men as those about us better than laugh at them ?

262

MENANDER AND EPICURUS

EPICURUS. Nothing with them, but much by keeping apart. If they laugh at each other for their weaknesses and their vices, these, countenanced and cherished by pleasantry, will become habitual and will increase.

MENANDER. If I exhorted them to be virtuous, they would ask me what virtue is. My father would have answered that patriotism is a main part of it ; and for such an assertion no Demosthenes could have saved him from the sword of the executioner. One wise man took the poison presented to him by the cup-bearer of the State ; another saved the State that ceremonial. Things are not so bad but we are still permitted to laugh ; if we wept, we should be called to a strict account for every tear.

EPICURUS. It would be folly to shed one. There are virtuous men among us who feel sorely the ignominy of living under the domination of the stranger. Inconsiderate ! Is this, which is now unavoidable, so low a condition as it is to be defrauded of freedom by those in whom we trusted, and to be unable or unwilling to make them responsible for their misdeeds ?

MENANDER. No slave is clever enough to tie his own hands behind him : only they who call themselves free have acquired this accomplishment.

EPICURUS. I live unmolested in my retirement. My philosophy does not irritate or excite. I have what I want of it for home-consumption, and am willing, but not anxious, that others should take the rest.

MENANDER. This indeed is true philosophy, yours exclusively. Socrates had a barking stomach for controversy and quibble ; Xenophon was half traitor, Plato complete sycophant. Perverseness actuated one, vanity the other : one left Philosophy outside the camp ; the other left her a prostitute in the palace. Far away from both, the graver and better Aristoteles was induced to be the guide of a wild youth, but unwilling and unable to be the keeper of a madman ; the Gods have given to Epicurus more than Epicurus could find among the Gods.

EPICURUS. Smile, my friend, as you will about them, they have given him a calm conscience, a spirit averse to disputation, and a friend to enjoy his garden with him uninterrupted ; a friend even dearer than solitude.

IMAGINARY CONVERSATIONS: GREEK

SECOND CONVERSATION

(*Wks.*, ii., 1876.)

MENANDER. Another year! another year! my old friend! *To the garden! to the garden once more*, said I to myself, as the dawn entered my chamber.

EPICURUS. Sit down by me; you seem fatigued.

MENANDER. The sun is now ascending the heavens at full speed. I prefer the white dapples of his horses, such as I saw when we were starting together, to their fume and foam which I now feel about me. Ah, Epicurus! I wish I was as thin as you are. A few stadions make me drag my heels after me with a chain about them.

EPICURUS. If you were as thin and angular as I am, the arts would have lost a rich ornament. Your statue, in a sitting posture, is the most beautiful and the most characteristic of any in our city. There is ease in thoughtfulness, and pleasantry in wisdom; there is also a warm day, like the present, in the attitude.

MENANDER. The Gods be gracious to me! but they have scarcely left breath enough in my body to walk twenty more paces.

EPICURUS. And why should you?

MENANDER. To gather another cyclamen. Since the last, Actene has bequeathed to you, I hear, the greater part of her property; just as if her wishes that you would espouse her Ternissa had been accomplished.

EPICURUS. We were born in the same Olympiad, if not in the same Archonate. Thramites, her husband, was willing and desirous that I should educate their daughter. He often brought her with him to hear me, while she was yet a child. Unlearned as he was, he had collected many books, some in Athens, some in Miletus, some on the borders of the Nile. Being a merchant, he was obliged to take in payment these occasionally; and he consulted me what authors the little girl should read. Never was I more puzzled; at last I re commended " Æsop's Fables " and the " Histories of Herodotus "; but under my tuition. The pious mother stealthily interfered, but I dissembled my knowledge of this interference. Ternissa was admonished by me to obey her in all things, especially in regard to the Gods.

MENANDER. You astonish me.

264

MENANDER AND EPICURUS

EPICURUS. My good Menander! obedience to parents, in all things lawful, is the most sacred of duties, and the earliest to be taught. We know not what the Gods may hereafter give us, or intend for us; but we do know that they have given us parents. We do know that parents love us instinctively, and that one of them hath suffered much for us ere she knew us. Gratitude then,[1] which is the better part of religion, and worth all the rest, even of the purer, draws us toward the sources of our existence.

MENANDER. Leontion has related to me that her friend Ternissa was averse to study.

EPICURUS. The fault, if there is any fault in it, is mine. I would not perplex, or suffer her to be perplexed, by systems of what we call philosophy. But we often read together a few pages of Natural History from the entertaining and instructive pages of Aristoteles.

MENANDER. What is become of the numerous volumes collected by her father?

EPICURUS. They are sold, and carried to Alexandria.

MENANDER. Actene, it is said, bequeathed them all to you, together with the rest of her property.

EPICURUS. She did.

MENANDER. And you sold them?

EPICURUS. No, indeed; but in my small house there is no room for books or property. It could, however, hold a porphyry vase large enough for a child to bathe in, and two additional volumes, one the Odyssea, the other the poems of Simonides.

MENANDER. Dissemble no more your love of poetry; one of these contains the most imaginative, the other the purest, the tenderest, the most elegant.

EPICURUS. The Odyssea was my delight in boyhood.

MENANDER. Simonides must have drawn forth some of your earliest and your latest tears.

EPICURUS. For which reason I was resolved they should draw forth none more precious. Two years before the death of Ternissa, I found her with these pages in her hands. " Ternissa," said I, " give me the smile that does not sparkle so." The sparkle ran down her cheeks, the smile left it. " Give me that book." She gave it, and I took it home. Within the hour I returned, carrying the

---

[1] The punctuation here is that of 1876; Crump gives dashes for commas enclosing the parenthesis.

Odyssea with me. She was sitting alone, not expecting me, yet looking as one expectant. " Thank you," said she, " thank you, Epicurus ! It was silly in me to shed a tear ; me who am so happy." The happy one sighed ; the wise one was confounded. " Ternissa," said I, " we will make an exchange. Here is a book containing more true tenderness than yours does, together with trials of endurance, victory over vain wishes, reward for fidelity, and return to domestic peace." One deeper sigh ensued.

MENANDER. Long treasured in the bosom of Epicurus, it now breathes softly on his friends.

EPICURUS. Seven years, nearly eight, has that shadow gone among those other shadows which vanish in succession from the earth. Can you tell me, could I ever tell myself, whether she has left me more of pain or pleasure ? It seems to me that I thought of her, while she was living, with less of tenderness than I do now. Often with anxiety then, now with none. Memory grows more and more merciful ; and the harrow roots up the weeds for wholesome seeds to grow.

MENANDER. When we met in this garden last year, we threw away on politics as much time as we could have counted a hundred in, and been better employed in doing it. Leontion tells me that you no longer are communicative with her about her younger friend. Hardly then can I expect that you will be more so with me, desirous as I am of hearing whatever I can learn about one who brought to you so much happiness.

EPICURUS. Incredulous as you must be, Leontion was jealous. No wonder you laugh.

MENANDER. Incredulity is not much addicted to laughter. Four years are somewhat more than an Olympiad in the days of women. Such, if I remember, was about the difference in theirs ; and Leontion must now have seen the lugubrious flight of thirty years. She speaks of you with reverence, which a man beyond fifty must do his best to bear.   I suspect that my seated figure would hardly have procured for me such an expression. And now, may I ask of you whether you possess any little statue of the sweet Ternissa ?

EPICURUS. None.

MENANDER. My question, I fear, is imprudent, and offends.

EPICURUS. Fear no such a thing.   Whatever is interesting to me, is interesting to my friend.

MENANDER AND EPICURUS

MENANDER. The spring, I remember, waited for Ternissa, and would not go without her.

EPICURUS. We crowned her with some of the flowers she had cherished. Maternal fondness, not without an apprehension that her beauty might attract the Macedonian, kept her within the house, when the fresh air might have been beneficial to her health.

MENANDER. O Epicurus! in my own despite, and in despite of my piety, you drive me again into politics. Never have I cursed the Macedonians so heartily for the shame and sorrow they have inflicted on us, as for the few of them which darkened the house of Ternissa. And now let me repeat to you a few verses which are neither comic nor consolatory; nor such perhaps as will ever be sung at the festivals of those barbarians. They are more applicable to the people of Attica, and some others :

> Ye whom your earthly gods condemn to heave
> The stone of Sisyphus uphill for ever,
> Do not, if ye have heard of him, believe,
> As your forefathers did, that he was clever.
>
> Strength in his arm, and wisdom in his head,
> He would have hurl'd his torment higher still,
> And would have brought them down with it, instead
> Of thus turmoiling at their wanton will.

EPICURUS. Methinks it would have been more godlike if they had inspired him to break the stone, and had kept him to mend the roads with it. But such imaginations are as ill adapted to our garden as iron benches would be, offering us rest, and giving us uneasiness and disquiet. If hereabout are only a few tufts of smooth and soft grass, we need not, however, peer into every quarter for the sharpest flints to set our feet on. If we have no images of nymphs and naiads, let us at least be exempt from such as represent the stronger animals tearing and devouring the weaker.

MENANDER. We have numerous artists chiselling in this school, who thrive prodigiously.

EPICURUS. Verily the stones are broken small enough, but the other party will never do the business, with their present overseers. You have taken me for a moment out of the chamber in which I love to linger.

MENANDER. If there is no indiscretion in the request, I would

267

entreat to enter it with you again ; for I much admire the chamber of that powerful and innocent girl, and I have often been desirous of seeing it reflected by you in some calm later hour ; the hour is now come.

EPICURUS. There is cheerfulness in the sunshine, but there is somewhat in the dusk beyond the best of cheerfulness. Light was withdrawn from me with Ternissa ; but it is not in the glare of day that we see the stars and feel the coolness of the heavens. In the morn of life we are alert, we are heated in its noon, and only in its decline do we repose.

MENANDER. But you in every stage of it have been temperate and serene.

EPICURUS. None are ; but some greatly more than others. Abstinence from public life, and from general society, has given me leisure for thought and meditation. Metrodorus and you are the only men I have admitted to familiarity.

MENANDER. Never were two more different.

EPICURUS. In habitudes and pursuits. You propell your thoughts into action, and throw wisdom into the gaping mouth of the laughing multitude. Metrodorus turns his little fish on the gridiron over a handful of charcoal, puts it between two slices of black bread and two rows of ready teeth, swallows a large cupful of fresh water, and sleeps soundly after it.

MENANDER. I doubt whether Ternissa would have been contented with his repast.

EPICURUS. She preferred her mother's, and even mine, although I seldom offered to her more than a small basketful of well-ripened fruit, which she usually carried home with her ; because the figs of this garden, especially the green and the yellow, were in favour with her mother.

MENANDER. And now tell me, if not disagreeable to you, how it happened that her mother, so fond of her, never thought of employing a sculptor to retain her youth and beauty.

EPICURUS. Earlier she might never have thought of losing her ; later, when I suggested that it should be done in the meridian of her health and loveliness, she laughed at my enthusiasm, " *Time enough yet*," said she. O Menander ! what miseries in all ages have these three words produced ! How many duties have they caused to be unfulfilled ! how many keen regrets have they excited ! When the mother saw, or fancied she saw, that her girl's slender form grew slenderer, she sent for the same sculptor who had been so successful in me. Ternissa was never disobedient to her mother, but she now was incompliant. Was it that I might be sent for to give my opinion? I was sent for, and went. Several days had passed since I had seen her. She was now sitting on the bedside, in a close yellow tunic, not reaching the grey sandals. " See how thin she is," said Actene. I stopped the hand that was on the shoulder! Ternissa smiled approvingly. " Do you desire my bust, O Epicurus? " " *Bust?* child! *statue* we want." She opened her eyes wide, turned them away from us, caught up her pillow, buried her face in it, and said, almost inaudibly, " O mother, mother! " " We will have Ternissa," said I, " we will have no statue, no bust." She turned round languidly and kissed my hand and cheek ; then, turning to her mother, she said to her, " Thank for me, bless for me, Epicurus." Little thought I, and little thought Actene, that our beloved one was so soon about to leave us. My visits had been frequent, but irregular. Usually I went to the house at noon when the citizens and soldiers were at dinner or asleep ; and the distance was short. Actene told me that one day, shortly after the customary hour, she found her child weak and fevered, and could not refrain from telling her. The reply was, " I may be weak and feverish, but Epicurus is wiser than either of us, and if he were not confident and certain of my speedy recovery, he would not have been absent from us three whole days." Indeed I was unaware of any danger. The first day Actene sent her maid for me, and I met her on the road. On my first inquiry, she told me her young mistress had recovered all her freshness, and had gained more. I found it true. The morning was excessively hot. I kissed her forehead ; she took my hand and kissed it. " Remember the strawberries," said she, and a faint blush and fainter smile played momentarily over her cheek. " The blossoms must be dropping fast, and the fruit must be setting ; water it for me ; I cannot go and help you." She sighed, leaned forward, and I caught her in my arms. " *Kind heart*," said Actene to me ; she might have said, *broken one*. Inconsiderate! inconsistent! When Ternissa had for ever ceased to weep, I wept.

XVII. RHADAMISTUS AND ZENOBIA

(*Imag. Convers. Gk. and Rom.*, 1853 ; transferred in *Wks.*, 1876, to " Famous Women " section.)

ZENOBIA. My beloved ! my beloved ! I can endure the motion of the horse no longer ; his weariness makes his pace so tiresome to me. Surely we have ridden far, very far from home ; and how shall we ever pass the wide and rocky stream, among the whirlpools of the rapid and the deep Araxes ? From the first sight of it, O my husband ! you have been silent : you have looked at me at one time intensely, at another wildly : have you mistaken the road ? or the ford ? or the ferry ?

RHADAMISTUS. Tired, tired ! did I say ? ay, thou must be. Here thou shalt rest : this before us is the place for it. Alight ; drop into my arms ; art thou within them ?

ZENOBIA. Always in fear for me, my tender thoughtful Rhadamistus !

RHADAMISTUS. Rhadamistus then once more embraces his Zenobia !

ZENOBIA. And presses her to his bosom as with the first embrace.

RHADAMISTUS. What is the first to the last !

ZENOBIA. Nay, this is not the last.

RHADAMISTUS. Not quite (O agony !), not quite ; once more.

ZENOBIA. So : with a kiss : which you forget to take.

RHADAMISTUS (*aside*). And shall this shake my purpose ? it may my limbs, my heart, my brain ; but what my soul so deeply determined, it shall strengthen : as winds do trees in forests.

ZENOBIA. Come, come ! cheer up. How good you are to be persuaded by me : back again at one word ! Hark ! where are those drums and bugles ? on which side are these echoes ?

RHADAMISTUS. Alight, dear, dear Zenobia ! And does Rhadamistus then press thee to his bosom ? Can it be ?

ZENOBIA. *Can it cease to be ?* you would have said, my Rhadamistus ! Hark ! again those trumpets ? on which bank of the

270

water are they ?   Now they seem to come from the mountains, and now along the river.   Men's voices too !   threats and yells !   You, my Rhadamistus, could escape.

RHADAMISTUS. Wherefor ?   with whom ?   and whither in all Asia ?

ZENOBIA. Fly ! there are armed men climbing up the cliffs.

RHADAMISTUS. It was only the sound of the waves in the hollows of them, and the masses of pebbles that rolled down from under you as you knelt to listen.

ZENOBIA. Turn round ; look behind ! is it dust yonder, or smoke ? and is it the sun, or what is it, shining so crimson ? not shining any longer now, but deep and dull purple, embodying into gloom.

RHADAMISTUS. It is the sun, about to set at mid-day ; we shall soon see no more of him.

ZENOBIA. Indeed ! what an ill omen ! but how can you tell that ?   Do you think it ?   I do not.   Alas ! alas ! the dust and the sounds are nearer.

RHADAMISTUS. Prepare then, my Zenobia !

ZENOBIA. I was always prepared for it.

RHADAMISTUS. What reason, O unconfiding girl ! from the day of our union, have I ever given you, to accuse, or to suspect me ?

ZENOBIA. None, none :   your love, even in these sad moments, raises me above the reach of fortune.   How can it pain me so ?   Do I repine ?   Worse may it pain me ; but let that love never pass away !

RHADAMISTUS. Was it then the loss of power and kingdom for which Zenobia was prepared ?

ZENOBIA. The kingdom was lost when Rhadamistus lost the affection of his subjects.   Why did they not love you ?   how could they not ?   Tell me so strange a thing.*

RHADAMISTUS. Fables, fables ! about the death of Mithridates and his children : declamations, outcries : as if it were as easy to bring men to life again as—I know not what—to call after them.

ZENOBIA. But about the children ?

RHADAMISTUS. In all governments there are secrets.

ZENOBIA. Between us ?

* From the seclusion of the Asiatic women, Zenobia may be supposed to have been ignorant of the crimes Rhadamistus had committed.—W. S. L.

RHADAMISTUS. No longer : time presses : not a moment is left us, not a refuge, not a hope !

ZENOBIA. Then why draw the sword ?

RHADAMISTUS. Wanted I courage ? did I not fight as becomes a king ?

ZENOBIA. True, most true.

RHADAMISTUS. Is my resolution lost to me ? did I but dream I had it ?

ZENOBIA. Nobody is very near yet ; nor can they cross the dell where we did. Those are fled who could have shown the pathway. Think not of defending me. Listen ! look ! what thousands are coming. The protecting blade above my head can only provoke the enemy. And do you still keep it there ? You grasp my arm too hard. Can you look unkindly ? Can it be ? O think again and spare me, Rhadamistus ! From the vengeance of man, from the judgments of heaven, the unborn may preserve my husband.

RHADAMISTUS. We must die ! They advance ; they see us ; they rush forward !

ZENOBIA. Me, me would you strike ? Rather let me leap from the precipice.

RHADAMISTUS. Hold ! Whither would thy desperation ? Art thou again within my grasp ?

ZENOBIA. O my beloved ! never let me call you cruel ! let me love you in the last hour of seeing you as in the first. I must, I must—and be it my thought in death that you love me so ! I would have cast away my life to save you from remorse : it may do that and more, preserved by you. Listen ! listen ! among those who pursue us there are many fathers ; childless by his own hand, none. Do not kill our baby—the best of our hopes when we had many—the baby not yet ours ! Who shall then plead for you, my unhappy husband ?

RHADAMISTUS. My honour ; and before me, sole arbiter and sole audience of our cause. Bethink thee, Zenobia, of the indigni-ties—not bearing on my fortunes—but imminent over thy beauty ! What said I ? did I bid thee think of them ? Rather die than imagine, or than question me, what they are ! Let me endure two deaths before my own, crueller than wounds or than age or than servitude could inflict on me, rather than make me name them.

272

RHADAMISTUS AND ZENOBIA

ZENOBIA. Strike! Lose not a moment so precious! Why hesitate now, my generous brave defender?

RHADAMISTUS. Zenobia! dost thou bid it?

ZENOBIA. Courage is no longer a crime in you. Hear the shouts, the threats, the imprecations! Hear them, my beloved! let *me* no more!

RHADAMISTUS. Embrace me not, Zenobia! loose me, loose me!

ZENOBIA. I can not: thrust me away! Divorce . . . but with death . . . the disobedient wife, no longer your Zenobia. (*He strikes.*) Oh! oh! one innocent head . . . in how few days . . . should have reposed . . . no, not upon this blood. Swim across! is there a descent . . . an easy one, a safe one, anywhere? I might have found it for you! ill-spent time! heedless woman!

RHADAMISTUS. An arrow hath pierced me: more are showering round us. Go, my life's flower! the blighted branch drops after. Away! forth into the stream! strength is yet left me for it. (*He throws her into the river.*) She sinks not! O last calamity! She sinks! she sinks! Now both are well, and fearless! One look more! grant one more look! On what? where was it? which whirl? which ripple? they are gone too. How calm is the haven of the most troubled life! I enter it! Rebels! traitors! slaves! subjects! why gape ye? why halt ye? On, on, dastards! Oh that ye dared to follow! (*He plunges armed into the Araxes.*)